Essays in Biochemistry

Other recent titles in the Essays in Biochemistry series:

Essays in Biochemistry volume 40: The Nuclear Receptor Superfamily
edited by I.J. McEwan
2004 ISBN 1 85578 150 6

Essays in Biochemistry volume 39: Programmed Cell Death
edited by T.G. Cotter
2003 ISBN 1 85578 148 4

Essays in Biochemistry volume 38: Proteases in Biology and Medicine
edited by N.M. Hooper
2002 ISBN 1 85578 147 6

Essays in Biochemistry volume 37: Regulation of Gene Expression
edited by K.E. Chapman and S. J. Higgins
2001 ISBN 1 85578 138 7

Essays in Biochemistry volume 36: Molecular Trafficking
edited by P. Bernstein
2000 ISBN 1 85578 131 X

Essays in Biochemistry volume 35: Molecular Motors
edited by G. Banting and S.J. Higgins
2000 ISBN 1 85578 103 4

Essays in Biochemistry volume 34: Metalloproteins
edited by D.P. Ballou
1999 ISBN 1 85578 106 9

Essays in Biochemistry volume 33: Molecular Biology of the Brain
edited by S.J. Higgins
1998 ISBN 1 85578 086 0

Essays in Biochemistry volume 32: Cell Signalling
edited by D. Bowles
1997 ISBN 1 85578 071 2

volume 41   2005

Essays in Biochemistry

The Ubiquitin–Proteasome System

Edited by R.J. Mayer
and R. Layfield

Portland Press

Essays in Biochemistry is published by Portland Press Ltd
on behalf of the Biochemical Society

Portland Press
Third Floor, Eagle House
16 Procter Street
London WC1V 6NX, U.K.
Fax: 020 7280 4169;
e-mail: editorial@portlandpress.com
www.portlandpress.com

All profits made from the sale of this publication are returned to the Biochemical Society for the promotion of the molecular life sciences.

British Library Cataloguing-in-Publication Data
A catalogue record for this book is available from the British Library

ISBN   1 85578 153 0
ISSN   0071 1365

Typeset by Portland Press Ltd
Printed in Great Britain by Cambrian Printers, Aberystwyth

Contents

1   Orchestra for assembly and fate of polyubiquitin chains

Kirsten Kuhlbrodt, Julien Mouysset and Thorsten Hoppe

2   E3 ubiquitin ligases

Helen C. Ardley and Philip A. Robinson

6   Ubiquitin and endocytic protein sorting
Sylvie Urbé

7   The role of the ubiquitin–proteasome system in ER quality control
Yihong Ye

8   Fluorescent reporters for the ubiquitin–proteasome system
Florian A. Salomons, Lisette G.G.C. Verhoef and Nico P. Dantuma

9   Transgenic manipulation of the ubiquitin–proteasome system
Douglas A. Gray

10   Targeting of host-cell ubiquitin pathways by viruses
Julia Shackelford and Joseph S. Pagano

11   The ubiquitin–proteasome system and neurodegenerative disorders
Robert Layfield, James Lowe and Lynn Bedford

12 The ubiquitin–proteasome system and skeletal muscle wasting

Didier Attaix, Sophie Ventadour, Audrey Codran, Daniel Béchet, Daniel Taillandier and Lydie Combaret

13 The ubiquitin–proteasome system and cancer

Anny Devoy, Tim Soane, Rebecca Welchman and R. John Mayer

14 Proteasome inhibitors as therapeutics

Constantine S. Mitsiades, Nicholas Mitsiades, Teru Hideshima, Paul G. Richardson and Kenneth C. Anderson

Preface

In the first book published on ubiquitin [M. Rechsteiner (ed.) (1988) *Ubiquitin*, Plenum Press, New York], Marty Rechsteiner wrote, "I believe that ubiquitin is a lucky molecule; almost everyone who has studied the protein has made fascinating observations." Some 17 years on, this statement still holds true. While of course it was not through luck, but largely through hard work and determination, that Avram Hershko along with Aaron Ciechanover and Irwin Rose were awarded the 2004 Nobel Prize for Chemistry for their discovery of ubiquitin-mediated protein degradation, it seems that few who have worked in the ubiquitin field have failed to be lucky in some way.

Ubiquitin, as its name suggests, is a ubiquitously expressed protein. Although this volume of *Essays in Biochemistry* is titled *The Ubiquitin–Proteasome System*, and considerable emphasis is placed on the role of ubiquitin as a co-factor for proteasome-mediated proteolysis throughout, it is now clear that ubiquitin conjugation cannot simply be regarded as a mechanism for regulating protein degradation. Indeed, ubiquitin conjugation is now seen to pervade almost every aspect of cell physiology. Accordingly, many of the non-degradative processes that ubiquitin conjugation regulates are also considered in this volume. It is not surprising that given the important roles of ubiquitin in controlling the fundamental mechanisms underlying normal cellular function, defects in ubiquitin-mediated processes can result in disease — this important relationship is also considered in detail.

The volume is divided broadly into four sections. The first four essays cover various aspects of ubiquitin enzymology. Following on from a discussion of E4 polyubiquitin chain conjugation factors (Kuhlbrodt and colleagues), which contains an excellent overview of the ubiquitin–proteasome system, the roles of E3 ubiquitin ligases, the enzymes that ultimately select target proteins for ubiquitination, are described (Ardley and Robinson). The next two essays focus on proteasomes, the molecular machines that are responsible for catalysing protein degradation (Dahlmann), and on ubiquitin-binding proteins, which afford precise regulation of ubiquitin-mediated processes (Andersen and colleagues). The following three essays describe how ubiquitin controls some of the most fundamental cellular processes. The different ways in which ubiquitin regulates transcription are discussed first (Dhananjayan and colleagues), followed by descriptions of how ubiquitin controls endocytic protein sorting (Urbé) and protein quality control in the endoplasmic reticulum (Ye). The next two essays highlight technological advances that have furthered our understanding of the operation of the ubiquitin–proteasome system.

Fluorescent reporters, which allow the efficacy of the ubiquitin–proteasome system to be monitored, are considered first (Salomons and colleagues), followed by a review of how transgenic approaches have been applied to manipulate the ubiquitin–proteasome system in a range of model systems (Gray). The remainder of the volume deals with the complex relationship between the ubiquitin–proteasome system and disease. The many ways in which viruses subvert the ubiquitin–proteasome system are reviewed first (Shackelford and Pagano). The emerging and central roles of the ubiquitin–proteasome system in neurodegenerative disorders (Layfield and colleagues), conditions associated with muscle atrophy (Attaix and colleagues), and cancer (Devoy and colleagues) are then covered. The final chapter highlights how the considerable efforts in understanding the basic biology of the ubiquitin–proteasome system have culminated in the development of compounds that are showing therapeutic potential in the treatment of certain cancers (Mitsiades and colleagues).

We would like to take this opportunity to thank all of the contributors to this volume for their considerable efforts. Likewise, we apologize to those whose work could not be properly cited because of space limitations. Thank you also to the many reviewers who took the time to provide comments and suggestions, which have significantly strengthened this volume. Finally, thanks to Mike Cunningham and Portland Press Ltd, for all their hard work.

We hope you enjoy reading this volume. We hope you find it useful and informative, and if you do not already have a research interest in ubiquitin, that you develop one. And we hope that you too are lucky.

John Mayer
Robert Layfield
Nottingham, UK
August 2005

Authors

Kirsten Kuhlbrodt studied biology at the University of Frankfurt, Germany, and then moved to the Centre for Molecular Neurobiology (ZMNH) in Hamburg, Germany, in Michael Wegner's laboratory, where she identified and characterized the transcription factor Sox10 during her PhD thesis. She did postdoctoral research in the ZMNH in the laboratory of Maike Sander, before she continued to work in the same institute as a research scientist in the laboratory of Thorsten Hoppe, focusing on the ubiquitin–proteasome system in *Caenorhabditis elegans*. Her research interests include the function of ataxin 3 in proteasomal degradation. **Julien Mouysset** studied in biology at the University Paris-Sud, France. He is now a graduate student in the laboratory of Thorsten Hoppe at ZMNH. His doctoral studies focus on the role of the CDC48$^{UFD1/NPL4}$ complex in *C. elegans*. **Thorsten Hoppe** obtained a PhD in Biology from the University of Heidelberg, Germany, in 2000, following work on ubiquitin–proteasome-dependent regulation of the transcription factor SPT23 under the supervision of Stefan Jentsch. He then undertook postdoctoral research on the regulation of myosin assembly in the laboratory of Ralf Baumeister at the Gene Center in Munich, Germany. At present, he is an independent research group leader at ZMNH. His research focuses on neuronal protein degradation and muscle development in *C. elegans*.

Helen Ardley studied biochemistry at the University of Sheffield. She became interested in ubiquitination while characterizing ubiquitin-conjugating enzymes as part of her PhD at the University of Leeds. As a postdoctoral fellow at the Molecular Medicine Unit at Leeds, she has expanded these interests to include ubiquitin–protein ligases, in particular their role in inclusion formation and neurodegeneration. Helen is currently funded by a Personal Fellowship from Research into Ageing. **Philip Robinson** is presently a Reader in Molecular Biology at the University of Leeds. He obtained a BSc degree in Biochemistry at the University of Birmingham in 1976, and a PhD at the University of Manchester in 1984. The intervening years were spent in industry as a Senior Scientific Officer at Roche Pharmaceuticals. Subsequently, much of his career has been spent on developing approaches to understand the underlying molecular causes of diseases, including cancer and neurodegenerative diseases. In the mid-1990s, these studies led to development of his interest in protein ubiquitination as a major regulator of disease processes.

Burkhardt Dahlmann is Professor of Biochemistry at the Charité-Universitätsmedizin-Berlin (Humboldt-Universität zu Berlin, Germany). At the Deutsches-Diabetes-Forschungsinstitut, Düsseldorf (Germany) his research interest in the mechanism of muscle protein breakdown lead to the discovery and characterization of proteasomes in muscle tissue and in archaea.

Rasmus Hartmann-Petersen is Assistant Professor at the Institute of Molecular Biology and Physiology at the University of Copenhagen, Denmark. **Kay Hofmann** is the head of the bioinformatics group at MEMO-REC, a biotechnology company that is based in Cologne, Germany. **Katrine M. Andersen** is a student working on ubiquitin-binding proteins at the University of Copenhagen, Denmark.

Zafar Nawaz received a PhD in biological sciences from the University of North Texas in 1992, and followed this with a postdoctoral fellowship at Baylor College of Medicine, Texas. He is currently an Associate Professor at the University of Miami School of Medicine, Florida. His research interests are in the area of steroid hormone receptor signalling, with an emphasis on the role of ubiquitin and the proteasome pathway in gene regulation, specifically oestrogen receptor-mediated transcription activation and degradation. **Sarath Dhananjayan** completed his Masters degree in Microbiology at Bharathidasan University, Trichy, India. He is currently a doctoral student in Zafar Nawaz's laboratory. He doctoral research involves the characterization of a novel protein WW domain binding protein-2 (WBP-2) as a co-activator of oestrogen and progesterone signalling pathways and its possible role in the ubiquitin–proteasome pathway. **Ayesha Ismail** obtained her Masters degree in Biochemistry from University of Hyderabad, India, followed by doctorate degree also in Biochemistry from National Institute of Nutrition, Osmania University, India. She is currently pursuing postdoctoral research in Zafar Nawaz's laboratory. She is involved in studying the role of the ubiquitin pathway enzymes, E6-AP, an E3 ubiquitin ligase, and UbcH7, an E2 ubiquitin-conjugating enzyme, in the regulation of gene expression, particularly of the oestrogen receptor.

Sylvie Urbé was born in Luxembourg and completed her graduate studies at the University of Heidelberg and in the Cell Biology Program at the European Molecular Biology Laboratory in Heidelberg, Germany. From here, she moved to the Imperial Cancer Research Fund in London, U.K., for her PhD studies on secretory granule biogenesis in the laboratory of Sharon Tooze. She then moved to Liverpool and worked as a post-doctoral fellow with Michael Clague's laboratory on endocytic trafficking processes. She has now established her own laboratory in Liverpool, where she is currently holding a Wellcome Trust Career Development Award and working on multi-vesicular body formation.

Yihong Ye received his PhD from the University of Pennsylvania in 2000. He then became a postdoctoral fellow in Tom Rapoport's laboratory in Harvard Medical School, where he studied the mechanism of protein retrotranslocation, a cellular pathway that deals with misfolded edoplasmic reticulum proteins. He is currently an Assistant Professor in the National Institute of Diabetes and Digestive and Kidney at the National Institutes of Health, Bethesda, MD, U.S.A.

Florian A. Salomons is currently a post-doctoral fellow at the Department of Cell and Molecular Biology of the Karolinska Institute in Stockholm, Sweden. He performed his doctorate research at the Eukaryotic Microbiology laboratory at the University of Groningen, The Netherlands and subsequently a post-doctoral research project at the Department of Radiation and Stress Cell Biology at the University of Groningen. His research is focused on the dynamics and activities of molecular chaperones and the ubiquitin–proteasome system in human pathologies using live-cell imaging with GFP (green fluorescent protein)-based fusion proteins. In 2002, **Lisette G.G.C. Verhoef** finished her Masters studies in biology at Utrecht University, The Netherlands. Since then she has been working as a PhD student at the Department of Cell and Molecular Biology, Karolinska Institute, in Stockholm, Sweden where she is studying the involvement of the ubiquitin–proteasome system in conformational diseases. **Nico P. Dantuma** received his PhD from Utrecht University. He is a principal investigator at the Department of Cell and Molecular Biology of the Karolinska Institute. His research team focuses on the role of the ubiquitin–proteasome system in diseases and regulation of proteasomal degradation. He developed GFP-based reporters to study the ubiquitin–proteasome system in cellular and animal models.

Douglas Gray obtained a PhD from the University of Western Ontario, Canada, and undertook post-doctoral training in the laboratory of Rudolf Jaenisch at the Whitehead Institute, Cambridge, MA, U.S.A. In 1993, he reported the cloning of *Unp* (later redesignated *Usp4*), a mouse gene that encodes a ubiquitin-specific protease (one of the first mammalian genes of this family to be identified). More recently, he has developed an expression system for the analysis of ubiquitin functions in transgenic mice. He is currently a Professor of Biochemistry, Microbiology and Immunology at the University of Ottawa and a Senior Scientist at the Ottawa Health Research Institute.

Julia Shackelford obtained her PhD in Cell Biology from Moscow State University. She is a Research Associate in the Lineberger Comprehensive Cancer Center at the School of Medicine, University of North Carolina at Chapel Hill. Her current research interests focus on studies of the mechanisms and biological role the ubiquitin system in lymphocytic malignancies associated with human tumour viruses. **Joseph S. Pagano**, MD, has worked with viruses since 1960 and with Epstein–Barr virus (EBV) for the last 35 years. He is Lineberger Professor of Cancer Research and Professor of Medicine and Microbiology and Immunology at the University of North Carolina at Chapel Hill. Interests, in addition to how EBV affects the ubiquitin–proteasome system, span interferon regulatory factors, viral induction of invasion, metastasis and angiogenic factors, regulation of EBV gene expression by the cell cycle, and mechanisms of action of antiviral drugs.

Robert Layfield is a Senior Lecturer in Biochemistry at the University of Nottingham, U.K. He was previously a Research into Ageing Queen Elizabeth the Queen Mother Research Fellow, and a Wellcome Trust Research Career Development Fellow. He received a BSc in Biochemistry and Biological Chemistry in 1990, and a PhD in 1994 (working with R. John Mayer), both from the University of Nottingham. With the exception of a year spent in the laboratory of Maria Spillantini at the Brain Repair Centre, University of Cambridge, he has remained in Nottingham researching the ubiquitin–proteasome system. **James Lowe** is Professor of Neuropathology at the University of Nottingham. He has worked closely with R. John Mayer on the ubiquitin system and neuropathology of neurodegenerative diseases since 1987. **Lynn Bedford** is an Alzheimer's Research Trust Junior Research Fellow at the University of Nottingham. She completed her BSc in Pharmacology in 1997 at the University of Sheffield and subsequently a PhD in Molecular Genetics at University College London in 2002. Since this time she has been working on the relationship between neurodegeneration and the ubiquitin–proteasome system in Nottingham.

Didier Attaix has worked in the field of skeletal muscle protein turnover at INRA (National Institute for Agricultural Research), Ceyrat, France, since 1979. After a post-doctoral position at Harvard University, he became Research Director and group leader in proteolysis. His major interest is the elucidation of the mechanisms responsible for muscle atrophy. **Sophie Ventadour** obtained a MSc degree in Nutrition from the Auvergne University, Clermont-Ferrand, France, in 2002. She is a senior PhD candidate in Biochemistry. **Audrey Codran** received her PhD in Virology and Molecular Biology from the Louis Pasteur University, Strasbourg, France, in 2003. She was then awarded a post-doctoral fellowship from Nestlé to study the regulation of proteolysis by nutrients. **Daniel Béchet** obtained a PhD in Applied Physiology at the University of Bristol, UK, in 1985. He then joined INRA and is a senior scientist with major interests in lysosomal proteolysis and proteomics. **Daniel Taillandier** obtained a PhD in Biochemistry at the Blaise Pascal University, Clermont-Ferrand, France, in 1993. He did post-doctoral work at the University of Utah, U.S.A, and is now a senior scientist at INRA. His main interests are the molecular mechanisms regulating the proteasome in skeletal muscle. **Lydie Combaret** received her PhD in Physiology from the Blaise Pascal University, Clermont-Ferrand, France, in 1996. After post-doctoral training at McGill University, Montréal, Canada, she joined INRA in 1998 and is now a senior scientist. Her research focuses on the regulation of the muscle ubiquitin–proteasome system by nutrients.

Anny Devoy was educated at the Victoria University of Wellington, New Zealand. She is studying for a PhD with R. John Mayer using gene targeting to delete conditionally a brain HECT (homologous to E6-AP C-terminus) ligase to recapitulate features of neurological illnesses. **Rebecca Welchman** was educated at University of Nottingham, U.K. She is studying for a PhD with R. John Mayer using yeast two-hybrid screens to identify interaction partners for the ubiquiton Urm1. **Tim Soane** was also educated at the University of Nottingham, U.K. He is studying for a PhD with R. John Mayer using gene targeting to delete conditionally a proteasomal deubiquitinating enzyme in the brain to recapitulate features of neurological illnesses. **R. John Mayer** is Professor of Molecular Cell Biology and has studied intracellular proteolysis for 35 years. He discovered the 'protein sequestration site for protein degradation by autophagy associated with the microtubule organising centre', now called 'the aggresome'. With colleagues, he discovered that all protein aggregates (inclusions) in chronic human neurodegenerative diseases contain ubiquitinated proteins and identified a new neurological illness, dementia with Lewy bodies. He was elected a Fellow of the Royal College of Pathologists for this work. Work from Nottingham and many laboratories around the world also indicates that dysfunction of the ubiquitin–proteasome system is a major cause of cancer.

Constantine S. Mitsiades, MD, PhD, is an Instructor in Medicine at the Department of Medical Oncology of the Dana-Farber Cancer Institute and the Department of Medicine of the Harvard Medical School in Boston, MA, U.S.A. **Nicholas Mitsiades**, MD, PhD, is an Instructor in Medicine at the Department of Medical Oncology of the Dana-Farber Cancer Institute and the Department of Medicine of the Harvard Medical School. **Teru Hideshima**, MD, PhD is a Principal Associate in the Jerome Lipper Multiple Myeloma Center of the Dana-Farber Cancer Institute. **Paul G. Richardson**, MD, is the Clinical Director of the Jerome Lipper Multiple Myeloma Center at the Dana-Farber Cancer Institute and an Assistant Professor at the Department of Medicine of Harvard Medical School. **Kenneth C. Anderson**, MD, is the Kraft Family Professor of Medicine at Harvard Medical School, and Director of the Jerome Lipper Multiple Myeloma Center of the Dana-Farber Cancer Institute.

Abbreviations

AAA	ATPase associated with various cellular activities
ABC	ATP-binding cassette
Aβ	amyloid β
ACC	accessory C-terminal zinc finger
AIP	apoptosis-linked-gene-2-interacting protein
AKAP	A-kinase anchoring protein
ALG2	apoptosis-linked gene 2
Alix	ALG2-interacting protein X
ALS	amyotrophic lateral sclerosis
AMFR	autocrine motility factor receptor (also known as gp78)
AML	acute myelogenous leukaemia
AMPK	AMP-activated protein kinase
AMSH	associated molecule with the SH3 domain of STAM
AP	adaptor protein
APC	anaphase-promoting complex
APCp	adenomatous polyposis coli tumour suppressor protein
AR-JP	autosomal recessive juvenile Parkinsonism
AS	Angelman syndrome
ATF	activating transcription factor
Avp	adenovirus proteinase
BAG-1	Bcl-2-associated athanogene
BARD1	BRCA1-associated RING domain 1
BMSC	bone marrow stromal cell
BPV	bovine papillomavirus
BRCA1	breast-cancer susceptibility gene 1
BTB	broad complex, tramtrak, bric a brac
CBC	Cullin-2 elongin B/C complex
CCV	clathrin-coated vesicle
Cdc	cell-division cycle
CDK	cyclin-dependent kinase
CDL	cullin-dependent ligase
CHIP	C-terminus of the heat-shock-protein-70-interacting protein
CHMP	charged multivesicular protein
CHN-1	*Caenorhabditis elegans* orthologue of CHIP

cIAP	cellular inhibitor of apoptosis protein
CLIM	cofactor of LIM-HD proteins
CLL	chronic lymphocytic leukaemia
ClpP	caseinolytic protease P
CMV	cytomegalovirus
COP	constitutive photomorphogenesis
CREB	cAMP-response-element-binding protein
CRL	Cullin–RING E3 (ubiquitin–protein ligase)
CSN	COP9 signalosome
CTL	cytotoxic T-lymphocyte
CUE	coupling of ubiquitin conjugation to endoplasmic reticulum degradation
Cul1	Cullin homologue 1
Doa10	degradation of α2-10
DUB	deubiquitinating enzyme
E1	ubiquitin-activating enzyme
E2	ubiquitin-conjugating enzyme
E3	ubiquitin ligase
E4	polyubiquitin chain conjugation factor
E6-AP	E6-associated protein
EAP	ELL-associated protein
EBNA1	Epstein–Barr virus nuclear antigen 1
EBV	Epstein–Barr virus
EGF	epidermal growth factor
EGFP	enhanced green fluorescent protein
EGFR	epidermal growth factor receptor
Emi1	early mitotic inhibitor-1
ENaC	epithelial Na^+ channel
END	endocytosis-defective
Eps15	epidermal growth factor receptor pathway substrate 15
ER	endoplasmic reticulum
ERAD	ER-associated degradation
ERK	extracellular-signal-regulated kinase
ESCRT	endosomal sorting complex required for transport
Fbs1	F-box only protein 2
Fbs2	F-box only protein 6
FGF	fibroblast growth factor
FLIP	FADD-like interleukin-1β-converting enzyme inhibitory protein
FoxO	forkhead box O
FP	fluorescent protein
GAP1	general amino acid permease

GAT	GGA and Tom1
GFP	green fluorescent protein
GGA	Golgi-associated γ-adaptin homologous
GHR	growth hormone receptor
GKAP	guanylate kinase-associated protein
GLUE	GRAM-like ubiquitin-binding in Eap45
gp	glycoprotein
GSK	glycogen synthase kinase
GST	glutathione S-transferase
GTF	general transcription factor
HAUSP	herpes virus-associated ubiquitin-specific protease
HBV	hepatitis B virus
HCC	hepatocellular carcinoma
HCMV	human cytomegalovirus
HCV	hepatitis C virus
HDlg	human discs large
Hdm2	human homologue of Mdm2
HECT	homologous to E6-AP C-terminus
HGF	hepatocyte growth factor
HHARI	human homologue of ariadne
HIF	hypoxia-inducible factor
HPV	human papillomavirus
Hrd1	hydroxymethylglutaryl reductase degradation
Hrs	hepatocyte growth factor-regulated tyrosine kinase substrate
Hsp	heat-shock protein
HSV	herpes simplex virus
HTLV-1	human T-cell lymphotropic virus type-1
IκB	inhibitory κB
IBR	in between RING fingers
ICP0	infected cell protein 0
IE	immediate-early
IFNγ	interferon-γ
IGF	insulin-like growth factor
IKK	inhibitory κB kinase complex
IL-2	interleukin-2
IL-6	interleukin-6
IRF7	interferon regulatory factor 7
ISG	interferon-stimulated gene
ITCH	itchy homologue E3 ubiquitin–protein ligase
JAMM	JAB1/MPN/Mov34
JCV	JC virus
KSHV	Kaposi's sarcoma-associated herpesvirus

LATS	large tumour suppressor
LC/MS/MS	liquid chromatography with tandem mass spectrometry
LEF	lymphoid enhancer factor
LIM-HD	LIM homeodomain
LMP-1	latent membrane protein 1
LMP2	low-molecular-mass polypeptide 2
MAFbx	muscle atrophy F-box protein
MAGI-1	membrane-associated guanylate kinase with inverted domain structure 1
MAPK	mitogen-activated protein kinase
MAPKK	mitogen-activated protein kinase kinase
MAPKKK	mitogen-activated protein kinase kinase kinase
MCL	mantle cell lymphoma
MDM2	murine double minute clone 2 oncoprotein
MECL-1	multicatalytic endopeptidase complex-like-1
Met4	transcriptional activator of sulphur metabolism
MIR	modulator of immune recognition
MJD	Machado–Joseph disease
MM	multiple myeloma
MND	motor neuron disease
MPN	Mpr1p Pad1p N-terminal
M-protein	monoclonal protein
MUPP-1	multiple PDZ domain-containing protein 1
MuRF-1	muscle-specific RING-finger 1
MVB	multi-vesicular body
NAC	nascent polypeptide-chain associated complex
ND10	nuclear domain 10
NEDD	neural precursor cell expressed developmentally down-regulated
NF-κB	nuclear factor κB
NHL	non-Hodgkin's lymphoma
NHR	nuclear hormone receptor
NMJ	neuromuscular junction
Npl4	nuclear protein localization gene 4
Ntn	N-terminal nucleophile
Nub1	Nedd8 ultimate buster-1
NZF	nuclear protein localization gene 4 zinc finger
ODC	ornithine decarboxylase
ORF	open reading frame
OTU	ovarian tumour
PAAF-1	proteasomal ATPase-associated factor-1
PACE	proteasome-associated control element

Pael-R	Parkin-associated endothelin-receptor-like receptor
PAN	proteasome-activating nucleotidase
PB1	Phox and Bem1
PC	proteasome/cyclosome
PCAF	p300/CREB (cAMP/Ca^{2+}-responsive element-binding protein)-binding protein-associated factor
PCNA	proliferating-cell nuclear antigen
PDB	Paget's disease of bone
PDGFR	platelet-derived growth-factor receptor
PGAM	phosphoglycerate mutase
PHD	plant homeodomain
PK	pharmacokinetic
PML	promyelocytic leukaemia
polyQ	polyglutamine
POMP	proteasome-maturation protein
pRb	retinoblastoma protein
PSD	postsynaptic density
P-TEFb	positive transcription elongation factor b
pVHL	von Hippel–Lindau tumour suppressor protein
Rbx	RING box protein
RING	really interesting new gene
RIP	receptor-interacting protein
RIR	RING in between RING–RING
rjs	runty–jerky–sterile
RLIM	RING-finger LIM domain-binding protein
RNA pol II	RNA polymerase II
ROS	reactive oxygen species
Rp	regulatory particle
RSV	Rous sarcoma virus
RTA	replication transcription activator
RTK	receptor tyrosine kinase
SCA	spinocerebellar ataxia
SCF	Skp1–Cdc53/Cul1–F-box protein
SCF$^{\beta TrCP}$	SCF β-transducin repeat-containing protein
SelS	selenoprotein S
SH	Src homology
siRNA	small interfering RNA
SKD1	suppressor of potassium transport growth defect 1
Skp	S-phase associated protein
SOCS	suppressor of cytokine signalling
STAM	signal-transducing adaptor molecule
STAT	signal transduction and activator of transcription
STI1	heat-shock chaperonin-binding motif

SUMO	small ubiquitin modifier
SV40	simian virus 40
TAB	TAK1-binding protein
TAD	transcriptional activation domain
TAK	TGF-β-activated-kinase
TAP	transporter associated with antigen processing
TBP	TATA-box binding protein
TCF	T-cell factor
TCR	transcription-coupled repair
TfR	transferrin receptor
TGF	transforming growth factor
TNF	tumour necrosis factor
tollip	toll-interacting protein
Tom	target of Myb
TPP II	tripeptidyl-peptidase II
TPR	tetratricopeptide repeat
TRAF	tumour-necrosis-factor-receptor-associated factor
β-TrCP	β-transducin repeat-containing protein
TRIP1	thyroid-hormone-receptor-interacting protein 1
TSG	tumour susceptibility gene
Ub	ubiquitin
UBA domain	ubiquitin-associated domain
UBAP	ubiquitin-associated protein
UbC	ubiquitin C
Ubc	ubiquitin-conjugating enzyme
UBL	ubiquitin-like
UBP	ubiquitin-binding protein
UBX domain	ubiquitin regulatory X domain
UCH	ubiquitin C-terminal hydrolase
UEV	ubiquitin E2 variant
UFD	ubiquitin fusion degradation protein-1
UIM	ubiquitin-interacting motif
UPR	unfolded-protein response
UPS	ubiquitin–proteasome system
USP	ubiquitin-specific protease
VCB	VHL elongin C–elongin B
VCP	valosin-containing protein
VEGF	vascular endothelial growth factor
VHL	von Hippel–Lindau
VIMP	VCP-interacting membrane protein
VP40	viral protein 40
vps	vacuolar protein sorting
VWA	von Willebrand factor A

WM	Waldenstrom's macroglobulinaemia
WW domain	protein–protein interaction domain containing two conserved tryptophan residues
XIAP	X-linked inhibitor of apoptosis protein
ZF	zinc finger
ZnF	A20-like zinc finger

1

Orchestra for assembly and fate of polyubiquitin chains

Kirsten Kuhlbrodt, Julien Mouysset
and Thorsten Hoppe[1]

Centre for Molecular Neurobiology (ZMNH), University of Hamburg, Falkenried 94, 20251 Hamburg, Germany

Abstract

Selective protein degradation by the 26 S proteasome usually requires a polyubiquitin chain attached to the protein substrate by three classes of enzymes: a ubiquitin-activating enzyme (E1), a ubiquitin-conjugating enzyme (E2), and a ubiquitin ligase (E3). This reaction can produce different polyubiquitin chains that, depending on size and linkage type, can provide distinct intracellular signals. Interestingly, polyubiquitination is sometimes regulated by additional conjugation factors, called E4s (polyubiquitin chain conjugation factors). Yeast UFD2 (ubiquitin fusion degradation protein-2), the first E4 to be described, binds to the ubiquitin moieties of preformed conjugates and catalyses ubiquitin-chain elongation together with E1, E2, and E3. Recent studies have illustrated that the E4 enzyme UFD2 co-operates with an orchestra of ubiquitin-binding factors in an escort pathway to transfer and deliver polyubiquitinated substrates to the 26 S proteasome. Here we propose a model in which E4-dependent polyubiquitination pathways are modulated by different ubiquitin-binding proteins, using ataxin-3 as an example.

[1]To whom correspondence should be addressed
(email thorsten.hoppe@zmnh.uni-hamburg.de).

Introduction

The ubiquitin–proteasome system (UPS) is the major pathway in eukaryotic cells responsible for selective proteolysis of intracellular proteins. In this system, proteins are marked for degradation by covalent modification with ubiquitin via isopeptide-bond formation between its C-terminus and ϵ-amino groups of internal lysine residues within the substrate protein.

Substrate conjugation generally requires a cascade of enzymes, which includes a ubiquitin-activating enzyme (E1), a ubiquitin-conjugating enzyme (E2) and a specific ubiquitin–protein ligase (E3) [1]. Most often, this reaction results in a polyubiquitin chain. A specific lysine residue of each ubiquitin molecule in the extending chain serves as a site for further ubiquitination. Ubiquitin itself contains seven internal lysines (Lys^6, Lys^{11}, Lys^{27}, Lys^{29}, Lys^{33}, Lys^{48} and Lys^{63}), all of which have been shown to be used for ubiquitin-chain formation *in vitro* [2]. Most polyubiquitinated substrates with a Lys^{48}-linked ubiquitin chain of four or more ubiquitin moieties are targeted to degradation by the 26 S proteasome, a multicatalytic protease complex that degrades modified substrates into small peptides and amino acids. In contrast, Lys^{63}-linked polyubiquitin chains appear to play non-proteolytic functions in DNA-repair pathways, endocytosis, signal transduction, transcriptional regulation and ribosomal function [3]. Recent studies provide evidence that different fates of polyubiquitinated substrates are determined not only by the size and linkage of polyubiquitin chains, but also by specific ubiquitin conjugate binding factors (for review, see Chapter 4). In yeast, for example, the proteins Rad23 and Dsk2, are known to be involved in targeting polyubiquitinated substrates for proteasomal degradation [4,5].

Polyubiquitin-chain assembly is a processive reaction, which is typically catalysed by E1, E2 and E3 enzymes alone. However, efficient polyubiquitination of certain substrates has been shown to be regulated by additional ubiquitin-chain assembly factors, termed E4s (polyubiquitin chain conjugation factors) [6]. One founding member of this enzyme class is the yeast protein UFD2 (ubiquitin fusion degradation protein-2), which binds to the ubiquitin moieties of preformed conjugates and catalyses polyubiquitin-chain elongation in collaboration with E1, E2 and E3. E4-dependent polyubiquitination appears to be tightly regulated by a set of different ubiquitin-binding proteins. This regulation results not only in the restriction of the number of ubiquitin molecules added by UFD2 to the growing polyubiquitin chain, but also in the subsequent targeting of the substrate to the proteasome [5]. Such an escort mechanism can provide another layer of regulation and specificity in the ubiquitin system. This review discusses the potential role of the ubiquitin conjugate binding factor, ataxin-3, to illustrate how alternatively used ubiquitin-chain-binding proteins can provide even more complexity in this pathway.

Ubiquitin-chain linkage: stamp for functionally distinct processes

Originally, it was assumed that polyubiquitinated proteins are exclusively targeted to the 26 S proteasome for degradation. However, recent studies have shown that the polyubiquitin signal is more versatile than expected. Different lysine residues of ubiquitin can be used for the linkage between ubiquitin monomers, which leads to polyubiquitin chains that are functionally distinct (Figure 1). Basically, two different types of polyubiquitin chains can be generated. In homopolymeric ubiquitin chains, several ubiquitin molecules are all linked to each other using the same donor lysine residue, and these have already been described for Lys^{48}-, Lys^{63}- and Lys^{6}-linked chains. In contrast, heteropolymeric chains contain more than one type of linkage [6]. There is, however, presently no experimental evidence for specific properties of these sporadically described heteropolymeric chains.

The role of the different lysine residues used for the assembly of polyubiquitin chains has been investigated by genetic approaches in budding yeast [3]. These experiments revealed that Lys^{48} of ubiquitin is essential for growth, which is directly linked to its central role in proteolysis. However, recent work by Flick et al. [7] demonstrated an additional proteolysis-independent role for Lys^{48}-linked chains. Polyubiquitination through Lys^{48} mediates inactivation of Met4 (transcriptional activator of sulphur metabolism), a transcription factor for genes involved in the biosynthesis of sulphuric amino acids.

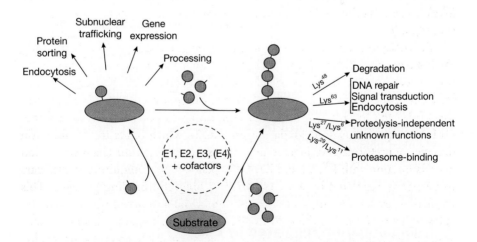

Figure 1. Ubiquitination serves as a versatile post-translational signal
Ubiquitination is performed by E1, E2, E3 and sometimes E4 enzymes together with additional cofactors, and leads to either mono- or poly-ubiquitinated substrates. Mono-ubiquitination, in most cases, regulates the activity of the substrate protein, providing signalling function in diverse processes. Throughout polyubiquitination, distinct ubiquitin chains can be formed depending on the lysine linkage used between the single ubiquitin molecules, which determines the fate of the substrate.

Surprisingly, in this case the polyubiquitin chain attached to Met4 stabilizes the protein, instead of inducing its proteasomal turnover. It has been suggested that the chain might be masked by interacting proteins and is therefore not recognized by the proteasome [7].

As well as Lys^{48}-linked chains, atypical chains linked through Lys^{29} and Lys^{11} could be similarly competent proteasomal targeting signals, since both are able to bind to the 26 S proteasome [3]. In contrast, Lys^{63}-linked chains act as non-proteolytic signals in several intracellular pathways, such as DNA repair, transcriptional regulation, protein trafficking and ribosomal protein synthesis. One example is the polyubiquitination via Lys^{63} of PCNA (proliferating-cell nuclear antigen) during error-free repair of damaged DNA, which controls its activity [8]. Lys^{63}-linked chains are also important for various regulation steps in inflammatory signalling pathways, induced by the transcriptional activator NF-κB (nuclear factor κB). In these steps, Lys^{63}-linkage-based polyubiquitination of the IKK [IκB (inhibitory κB) kinase complex] is necessary for the activation of the complex, which then phosphorylates IκB proteins that sequester NF-κB transcription factors into the cytosol. It has been shown that such modifications promote various protein–protein associations (for review, see [9]).

The less frequently used Lys^{27}-linked and Lys^{6}-linked polyubiquitin chains additionally provide functions that are distinct from proteasomal targeting. Attachment of Lys^{27}-linked polyubiquitin chains to the co-chaperone and ubiquitin domain protein, BAG-1 (Bcl-2-associated athanogene), does not induce proteasomal degradation, but rather promotes the association of BAG-1 with the proteasome ([10], but see [10a]). This enables BAG-1 to act as one of the coupling factors between molecular chaperones and the proteasomal complex. As yet, Lys^{6}-linked polyubiquitin chains have only been reported to affect the activity of DNA repair factors.

Taken together, the generation of these different polyubiquitin chains provides an important level of complexity. However, the molecular mechanism by which the different chain linkages are determined remains elusive. Perhaps linkage formation is regulated by specialized E3s. Indeed, the formation of Lys^{6}-linked ubiquitin chains is catalysed by an unusual E3 activity provided by a heterodimer consisting of BRCA1 (breast-cancer susceptibility gene 1), a breast and ovarian tumour suppressor, and BARD1 [BRCA1-associated RING (really interesting new gene) domain 1] [11,12].

Polyubiquitination regulated by E4s

A new family of conjugation factors has been identified, which seems to regulate polyubiquitination at the level of ubiquitin-chain elongation [6]. Such factors, able to catalyse an extension of the polyubiquitin chain in collaboration with E1, E2, and E3, have been termed E4s (Figure 2). The first E4 to be described was the yeast protein UFD2, which is required for efficient

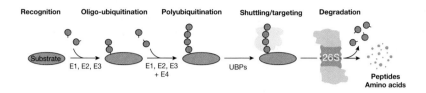

Figure 2. E4-dependent polyubiquitination and targeting
Substrate proteins are recognized for proteasomal targeting and are polyubiquitinated by the sequential activity of E1, E2 and E3 enzymes. In some cases, the additional function of E4 enzymes is required for efficient polyubiquitination. Chains with four to six ubiquitin moieties are an optimal length for interacting with UBPs (ubiquitin-binding proteins) that shuttle polyubiquiti-nated substrates to the 26 S proteasome for subsequent degradation into peptides and amino acids. Concomitantly with degradation, ubiquitin moieties are recycled.

polyubiquitination of ubiquitin-fusion-degradation-model (UFD) substrates and the transcription factor SPT23 [13]. Genetic and biochemical studies have revealed that UFD2 binds to substrates conjugated with one to three ubiquitin molecules, and catalyses the addition of further ubiquitin moieties in the presence of E1, E2 and E3s, yielding polyubiquitinated substrates that are targets for the 26 S proteasome. UFD2 defines the first identified family of E4s, which is characterized by a conserved C-terminal U-box (modified RING motif without the full complement of Zn^{2+}-binding ligands), a UFD2-homology domain, of approx. 70 amino acids, that is structurally related to the RING finger motif found in RING finger E3s (Figure 3). This UFD2 family includes human members and homologues in mouse, fission yeast, *Dictyostelium*, *Arabidopsis* and *Caenorhabditis elegans*, suggesting that alternative E4-dependent degradation pathways exist.

Another member of this family is CHIP [C-terminus of the Hsp (heat-shock-protein)-70-interacting protein], previously identified as a negative regulator of Hsp70 ATPase activity. In addition to the U-box, CHIP bears three tandem TPR (tetratricopeptide repeat) motifs at its N-terminus (Figure 3) that bind to the chaperones Hsp70 and Hsp90. Several studies revealed that CHIP displays E3 activity and mediates the ubiquitination of a variety of chaperone-bound substrates. Thus CHIP is likely to be involved in regulating the cellular balance between protein folding and degradation. However, CHIP has been shown to display E4 function, by regulating the ubiquitination activity of the E3 Parkin [14].

Our recent work identified a novel functional interaction between the *C. elegans* orthologues of CHIP and UFD2, CHN-1 and UFD-2, respectively, and the myosin chaperone UNC-45. Both UFD-2 and CHN-1 alone, in collaboration with E1 and E2, conjugate one to three ubiquitin moieties to the substrate UNC-45. Therefore, in *C. elegans*, both CHN-1 and UFD-2 work independently as E3 enzymes in this pathway. However, in combination, CHN-1 and UFD-2 are able to increase the ubiquitination of UNC-45. These

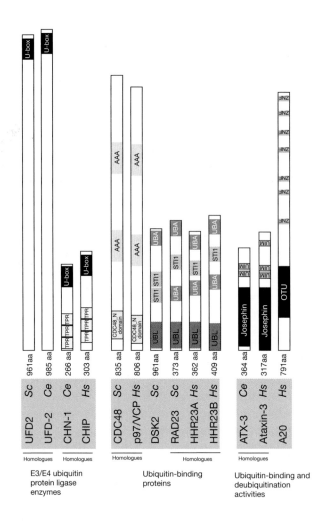

Figure 3. Schematic drawing of the primary structures of escort-pathway components and homologues
Functionally distinct domains are marked by boxes: Josephin domain, OTU domain, UBA domain, UBL domain, U-box, UFD2 homology domain (a modified RING motif without the full complement of Zn^{2+}-binding ligands). aa, amino acid; CDC48_N domain, N-terminal domain of CDC48; Ce, C. elegans; Hs, Homo sapiens; Sc, S. cerevisiae; STI1, heat-shock chaperonin-binding motif; ZnF, A20-like zinc finger.

results suggest a novel mechanism in which two E3 enzymes 'team up' to achieve E4 function. The assembly of such an E3/E4 complex in multicellular organisms could be controlled by developmentally-regulated co-expression of both enzymes in specific tissues. Furthermore, it is conceivable that different combinations of E3 enzymes could result in alternative substrate-specific complexes with E4 activity [15].

However, E4 activity does not necessarily depend on the existence of a U-box domain. In contrast to UFD2 and CHIP, a different type of E4 enzyme is represented by p300, previously known as a transcriptional cofactor and histone acetyltransferase. p300 has been shown to polyubiquitinate mono-ubiquitinated species of the tumour suppressor p53 in collaboration with the E3 enzyme MDM2 (murine double minute clone 2 oncoprotein), whereas p300 alone is not able to conjugate ubiquitin to p53. The regulation of the GAP1 (general amino acid permease) of *Saccharomyces cerevisiae* again shows that E4 activity is not exclusively restricted to single proteins. In this case, the BUL1/BUL2 complex possesses E4 activity, necessary for ubiquitin-chain elongation of mono-ubiquitinated GAP1. p300 and the BUL1/BUL2 complex are the only E4 enzymes without a U-box that have been identified so far [16].

It is intriguing to speculate that E4 might regulate the selection of lysine residues used for ubiquitin–ubiquitin linkages during polyubiquitin-chain assembly. Indeed, as has been shown by Saeki et al. [17], yeast UFD2 catalyses a linkage switch from Lys^{29}, used for mono-ubiquitination, by further elongation of the ubiquitin chain through Lys^{48}.

Modulation of the polyubiquitin chain

Such a linkage-type switch, mediated by the yeast E4 enzyme, offers another level of control in polyubiquitin-chain assembly. An additional example of such a mechanism is the switch from mono- to poly-ubiquitination by the yeast proteins RAD5, MMS2, and UBC13, which appears to control the activity of PCNA during DNA repair [8]. Representing another fine-tuning mechanism, modulation of polyubiquitination can be reversed by the action of DUBs (deubiquitinating enzymes). This defines ubiquitination as a post-translational modification that is regulated by feedback mechanisms comparable to signals in other regulatory processes, such as phosphorylation [9,18]. Polyubiquitin-chain attachment and removal act as on- and off-switches at several points along signal-transduction cascades, as has been illustrated for the regulation of the TNF (tumour necrosis factor)-induced signal transduction pathway that leads to activation of the NF-κB family of transcription factors (for review, see [19]).

Intriguingly, the NF-κB inhibitor A20 has been discovered to be an enzyme with dual ubiquitin editing functions in the NF-κB signalling pathway. The N-terminal OTU (ovarian tumour) domain of A20, which is characteristic of DUBs of the OTU family, disassembles Lys^{63}-linked ubiquitin chains from RIP (receptor-interacting protein), an essential mediator of the TNF receptor 1 signalling complex. RIP deubiquitination works as a prerequisite for the subsequent attachment of Lys^{48}-linked chains mediated by the C-terminal E3 activity of A20, targeting RIP for proteasomal degradation. These two opposing activities of deubiquitination and ubiquitination are united within the same protein (Figure 3) in order to change the linkage of the polyubiquitin chain [19].

The ubiquitin-binding protein ataxin-3

Another ubiquitin-binding protein that comprises two distinct catalytic activities that are functionally related to the ubiquitin system is ataxin-3 [20]. Mutations in the human *ataxin-3* gene have been associated with the neurodegenerative disease spinocerebellar ataxia type 3 (SCA3) [21]. This disorder, also known as Machado–Joseph disease (MJD), is the most common dominantly inherited ataxia and one of at least nine neurodegenerative polyQ (polyglutamine) diseases, including Huntington's disease. PolyQ diseases are caused by the pathological expansion of a polyQ region in the disease protein, which leads to a misfolding process and subsequent accumulation of insoluble protein aggregates. In this context, it is very interesting that a variety of genes of the ubiquitin pathway seem to be implicated in the development of neurodegenerative diseases. Genes implicated in Parkinson's disease, for example, encode the E3 enzyme Parkin and the ubiquitin C-terminal hydrolase L1 (UCH-L1). In the case of SCA3/MJD, the disease pathology is also attributed to alterations in ubiquitin-pathway functions, since ataxin-3 has been shown to interact with ubiquitinated substrates [20,22,23].

Ataxin-3 possesses two different functional domains [24,25]: an N-terminal deubiquitinating Josephin domain and two to three UIM (ubiquitin-interacting motif) domains at the flexible C-terminal tail, which also contains the polyQ region expanded in SCA3/MJD (Figure 3). It has recently been shown that ataxin-3 binds ubiquitinated proteins [20,22]. This interaction is mediated by the UIMs, which contain a conserved cluster of amino acids, including a nearly invariant serine and a conserved leucine, which is often essential for ubiquitin binding [24]. The Josephin domain of ataxin-3 includes highly conserved amino-acid stretches reminiscent of the catalytic residues of deubiquitinating cysteine proteases [25]. Cysteine proteases in this context are also known as DUBs and have been divided into four families: USPs (ubiquitin-specific proteases), UCHs and two novel ubiquitin-specific families, comprising the Jab/Csn5 and MPN (Mpr1p Pad1p N-terminal) domain-containing proteins [the JAMM (JAB1/MPN/Mov34) group of hydrolases] and a family of cysteine proteases that contains an OTU domain (for review, see [26]). Structural studies have confirmed that ataxin-3 is evolutionarily related to deubiquitinating cysteine proteases of the UCH family. This has been substantiated by *in vitro* experiments in which ataxin-3 was able to remove ubiquitin from polyubiquitin chains [20]. Cys^{14} has been identified as the major catalytic amino acid essential for the deubiquitination activity, since the abolition of protease activity by mutation of Cys^{14} inhibits the cleavage of ubiquitinated proteins. Interestingly, the Josephin domain, which harbours this ubiquitin-specific protease activity, also mediates protein–protein interactions [27], specifically binding to the two

ubiquitin chain recognition factors HHR23A and HHR23B, the human homologues of the yeast protein RAD23.

Ataxin-3 might modulate E4-dependent polyubiquitin-chain assembly

A recent study has described that the yeast proteins RAD23 and DSK2 bind
preferentially to UFD2-assembled polyubiquitin chains, which are restricted
in size to an average of four to six ubiquitin molecules by the concerted action
of a CDC48 complex [5]. The AAA (ATPase associated with various cellular
activities)-ATPase CDC48, which binds to ubiquitin via its N-terminus
(Figure 3), exerts its function in co-operation with the cofactors NPL4 and
UFD1, forming the specialized CDC48–UFD1–NPL4 complex. It seems that
CDC48 is a substantial component of a pathway which shuttles ubiquitin
conjugates, together with additional interacting factors, to the 26 S proteasome
[5]. In this escort pathway, oligo-ubiquitinated substrates are recognized by
the substrate-recruiting cofactors of CDC48, relocated on to the bound E4
enzyme UFD2 for polyubiquitination, and subsequently handed over to
RAD23 and DSK2, which finally mediate the delivery of ubiquitinated
substrates to the 26 S proteasome.

Supporting this model, it has become evident from previous studies on
Lys^{48}-linked chains that the affinity to the proteasome is influenced by the
length of the ubiquitin chain. Binding affinity and chain length are related in a
non-linear manner, since affinity increases more than 100-fold as the chain is
lengthened from two to four ubiquitins, in contrast with a further increase of
only 10-fold when eight more ubiquitin moieties are added to the chain [28].
Chains of four ubiquitin molecules act as a minimum signal for high-affinity
binding to the 26 S proteasome and efficient degradation [20,28]. These chains
contain enough ubiquitin molecules for optimal binding to the C-terminal
UBA (ubiquitin-associated) domains of HHR23A and HHR23B (see Figure 3
and [29]).

Interestingly, *in vitro* ataxin-3 binds preferentially to Lys^{48}-linked tetra-
ubiquitin chains [30] and to different components of the escort pathway.
Doss-Pepe et al. [22] reported that ataxin-3 interacts with both HHR23B and
p97/VCP (valosin-containing protein), the mammalian CDC48 homologue.
Specifically, the Josephin domain of ataxin-3 interacts with the UBL (ubiquitin-like) domain of HHR23B, and the C-terminal region of ataxin-3 interacts
with the N-terminal domain of p97/VCP. The authors propose a model in
which ubiquitinated substrates are transferred from HHR23B to ataxin-3, the
latter of which may function as a transiently associated polyubiquitin-chain
recognition subunit of the 26 S proteasome. This implies that the activity of
p97/VCP seems to be required for a concerted delivery of ubiquitinated substrates to the proteasome. Thus it is likely that ataxin-3 might play a role in
the escort pathway.

Moreover, recent studies indicate that UFD2a, the human homologue of yeast UFD2, in conjunction with p97/VCP forms a ternary complex with ataxin-3 [23]. Another factor implicated in binding to ataxin-3 is the ubiquitin–protein ligase CHIP [31], whose *C. elegans* orthologue CHN-1 acts in concert with *C. elegans* UFD-2 to form an E3–E4 polyubiquitination complex [15]. Since ataxin-3 interacts both with CHIP and UFD2a, it is intriguing to speculate that ataxin-3, together with CHIP and UFD2a, is involved in regulating the ubiquitination status of specific substrates. Indeed, the conservation of this complex in *C. elegans* (K. Kuhlbrodt and T. Hoppe, unpublished work) leads to the attractive idea that *C. elegans* ataxin-3 (ATX-3), in collaboration with CHN-1 and UFD-2, could be directly involved in the regulation of the myosin assembly chaperone UNC-45, a known substrate of the E3–E4 complex formed by CHN-1 and UFD-2 [15].

Taken together, it is tempting to speculate that ataxin-3 is not mainly a substrate for ubiquitination, but that it appears to be involved in an escort pathway. Moreover, the combination of deubiquitination activity and ubiquitin-binding properties indicates that ataxin-3 plays a general regulatory role in the ubiquitin system. To down-regulate its activity, ataxin-3 seems to be ubiquitinated and degraded by the proteasome *in vivo*, which is not unusual, as it has already been shown for E3 enzymes such as TRAF (TNF-receptor-associated factor)-2 and TRAF-6 in the NF-κB pathway [32].

Conclusion

In the UPS pathway, polyubiquitination regulated by E4 enzymes is required for efficient targeting of certain protein substrates for proteasomal degradation. Ubiquitin-binding proteins help to shuttle E4-catalysed polyubiquitinated chains to the 26 S proteasome. This course of events has recently been described in yeast, providing evidence for the existence of an escort pathway associated with a size-restriction mechanism [5]. It is conceivable that such an escort pathway might be a general mechanism for shuttling polyubiquitinated substrates to the proteasome in a regulated manner. Consequently, size-restriction of polyubiquitin chains could be a widespread mechanism accomplished by several ubiquitin-binding proteins, which subsequently escort the size-restricted ubiquitin conjugates for degradation. Richly et al. [5] proposed that a loose ubiquitin number code might exist for the size of a polyubiquitin chain, which, depending on the different binding properties of these escort factors, directs specificity and efficiency in proteasomal targeting.

It is an attractive idea that diversity in the escort pathway is created by modulating polyubiquitin-chain signals. A particularly striking example could be provided by the function of ataxin-3. Here, we propose a model in which ataxin-3 regulates the ubiquitination status of proteins destined for degradation. Ataxin-3 might act antagonistically to the escort complex by reversing the transfer direction of UFD2-polyubiquitinated protein substrates. Its deubiquitination activity would provide a feedback mechanism, enabling fine-tuning of the polyubiquitin signal, which otherwise would be the concomitant signal for degradation (Figure 4A). Alternatively, ataxin-3 might assist the CDC48 complex in restricting the polyubiquitin-chain length to ensure maximum efficiency for proteasomal targeting. In this scenario, a proofreading mechanism for size-restricted ubiquitin chains would be provided by ataxin-3 (Figure 4B). Other potential functions of the ataxin-3 protease activity could include editing functions that regulate the polyubiquitin-chain linkage.

It is tempting to speculate that each substrate is accompanied by an orchestra of distinct escort components and modulating factors, contributing to courses of events which might occur directly at the proteasome. An important future challenge will be to unravel the prominence of such regulat-

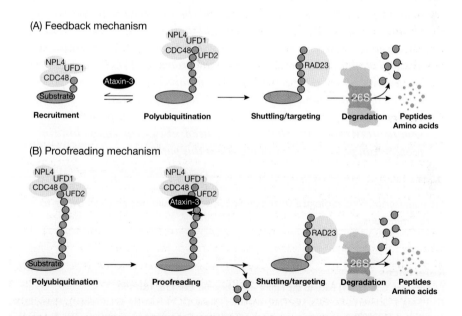

Figure 4. Hypothetical model for a function of ataxin-3 in the escort pathway
UFD2-assembled polyubiquitin chains are regulated to an optimal length of four to six ubiquitin molecules by the concerted action of the CDC48–UFD1–NPL4 complex. Substrates linked to these size-restricted chains are subsequently escorted to the 26 S proteasome for degradation by a succession of interacting factors. Based on its interaction with p97/VCP and UFD2a, the mammalian homologues of yeast CDC48 and UFD2, ataxin-3 might play a role in a conserved escort pathway. Ataxin-3 could be involved in the size-restriction mechanism of this pathway by two alternative modes of action. (**A**) In association with the deubiquitination activity, ataxin-3 could stabilize the substrate by shortening the ubiquitin chain. (**B**) Alternatively, ataxin-3 could support substrate degradation by controlling the efficient length of size-restricted chains in a proofreading mechanism. Moreover, the ability of ataxin-3 to bind to the proteasome [22] suggests that the whole pathway might take place directly at the 26 S proteasome.

ed networks by the identification of additional ubiquitin-binding factors and of specific substrates.

Summary

- *The ubiquitin system usually marks proteins for proteasomal degrada-tion by covalent modification with ubiquitin. This ubiquitination process is mediated by E1, E2 and E3 enzymes.*
- *Each individual lysine residue of ubiquitin can be used for ubiquitin-chain formation (Lys^6-, Lys^{11}-, Lys^{27}-, Lys^{29}-, Lys^{33}-, Lys^{48}-, or Lys^{63}-based linkages), resulting in functionally distinct polyubiquitin chains.*
- *Polyubiquitination is sometimes regulated by additional conjugation factors, called E4 enzymes. The yeast E4 enzyme UFD2 co-operates with an orchestra of ubiquitin-binding factors in an escort pathway to transfer and deliver polyubiquitinated substrates to the 26 S protea-some.*
- *The affinity of polyubiquitin chains for the proteasome is influenced by the length of the chain; four to six ubiquitin molecules are enough for optimal binding to RAD23 and DSK2, which finally mediate the delivery of ubiquitinated substrates to the proteasome.*
- *Alternative escort pathways might be involved in modulating poly-ubiquitin-chain signals. Speculation about a potential role for the ubiquitin-conjugate-binding factor ataxin-3 in this escort mechanism should illustrate how alternatively used ubiquitin-chain-binding proteins can provide more complexity in this pathway.*

We thank Johnny Kim and Heather P. Ostendorff for discussions and comments on the manuscript. We apologize to those whose work could not be cited owing to space limitations.

References

1. Pickart, C.M. (2004) Back to the future with ubiquitin. *Cell* **116**, 181–190
2. Peng, J., Schwartz, D., Elias, J.E., Thoreen, C.C., Cheng, D., Marsischky, G., Roelofs, J., Finley, D. & Gygi, S.P. (2003) A proteomics approach to understanding protein ubiquitination. *Nat. Biotechnol.* **21**, 921–926
3. Pickart, C.M. & Fushman, D. (2004) Polyubiquitin chains: polymeric protein signals. *Curr. Opin. Chem. Biol.* **8**, 610–616
4. Madura, K. (2004) Rad23 and Rpn10: perennial wallflowers join the melee. *Trends Biochem. Sci.* **29**, 637–640
5. Richly, H., Rape, M., Braun, S., Rumpf, S., Hoege, C. & Jentsch, S. (2005) A series of ubiquitin binding factors connects CDC48/p97 to substrate multiubiquitylation and proteasomal targeting. *Cell* **120**, 73–84
6. Koegl, M., Hoppe, T., Schlenker, S., Ulrich, H.D., Mayer, T.U. & Jentsch, S. (1999) A novel ubiquitination factor, E4, is involved in multiubiquitin chain assembly. *Cell* **96**, 635–644

7.   Flick, K., Ouni, I., Wohlschlegel, J.A., Capati, C., McDonald, W.H., Yates, J.R. & Kaiser, P. (2004)
      Proteolysis-independent regulation of the transcription factor Met4 by a single Lys[48]-linked
      ubiquitin chain. Nat. Cell Biol. **6**, 634–641

8.   Hoege, C., Pfander, B., Moldovan, G.L., Pyrowolakis, G. & Jentsch, S. (2002) RAD6-dependent
      DNA repair is linked to modification of PCNA by ubiquitin and SUMO. Nature (London) **419**,
      135–141

9.   Sun, L. & Chen, Z.J. (2004) The novel functions of ubiquitination in signaling. Curr. Opin. Cell Biol.
      16, 119–126

10.   Alberti, S., Demand, J., Esser, C., Emmerich, N., Schild, H. & Hohfeld, J. (2002) Ubiquitylation of
      BAG-1 suggests a novel regulatory mechanism during the sorting of chaperone substrates to the
      proteasome. J. Biol. Chem. **277**, 45920–45927

10a   Iberti, S., Demand, J., Esser, C., Emmerich, N., Schild, H. & Hohfeld, J. (2003) Erratum. J. Biol.
      Chem. **278**, 15702–15703

11.   Wu-Baer, F., Lagrazon, K., Yuan, W. & Baer, R. (2003) The BRCA1/BARD1 heterodimer
      assembles polyubiquitin chains through an unconventional linkage involving lysine residue K6 of
      ubiquitin. J. Biol. Chem. **278**, 34743–34746

12.   Morris, J.R. & Solomon, E. (2004) BRCA1:BARD1 induces the formation of conjugated ubiquitin
      structures, dependent on K6 of ubiquitin, in cells during DNA replication and repair. Hum. Mol.
      Genet. **13**, 807–817

13.   Hoppe, T., Matuschewski, K., Rape, M., Schlenker, S., Ulrich, H.D. & Jentsch, S. (2000) Activation
      of a membrane-bound transcription factor by regulated ubiquitin/proteasome-dependent
      processing. Cell **102**, 577–586

14.   Imai, Y., Soda, M., Hatakeyama, S., Akagi, T., Hashikawa, T., Nakayama, K.I. & Takahashi, R. (2002)
      CHIP is associated with Parkin, a gene responsible for familial Parkinson's disease, and enhances
      its ubiquitin ligase activity. Mol. Cell **10**, 55–67

15.   Hoppe, T., Cassata, G., Barral, J.M., Springer, W., Hutagalung, A.H., Epstein, H.F. & Baumeister, R.
      (2004) Regulation of the myosin-directed chaperone UNC-45 by a novel E3/E4-
      multiubiquitylation complex in C. elegans. Cell **118**, 337–349

16.   Hoppe, T. (2005) Multiubiquitylation by E4 enzymes: 'one size' doesn't fit all. Trends Biochem. Sci.
      30, 183–187

17.   Saeki, Y., Tayama, Y., Toh-e, A. & Yokosawa, H. (2004) Definitive evidence for UFD2-catalyzed
      elongation of the ubiquitin chain through Lys[48] linkage. Biochem. Biophys. Res. Commun. **320**,
      840–845

18.   Ravid, T. & Hochstrasser, M. (2004) NF-kB signaling: flipping the switch with polyubiquitin chains.
      Curr. Biol. **14**, R898–R900

19.   Heyninck, K. & Beyaert, R. (2005) A20 inhibits NF-kB activation by dual ubiquitin-editing
      functions. Trends Biochem. Sci. **30**, 1–4

20.   Burnett, B., Li, F. & Pittman, R.N. (2003) The polyglutamine neurodegenerative protein ataxin-3
      binds polyubiquitylated proteins and has ubiquitin protease activity. Hum. Mol. Genet. **12**,
      3195–3205

21.   Kawaguchi, Y., Okamoto, T., Taniwaki, M., Aizawa, M., Inoue, M., Katayama, S., Kawakami, H.,
      Nakamura, S., Nishimura, M., Akiguchi, I. et al. (1994) CAG expansions in a novel gene for
      Machado–Joseph disease at chromosome 14q32.1. Nat. Genet. **8**, 221–228

22.   Doss-Pepe, E.W., Stenroos, E.S., Johnson, W.G. & Madura, K. (2003) Ataxin-3 interactions with
      rad23 and valosin-containing protein and its associations with ubiquitin chains and the protea-
      some are consistent with a role in ubiquitin-mediated proteolysis. Mol. Cell. Biol. **23**, 6469–6483

23.   Matsumoto, M., Yada, M., Hatakeyama, S., Ishimoto, H., Tanimura, T., Tsuji, S., Kakizuka, A.,
      Kitagawa, M. & Nakayama, K.I. (2004) Molecular clearance of ataxin-3 is regulated by a
      mammalian E4. EMBO J. **23**, 659–669

24.   Masino, L., Nicastro, G., Menon, R.P., Dal Piaz, F., Calder, L. & Pastore, A. (2004)
      Characterization of the structure and the amyloidogenic properties of the Josephin domain of the
      polyglutamine-containing protein ataxin-3. J. Mol. Biol. **344**, 1021–1035

25. Scheel, H., Tomiuk, S. & Hofmann, K. (2003) Elucidation of ataxin-3 and ataxin-7 function by integrative bioinformatics. *Hum. Mol. Genet.* **12**, 2845–2852
26. Guterman, A. & Glickman, M.H. (2004) Deubiquitinating enzymes are IN/(trinsic to proteasome function). *Curr. Protein Pept. Sci.* **5**, 201–211
27. Wang, G., Sawai, N., Kotliarova, S., Kanazawa, I. & Nukina, N. (2000) Ataxin-3, the MJD1 gene product, interacts with the two human homologs of yeast DNA repair protein RAD23, HHR23A and HHR23B. *Hum. Mol. Genet.* **9**, 1795–1803
28. Thrower, J.S., Hoffman, L., Rechsteiner, M. & Pickart, C.M. (2000) Recognition of the polyubiquitin proteolytic signal. *EMBO J.* **19**, 94–102
29. Raasi, S., Orlov, I., Fleming, K.G. & Pickart, C.M. (2004) Binding of polyubiquitin chains to ubiquitin-associated (UBA) domains of HHR23A. *J. Mol. Biol.* **341**, 1367–1379
30. Chai, Y., Berke, S.S., Cohen, R.E. & Paulson, H.L. (2004) Poly-ubiquitin binding by the polyglutamine disease protein ataxin-3 links its normal function to protein surveillance pathways. *J. Biol. Chem.* **279**, 3605–3611
31. Jana, N.R., Dikshit, P., Goswami, A., Kotliarova, S., Murata, S., Tanaka, K. & Nukina, N. (2005) Co-chaperone CHIP associates with expanded polyglutamine protein and promotes their degradation by proteasomes. *J. Biol. Chem.* **280**, 11635–11640
32. Kovalenko, A., Chable-Bessia, C., Cantarella, G., Israel, A., Wallach, D. & Courtois, G. (2003) The tumour suppressor CYLD negatively regulates NF-kB signalling by deubiquitination. *Nature (London)* **424**, 801–805

2

E3 ubiquitin ligases

Helen C. Ardley[1] and Philip A. Robinson

Molecular Medicine Unit, University of Leeds, Clinical Sciences Building, St. James's University Hospital, Leeds LS9 7TF, U.K.

Abstract

The selectivity of the ubiquitin–26 S proteasome system (UPS) for a particular substrate protein relies on the interaction between a ubiquitin-conjugating enzyme (E2, of which a cell contains relatively few) and a ubiquitin–protein ligase (E3, of which there are possibly hundreds). Post-translational modifications of the protein substrate, such as phosphorylation or hydroxylation, are often required prior to its selection. In this way, the precise spatio-temporal targeting and degradation of a given substrate can be achieved. The E3s are a large, diverse group of proteins, characterized by one of several defining motifs. These include a HECT (homologous to E6-associated protein C-terminus), RING (really interesting new gene) or U-box (a modified RING motif without the full complement of Zn^{2+}-binding ligands) domain. Whereas HECT E3s have a direct role in catalysis during ubiquitination, RING and U-box E3s facilitate protein ubiquitination. These latter two E3 types act as adaptor-like molecules. They bring an E2 and a substrate into sufficiently close proximity to promote the substrate's ubiquitination. Although many RING-type E3s, such as MDM2 (murine double minute clone 2 oncoprotein) and c-Cbl, can apparently act alone, others are found as components of much larger multi-protein complexes, such as the anaphase-promoting complex. Taken together, these multifaceted properties and interactions enable E3s to provide a powerful, and specific, mechanism for protein clearance within all cells of eukaryotic organisms. The importance of E3s is highlighted by the number of

[1]*To whom correspondence should be addressed (email h.c.ardley@leeds.ac.uk).*

normal cellular processes they regulate, and the number of diseases associated with their loss of function or inappropriate targeting.

Introduction

Over the last decade, our knowledge and understanding of the UPS (ubiquitin–proteasome system) has expanded enormously. In particular, we have come to realize the importance of E3s (ubiquitin–protein ligases) for substrate recognition and ubiquitination within the system. Particular interest in these molecules has developed since the discovery that E3s are often found to be mutated, absent or malfunctioning in many diseases, including neurodegenerative disorders and cancer (Table 1) [1–3]. Indeed, the pharmaceutical industry is currently assessing whether E3s are suitable therapeutic targets for such disorders [4].

E2s (ubiquitin-conjugating enzymes) are characterized by a highly conserved domain adjacent to the cysteine residue that forms the thioester bond with ubiquitin. By contrast, E3s are a much more diverse group of proteins in terms of size and domain structure. Although such diversity made their initial identification difficult, many E3s have now been characterized. These proteins generally contain one of several different defining E3 domain structures. These motifs are found in hundreds of sequences in mammalian, plant and viral genomes, leading to the suggestion that many of these may also be E3s. In general, like most components of the ubiquitin system, they are highly conserved throughout evolution.

Different types of E3 often display different modes of action (Figure 1). Whereas some promote monoubiquitination of substrate, others catalyse polyubiquitination. The specificity and timing of substrate ubiquitination may be dependent on a number of other factors. These may include the requirement for post-translational modification of the substrate, such as phosphorylation or hydroxylation. The respective intracellular locations of E3, substrate and post-translational modifying complex may also be critical. The combination of these factors presents the cell with a powerful and precise mechanism for the specific spatio-temporal clearance of individual proteins.

A major function of E3s is to regulate the polyubiquitination, and subsequent degradation, of target proteins. Complete breakdown of proteins, however, is not always the primary function of the ubiquitination. For example, polyubiquitination by the RING (really interesting new gene) E3, TRAF6 (tumour necrosis factor-receptor-associated factor 6), is required during IκB (inhibitory κB) processing and NF-κB (nuclear factor κB) activation.

Protein monoubiquitination has been shown to play key functional roles that are apparently independent of degradation. In particular, regulation of endocytosis of cell surface receptors, DNA-repair mechanisms and transcription regulation are controlled by monoubiquitination of target proteins [5].

Table 1. E3s associated with disease

Disease	E3	E3 type	Target(s)
Cancer			
Breast/ovarian	BRCA1, BARD1	RING, RING	H2A, H2B, H3, H4
Colonic, gastric	SCF$^{\beta TrCP}$	Multi-complex	β-catenin, NFκB
Renal cell carcinoma and others	VCB	Multi-complex	HIF-1α, HIF-2α
Sarcoma, leukaemia	MDM2, MDMX	RING, RING	p53
Ewings sarcoma, acute leukaemia	c-Cbl	RING	EGFR
Neurological disorders			
Angelman syndrome	E6-AP1	HECT	p53
Parkinson's disease	Parkin, Dorfin, Siah-1, CHIP	RIR, RIR, RING, U-box	Multiple
Alzheimer's disease	CHIP	U-box	(Phosphorylated)* tau
ALS	Dorfin, CHIP	RIR, U-box	Mutant SOD1
Lafora disease	Malin	RING	Unknown
Miscellaneous			
Liddle's disease	NEDD4	HECT	ENaC
Muscle cachexia	E3α, MuRF1, MAFbX	RING, RING, multi-complex	Multiple
HIV/AIDS	NEDD4	HECT	HIV gag

Specific E3s have now been demonstrated to have a role in disease processes, in particular in cancer and neurodegenerative disorders. For many of these diseases, E3s appear to play an essential role in the aetiology of the condition either due to mis-targeting of (mutant) substrates or through deletion/amplification/mutation of the E3 itself. Both scenarios would result in altered ubiquitination of proteins, leading to disease. *Both phosphorylated [33] and unphosphorylated [34] tau are reported to be ubiquitinated by CHIP. ALS, amyotrophic lateral sclerosis; BARD1, BRCA1-associated RING domain 1; BRCA1, breast-cancer susceptibility gene 1; SOD1, superoxide dismutase 1.

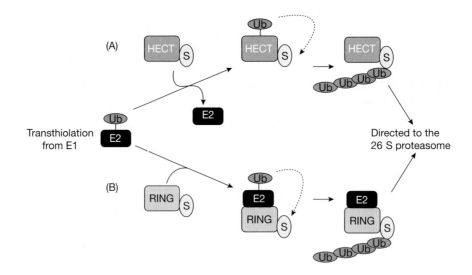

Figure 1. Mechanisms of ubiquitin transfer by HECT and RING E3s
Ubiquitin (Ub) is transferred via transthiolation from an E1 to an E2. E3s then facilitate ubiquiti-nation of the substrate protein (S). (**A**) HECT E3s transfer ubiquitin directly to the substrate. (**B**) RING E3s do not directly catalyse the ubiquitination of the target protein and require the pres-ence of the E2 and often additional components (e.g. in the case of SCF complexes) for ubiquit-ination to proceed. U-box E3s have a similar mode of action to RING E3s. Multiple ubiquitination of substrate is required for recognition by the 26 S proteasome. This may require the involve-ment of additional E2s and E3s.

Interestingly, the levels of E3s themselves can also be regulated by UPS-mediated proteolysis. Indeed, many E3s are capable of self-regulation by 'autoubiquitination' [1–4]. Autoubiquitination may have evolved as a gain-of-function, and protective, cellular mechanism. Programmed self-destruction would help to prevent damaging cellular consequences that may occur if intra-cellular concentrations of E3 became too high. This also raises the possibility that proteins initially identified as E3s as a consequence of their autoubiquiti-nation activity may also display a secondary unrelated function. Loss of E3 autoubiquitination activity through mutation, for example, may not affect its secondary function. This could lead to increased intracellular concentration and secondary function. This property may be particularly relevant in neuro-logical disorders associated with aging, because the UPS becomes less efficient at processing proteins as we age.

E3s: a diverse group of proteins

Three major classes of E3 have been identified, termed the HECT (homologous to E6-associated protein C-terminus), RING finger and U-box (a modified RING motif without the full complement of Zn^{2+}-binding ligands) E3s. In addition, two subclasses of RING E3s have been defined: RIR (RING in between RING–RING) domain, and multi-protein complex E3s

[CRL (Cullin-RING E3)] (Figures 2 and 3). However, there is also a minor group of proteins that are not characterized by any of these domain structures, but can act as E3s. For example, the DUB (deubiquitinating enzyme), UCH-L1 (ubiquitin C-terminal hydrolase L1), a protein highly expressed in the brain, displays dimerization-dependent E3 activity *in vitro* [6]. Why an enzyme should have two opposing functions is somewhat intriguing and warrants further investigation. Whether other DUBs also share this dual function remains to be determined.

HECT domain E3s

One of the first E3s to be identified and characterized was E6-AP1 (E6-associated protein 1) (Figure 2) [7]. Subsequently, many other proteins with a similar 350-amino-acid catalytic domain were identified through database searches. These HECT domain E3s function in a similar manner to E1 and E2s. Each contains a central cysteine residue within the HECT domain, which acts as an acceptor for ubiquitin. The thiol group of the cysteine residue forms a thioester bond with the carboxy group of the C-terminal glycine residue prior to its transfer to substrate (Figure 1). Whereas the C-terminal HECT

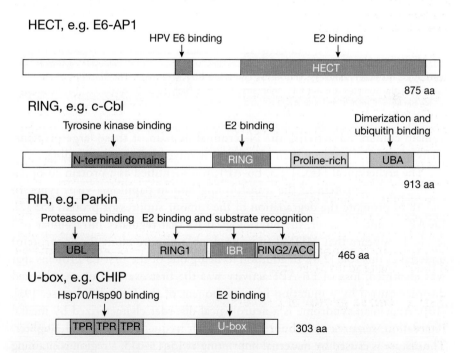

Figure 2. Domain structure of E3s

Structures of the main types of E3. Each contains a specific domain: HECT, RING, RIR or U-box. RING motifs of RIR E3s are of the RING-HC type. Most E3s also contain other protein interaction domains. These vary widely between members of the same E3 type. An example of each type of E3 is shown. HPV, human papillomavirus; UBL, ubiquitin-like domain; TPR, tetratricopeptide repeat.

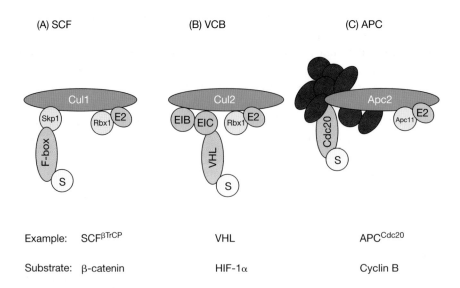

Figure 3. CRLs: multi-protein complexes
An increasing number of large multi-subunit E3s have been identified. CRLs are all based on a Cullin–RING-H2 complex and auxiliary proteins. (**A**) SCF based on Skp1–Cullin 1(Cul1)–F-box proteins. The RING protein, Rbx1, is required for E3 activity. Interaction with different F-box proteins changes substrate specificity. For example, SCF^{Skp2} can degrade p27^{kip1} and E2F-1; SCF$^{\beta TrCP}$ degrades IκB α and β-catenin. (**B**) VCB complex. VCB forms a complex with Cullin 2 and Rbx1 to act as an E3. Substrates (HIF-1α/2α) are recognized by the tumour suppressor protein VHL, which interacts with elongin C, via a SOCS box domain. EIB, elongin B; EIC, elongin C. (**C**) The APC. A large complex consisting of at least eleven subunits, which is activated by the regulatory subunits Cdc20 or Cdh1 (not shown) to degrade mitotic cyclins, securin and other cell-cycle regulatory proteins. Apc2 has cullin homology, and Apc11 contains a RING-H2 motif. The functions of the other subunits in the complex are not fully understood. Each is likely to be involved in either providing a bridge between Cdc20/Cdh1 and Apc2 or aiding in substrate recognition and degradation.

domain confers E3 activity, the N-terminal domain of these large proteins, many of which are greater than 100 kDa, is involved in substrate binding.

The archetypical HECT E3, E6-AP1, was identified as a protein co-opted by the E6 oncoprotein of the transforming human papilloma virus types 16 and 18 to promote the degradation of the tumour suppressor protein p53 [7]. E6-AP1 is not, however, the physiological E3 that regulates intracellular p53 levels. It appears that MDM2 (murine double minute clone 2 oncoprotein) undertakes this role [2,8]. In addition to being one of the first E3 proteins that was identified, loss of E6-AP1 activity was the first example of an inherited disorder caused by a mutation in a component of the UPS ([9], but see [9a], [10]). Angelman syndrome is a neurological disorder characterized by mental retardation, seizures and abnormal gait, with frequent smiling and laughter. The disease is caused by maternal imprinting at 15q11–q13, a region containing *UBE3A*, the gene that encodes E6-AP1 ([9], but see [9a], [10]). Maternal loss of activity of E6-AP1 can occur due to deletions, imprinting mutations, paternal uniparental disomy or point mutations in the *UBE3A* gene. Imprinting defects cause silencing of the paternal allele in neurons, but not in the glial cells of the brain. However, as the physiological substrates of E6-AP1 remain to be determined, the mechanism by which loss of activity causes the neurological phenotype remains unclear.

It is interesting that the gene encoding the human HECT protein, HERC2 [C-terminal HECT domain and three RCC1 (regulator of chromatin condensation)-like domains], and its pseudogenes also flank the chromosomal deletion that characterizes the Prader–Willi and Angelman syndromes at chromosome 15q11–q13 [11]. Murine Herc2 is a large protein of 4834 amino acid residues that demonstrates a remarkable 95% identity and 99% similarity to human HERC2. Loss of Herc2 function leads to the neurological defects associated with the *rjs* (runty–jerky–sterile) mouse [11,12].

RING finger E3s

The RING finger family of proteins potentially represents the largest group of E3s, with hundreds of proteins containing a RING finger domain being present in mammalian genomic databases [13,14]. Although their structures suggest an E3 function, such an activity has not been proven *in vivo* in most instances. Unlike HECT domain proteins, RING finger E3s do not appear to have a direct catalytic role in protein ubiquitination. Instead, RING E3s act as scaffolding partners, facilitating the interaction between an E2 and a substrate (Figure 1) [13,14].

The RING finger domain is a cysteine/histidine-rich, zinc-chelating domain that promotes both protein–protein and protein–DNA interactions. It is defined as Cys^1-Xaa_2-Cys^2-Xaa_{9-39}-Cys^3-Xaa_{1-3}-His^4-Xaa_{2-3}-Cys/His^5-Xaa_2-Cys^6-Xaa_{4-48}-Cys^7-Xaa_2-Cys^8 (where Xaa can be any amino acid residue) [13]. Two zinc atoms are complexed by the cysteine/histidine residues in a 'cross-brace' manner, to provide correct folding and biological activity of the RING domain (Figure 4A). RING finger motifs are further subdivided, depending on whether a cysteine or histidine residue is found at Cys/His^5 within the motif. Thus they are classified as being either a RING-HC (Cys^5) or a RING-H2 (His^5) type. The presence of Cys^5 or His^5 appears to be structurally important for E2 recognition, because substituting cysteine for histidine prevents E2–E3 binding for several RING-containing proteins, including HHARI (human homologue of *Drosophila* ariadne) [15]. It is of note that the second RING domain that characterizes the RIR E3s displays a modified structure that is capable of binding only one Zn^{2+} ion [16].

c-Cbl is a RING finger E3 required for endocytosis and degradation of RTKs (receptor tyrosine kinases) [17,18]. It is required for the early-endosome-to-late-endosome/lysosome sorting step of EGFR (epidermal growth factor receptor) down-regulation. As many membrane receptors signal via a 'triple membrane passing signal' through the EGFR, the control of its levels and activity is fundamental to many signalling pathways. Endocytosis of EGFR by c-Cbl is dependent on phosphorylation. c-Cbl recognizes phosphorylated tyrosines on

(A)

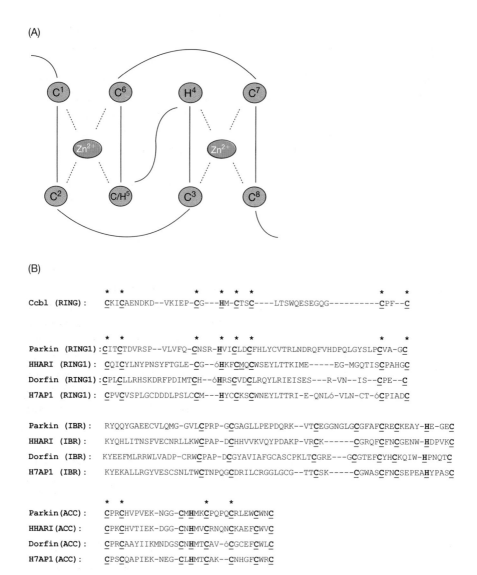

(B)

```
                       *  *              *   *  *  *                              *       *
Ccbl  (RING):      CKICAENDKD--VKIEP-CG---HM-CTSC----LTSWQESEGQG---------CPF--C


                       *  *              *   *  *  *                              *       *
Parkin (RING1):CITCTDVRSP--VLVFQ-CNSR-HVICLDCFHLYCVTRLNDRQFVHDPQLGYSLPCVA-GC

HHARI  (RING1): CQICYLNYPNSYFTGLE-CG--6HKFCMQCWSEYLTTKIME-----EG-MGQTISCPAHGC

Dorfin (RING1):CPLCLLRHSKDRFPDIMTCH--6HRSCVDCLRQYLRIEISES---R-VN--IS--CPE--C

H7AP1  (RING1): CPVCVSPLGCDDDLPSLCCM---HYCCKSCWNEYLTTRI-E-QNL6-VLN-CT-6CPIADC


Parkin (IBR):  RYQQYGAEECVLQMG-GVLCPRP-GCGAGLLPEPDQRK--VTCEGGNGLGCGFAFCRECKEAY-HE-GEC

HHARI  (IBR):  KYQHLITNSFVECNRLLKWCPAP-DCHHVVKVQYPDAKP-VRCK------CGRQFCFNCGENW-HDPVKC

Dorfin (IBR):  KYEEFMLRRWLVADP-CRWCPAP-DCGYAVIAFGCASCPKLTCGRE---GCGTEFCYHCKQIW-HPNQTC

H7AP1  (IBR):  KYEKALLRGYVESCSNLTWCTNPQGCDRILCRGGLGCG--TTCSK-----CGWASCFNCSEPEAHYPASC


                       *  *              *   *
Parkin(ACC):   CPRCHVPVEK-NGG-CMHMKCPQPQCRLEWCWNC

HHARI (ACC):   CPKCHVTIEK-DGG-CNHMVCRNQNCKAEFCWVC

Dorfin(ACC):   CPRCAAYIIKMNDGSCNHMTCAV-6CGCEFCWLC

H7AP1(ACC):    CPSCQAPIEK-NEG-CLHMTCAK--CNHGFCWRC
```

Figure 4. Structure of the RING finger and comparison of RIR domains
(**A**) Schematic showing the RING finger domain. Conserved zinc-binding ligands are numbered and shown in circles (C, cysteine; H, hisidine). Each zinc ion is co-ordinated by four binding ligands. (**B**) A comparison of the structure of the RING1, IBR and ACC domains of Parkin, HHARI, Dorfin and H7-API (Parc). RING1 of these proteins is aligned with the RING domain of c-Cbl. Amino acid residue positions are as indicated. The cysteine and histidine residues that define the RING finger domains are underlined and in bold. '*' indicates a residue required for zinc chelation. '–' denotes a shift in amino acid sequence to maintain alignment.

RTKs through its N-terminal SH2 (Src homology 2) domain. When the ligand binds to EGFR, its tyrosine kinase activity is activated, catalysing autophosphorylation. In the presence of endophilin and Cbl-interacting protein of 85 kDa (also called SH3-domain kinase binding protein 1), c-Cbl then causes rapid endocytosis of EGFR into endosomes. This process is facilitated by receptor ubiquitination. The receptor can then be recycled or processed by the ESCRT (endosomal sorting complex required for transport) system.

Another member of the Cbl family is Cbl3. This protein is structurally similar to c-Cbl, but it lacks the UBA (ubiquitin-associated) domain and pro-line-rich domains. Cbl3 also regulates the EGFR; however, in this instance it requires an interaction with the HECT E3, ITCH (itchy homologue E3 ubiquitin–protein ligase), before ubiquitination can occur [19]. Interestingly, ITCH itself does not interact directly with EGFR. This suggests that Cbl3 may be required for the initial ubiquitination step with ITCH, enhancing polyubiquitination of the receptor. Cbl proteins have also been described as suppressors of other EGFR superfamily members, including the HER2/Neu oncogene. Up-regulation of EGFR-superfamily signalling is a major contributor to uncontrolled proliferation in many malignant conditions.

As noted above, p53 is usually targeted for cellular removal by the RING finger protein, MDM2 [2,8]. Ubiquitination of p53 by MDM2 may also regulate the nuclear export of p53 to the cytoplasm for proteasomal degradation, although this role of MDM2 remains controversial [4]. MDM2 regulation of p53 turnover is complex. Under normal cellular conditions, p53 up-regulates *MDM2* gene expression while MDM2 down-regulates p53. Other proteins, including cyclin-dependent kinase 2A (CDKN2A) and MDMX, and post-translational modifications (such as phosphorylation of both p53 and MDM2) add extra layers of complexity to the regulation of p53 by MDM2. Whereas ARF acts to inhibit MDM2 activity, MDMX enhances its activity. MDMX is a RING finger protein highly related to MDM2. The MDM2–MDMX dimer forms via RING domain interactions between the two proteins and prevents autoubiquitination of MDM2. The resultant increased stability of MDM2 was expected to result in lower levels of p53. However, it also caused the stabilization of p53. This occurs because the MDM2–MDMX complex ubiquitinates p53, but the latter polyubiquitinated product accumulates in the nucleus and is not degraded by the 26 S proteasome. Interestingly, when CDKN2A blocks MDM2's activity towards p53, MDM2 targets the degradation of MDMX.

Complex RING E3s

RING-IBR-RING E3s

The RIR E3 family consist of a central Cys/His-rich region called the IBR [in between RING fingers; alternatively termed the double RING linked (DRIL)] domain. It links a classic RING finger domain to a second RING-finger-like or ACC (accessory C-terminal zinc finger) domain [20,21]. This specialized group of E3s appear to be RING-HC type E3s. They rely on the highly homologous E2s, UbcH7 (ubiquitin-conjugating enzyme H7) or UbcH8, for their activity. The RING1 domain is structurally similar to many other RING-finger-containing proteins, such as c-Cbl (Figure 4B). However, it is generally a little

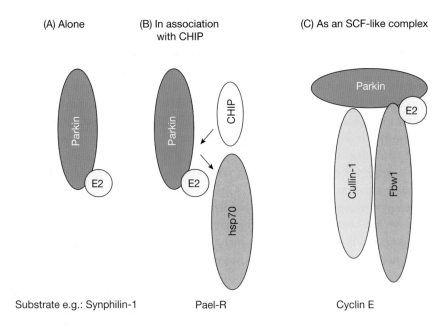

(A) Alone

(B) In association
with CHIP

(C) As an SCF-like complex

Substrate e.g.: Synphilin-1   Pael-R   Cyclin E

Figure 5. Parkin can act alone or as part of a multi-protein complex
Multiple substrates for Parkin have been described. Some, including synphilin-1 and α–synuclein, require Parkin–E2 for degradation (**A**). However, Parkin is also capable of forming E3 complexes. (**B**) Parkin E3 activity and subsequent degradation of Pael-R is enhanced when CHIP displaces hsp70 binding to Parkin. (**C**) Cyclin E is degraded by Parkin as part of an SCF-like complex containing Cullin 1 and F-box[Fbw1].

larger and is essential for E2 and substrate binding. The IBR domain is characterized by the canonical structure, C_6HC [20]. The purpose of the IBR remains unknown. It may promote protein–protein interactions or, alternatively, it may act as a spacer, or flexible region, that accurately positions the RING1 and ACC domains for E2/substrate recognition and binding. Indeed, a 20-amino-acid essential spacer region is required for UbcH7 binding to the RIR of HHARI [15]. The RING2, or the ACC, domain is smaller (but similar in size between family members) than RING1. Although this was originally thought to be an additional RING finger, structural studies have now established that this domain has a distinctly different topology from classical RING finger domains [16]. The Cys^1, Cys^2, Cys^4 and Cys^6 residues are required for binding of only a single zinc atom. As a consequence, the unique structure of the ACC domain resembles a zinc ribbon motif with a 'criss-cross' appearance, similar to that of subunit Rbp12 of RNA polymerase II [16].

Whereas it is generally accepted that RING1 is essential for E3 activity, the ACC may also be required for the recognition and binding of both E2 and substrate. This is the case with Parkin. Although the ACC domain in isolation can interact with E2s and cause ubiquitination in *in vitro* assays [16], they have not been identified independently of the RIR. Hence, the significance of this observation to *in vivo* activity remains unclear.

RIR E3s, such as Parkin, can act both alone with the E2 to facilitate ubiquitination, or with cullin-containing proteins, as part of a multi-protein complex (Figure 5). Parkin mutations are responsible for more than 50% of all cases of AR-JP (autosomal recessive juvenile Parkinsonism) [22–24]. AR-JP patients suffer from an early onset form of Parkinson's disease, with symptoms often manifesting in the third decade of life. Because of the importance of Parkin, many studies have been undertaken to identify substrates of this E3, with the aim of understanding why it causes disease. Substrates include synphilin-1, synaptotagmin XI and Pael-R (Parkin-associated endothelin-receptor-like receptor) [24–27]. It is proposed that Pael-R accumulates in the ER (endoplasmic reticulum) of dopaminergic neurons to cause ER stress and neurodegeneration in Parkin-associated AR-JP patients. Under normal conditions, Parkin degrades unfolded Pael-R before it is able to accumulate [27]. This mechanism involves the chaperone hsp70 (heat-shock protein 70), and CHIP (C-terminus of the hsp-70-interacting protein) (Figure 5B) [27]. Both CHIP and hsp70 interact with Parkin to regulate Pael-R degradation. The E3 activity of Parkin is inhibited when hsp70 transiently forms a complex with unfolded Pael-R and Parkin. The presence of CHIP, however, causes the dissociation of hsp70 from the Pael-R–Parkin complex, enhancing Parkin activity and breakdown of the Pael-R protein. The interplay between hsp70, Parkin and CHIP is particularly interesting, given that CHIP can independently act as both a co-chaperone and an E3 (see the section on U-boxes below). These combined activities provide a direct link between the chaperone system and the UPS.

By contrast, Parkin has also been demonstrated to be part of an SCF (Skp1–Cul1–F-box protein)-like E3, composed of Cullin-1 and the F-box protein Fbw7, which targets cyclin E for degradation (Figure 5C) [28]. Interestingly, Skp1 is not required for E3 activity in this complex [28]. Since elevated levels of cyclin E cause apoptosis in post-mitotic neurons, AR-JP-associated Parkin mutations may also cause neuronal loss because of increased cyclin E-mediated apoptosis.

The flexible nature of Parkin E3 activity may explain why it can target many different substrates. Furthermore, the broad range of cellular functions of these targets may explain why the molecular mechanisms underlying Parkinson's disease have been so difficult to elucidate.

CRLs

The multi-component, modular CRLs are a large and diverse group of ligases [3,4,14,29]. They comprise at least a Cullin and a RING protein (Figure 3). The principal groups are the F-box (in SCF), BTB (broad complex, tramtrak, bric a brac) and SOCS (suppressor of cytokine signalling)/BC (elongin B, elongin C) types of E3 complexes (Figures 3A and 3B) [4,13,29]. The Cullin proteins (CUL1, CUL3 and CUL2A, respectively) provide the central scaffolding component of each of these complexes. For example, for the SCF complexes, Skp1 interacts with its N-terminal sequence to recruit the substrate receptors (F-box proteins). By contrast, Rbx1 (RING box protein 1) (or ROC1/HRT1) binds the C-terminal domain to recruit the E2 to form the active complex. The C-terminal region is also modified by the ubiquitin-like protein, NEDD8 (neural precursor cell expressed developmentally down-regulated 8) [4,14,29]. This post-translational modification appears to improve the ligase activity of the E3, possibly by enhancing the binding of ubiquitin-loaded E2s.

The presence of multiple F-box, BTB and SOCS/BC box proteins in genome databases suggests that changing just one component of these com-plexes can potentially allow the formation of many different E3s, each with their own targeting specificity. For example, SCF$^{\beta TrCP}$ (SCF β-transducin repeat-containing protein) can target the degradation of β-catenin or IκBα, whereas substrates of SCF^{SKP2} include p27^{KIP1}, c-Myc and cyclin E. Recognition of these substrates often requires their phosphorylation prior to their targeted ubiquitination.

In the case of β-catenin, phosphorylation requires a complex of GSK-3β (glycogen synthase kinase 3β), axin and the APCp (adenomatous polyposis coli tumour suppressor protein). UPS-mediated breakdown of β-catenin is essential to limit the amount of cytosolic β-catenin entering the nucleus, there-by inhibiting its role as an activator of TCF4 (T-cell factor 4)-driven transcrip-tion. Without this tight regulation, increased levels of transcriptional activation of downstream genes occur. Mutations in APCp or β-catenin that prevent their interaction lead to the malignant transformation of colonic epithelium.

The VCB [VHL (von Hippel–Lindau) E3 or VHL elongin C–elongin B] complex is made up of the VHL tumour suppressor, elongins B and C (ubiqui-tin-like and Skp1-related, respectively), Rbx1 and an E2 (Figure 3B) [4,14]. Despite its ubiquitin-like homology, the role of elongin B within the complex is unclear. The VCB is involved in down-regulation of the HIF-1α (hypoxia-inducible factor-1α) and HIF-2α. Under normoxic conditions, HIF-1α is hydroxylated and targeted for degradation by VCB. However, under hypoxic conditions, hydroxylation of the key proline residue in HIF-1α/2α does not occur. This has the consequence that HIF-1α/2α is stabilized, as it is no longer recognized by the VCB complex. Mutations in VHL also result in a loss of VCB activity. The consequence of stabilization of HIF-1α/2α is increased transcription of downstream genes, such as that encoding vascular endothelial growth factor. This can lead to the development of a variety of highly vascu-larized tumours, such as those observed in renal cell carcinoma.

The APC (anaphase-promoting complex) is key to many cell cycle events, including chromosome segregation and exit from mitosis. It is a large multi-component complex consisting of at least eleven subunits (Figure 3C) [3,4,14]. Its core structure is highly similar to that of the SCF complexes. The APC2 sub-unit contains a cullin-like domain and APC11 is a RING finger protein which binds the E2. The interchangeable regulatory subunits Cdc20 (cell-division cycle

20) or Cdh1 (Cdc20 homologue 1; also known as fizzy) are required for its activation [3]. They act in a similar way to the F-box proteins, providing substrate specificity. The additional subunits are likely to act as scaffolding molecules, promoting interactions that bring a substrate and the E2–E3 core complex into sufficient proximity to promote ubiquitination of its various substrates. Indeed, recent data suggest that APC1, APC4 and APC5 are involved in polyubiquitin chain assembly, APC3 and APC7 can recruit Cdh1 to the APC complex, APC10 is involved in substrate recognition, and APC9 provides structural stability to the complex [30,31].

U-box E3s

The U-box is a 74-amino-acid domain that is structurally similar to the RING finger domain [32,33]. However, it lacks the key residues required for metal chelation. It has been proposed that it utilizes salt bridges to maintain its structure. The U-box was first described in the yeast protein Ufd2 (ubiquitin fusion degradation protein 2), a protein involved in ubiquitin-chain elongation in conjunction with an E1, E2 and a HECT E3. This new type of enzyme was termed an E4. Initially, all U-box proteins were thought to be auxiliary proteins, supplementing the activity of E2–E3 interactions. However, subsequent studies have demonstrated that other U-box proteins can interact with E2s and display E3 activity independently of another E3 [32,33]. Whether these proteins act as an E3 or E4 may depend on which components of the UPS are present, and the nature of the substrate. Given their similarity in structure, it is perhaps not surprising that U-box E3s show similar modes of action to the RING E3s, sometimes acting alone, and sometimes as part of multi-protein complexes.

CHIP is the best characterized of the U-box proteins [32,33]. It was first identified as a co-chaperone that interacts with hsp70 or hsp90 through the N-terminal tetratricopeptide repeat regions. It is involved in quality control, regulating decisions between folding of the protein by the chaperones or degradation by the UPS [26,32,33]. Recently, CHIP was demonstrated to be an E3 that uses UbcH5 as its E2 partner. Its substrates include: the cystic fibrosis transmembrane conductance regulator; the Alzheimer's-disease-associated protein, tau; the glucocorticoid receptor; and the transcription factor E2A [32–35]. Hsp70 or hsp90 appear to direct the substrate specificity of CHIP.

Analogous to RING E3s, CHIP also interacts with other U-box proteins. For example, the *Caenorhabditis elegans* orthologues of CHIP and Ufd2 interact to degrade unc-45, a (co-)chaperone required during thick myosin filament assembly [36]. Furthermore, as mentioned above, CHIP has a role in enhancing Parkin E3 activity [27].

Conclusion

E3 proteins are now recognized as performing a pivotal role in ubiquitin-mediated intercellular protein degradation. The majority of E3s are proteins that contain HECT, RING or U-box motifs within their structure. Different families of E3s have members which can act alone, with other proteins or E3s, or as part of larger, multi-protein complexes. Under certain circumstances, additional proteins may also be required to enhance the activity of an E3. E4 proteins may act in conjunction with E3s, but some also have E3 properties themselves, making the characterization of these molecules difficult. Other proteins containing DOC (deleted in oral cancer), SOCS or CUE (coupling of ubiquitin conjugation to ER degradation) domains (involved with substrate recognition and interaction with E2s respectively) can also enhance ubiquitination reactions.

E3 proteins, with their myriad of combinations and their need for post-translational modifications and/or additional proteins, ensure the precise spatio-temporal targeting and breakdown of individual substrates within cells. Much is still to be learnt about the regulation of protein levels by this complex group of proteins, especially *in vivo*.

Summary

- *E3s are essential for substrate recognition and ubiquitination.*
- *Substrate recognition may require post-translational modification of the substrate.*
- *The major classes of E3 proteins contain either HECT, RING or U-box domains.*
- *HECT domain proteins are directly involved in ubiquitination of substrate proteins. By contrast, RING and U-box proteins act as facilitators of ubiquitination reactions.*
- *Many RING finger proteins are core components of multi-protein E3 complexes.*
- *Many RING finger E3s interact with other E3s, thereby promoting greater targeting specificity or enhanced ubiquitination.*
- *Many E3s possess the potential to regulate their own levels through autoubiquitination.*

Literature covering the topic of E3s is increasing at an exponential rate. Consequently, it has been impossible to cite many exceptional articles within the constraints of this review. We apologize to those whose work we have not quoted. However, many additional E3 references can be found at: http://www.leeds.ac.uk/medicine/res_school/mol_med/res_robinson.htm

H.C.A is a recipient of a Research into Ageing Fellowship Award. Work in the authors' laboratory is also supported by The Parkinson's Disease Society (UK) and Yorkshire Cancer Research. H.C.A. would like to dedicate this essay to Jessica and Thomas Carey.

References

1.   Ardley, H.C. & Robinson, P.A. (2004) The role of ubiquitin protein ligases in neurodegenerative disease. *Neurodegen. Dis.* **1**, 71–87

2.   Michael, D. & Oren, M. (2002) The p53 and Mdm2 families in cancer. *Curr. Opin. Genet. Dev.* **12**, 53–59

3.   Wasch, R. & Engelbert, D. (2005) Anaphase-promoting complex-dependent proteolysis of cell cycle regulators and genomic instability of cancer cells. *Oncogene* **24**, 1–10

4.   Robinson, P.A. & Ardley, H.C. (2004) Ubiquitin protein ligases — novel therapeutic targets? *Curr. Protein Pept. Sci.* **5**, 163–176

5.   Hicke, L. (2001) Protein regulation by monoubiquitin. *Nat. Rev. Mol. Cell Biol.* **2**, 195–201

6.   Liu, Y., Fallon, L., Lashuel, H.A., Liu, Z. & Lansbury, Jr, P.T. (2002) The *UCH-L1* gene encodes two opposing enzymatic activities that affect alpha-synuclein degradation and Parkinson's disease susceptibility. *Cell* **111**, 209–218

7.   Scheffner, M., Huibregtse, J.M., Vierstra, R.D. & Howley, P.M. (1993) The HPV-16 E6 and E6-AP complex functions as a ubiquitin-protein ligase in the ubiquitination of p53. *Cell* **75**, 495–505

8.   Moll, U.M. & Petrenko, O. (2003) The MDM2-p53 interaction. *Mol. Cancer Res.* **14**, 1001–1008

9.   Kishino, T., Lalande, M. & Wagstaff, J. (1997) UBE3A/E6-AP mutations cause Angelman syndrome. *Nat. Genet.* **15**, 70–73

9a. Kishino, T., Lalande, M. & Wagstaff, J. (1997) Erratum *Nat. Genet.* **15**, 411

10. Matsuura, T., Sutcliffe, J.S., Fang, P., Galjaard, R.J., Jiang, Y.H., Benton, C.S., Rommens, J.M. & Beaudet, A.L. (1997) De novo truncating mutations in E6-AP ubiquitin-protein ligase gene (UBE3A) in Angelman syndrome. *Nat. Genet.* **15**, 74–77

11. Ji, Y., Walkowicz, M.J., Buiting, K., Johnson, D.K., Tarvin, R.E., Rinchik, E.M., Horsthemke, B., Stubbs, L., Nicholls, R.D. (1999) The ancestral gene for transcribed, low-copy repeats in the Prader–Willi/Angelman region encodes a large protein implicated in protein trafficking, which is deficient in mice with neuromuscular and spermiogenic abnormalities. *Hum. Mol. Genet.* **8**, 533–542

12. Lehman, A.L., Nakatsu, Y., Ching, A., Bronson, R.T., Oakey, R.J., Keiper-Hrynko. N., Finger, J.N., Durham-Pierre, D., Horton, D.B., Newton, J.M. et al. (1998) A very large protein with diverse functional motifs is deficient in rjs (runty, jerky, sterile) mice. *Proc. Natl. Acad. Sci. U.S.A.* **95**, 9436–9441

13. Borden, K.L. & Freemont, P.S. (1996) The RING finger domain: a recent example of a sequence-structure family. *Curr. Opin. Struct. Biol.* **6**, 395–401

14. Jackson, P.K., Eldridge, A.G., Freed, E., Furstenthal, L., Hsu, J.Y., Kaiser, B.K. & Reimann, J.D. (2000) The lore of the RINGs: substrate recognition and catalysis by ubiquitin ligases. *Trends Cell Biol.* **10**, 429–439

15. Ardley, H.C., Tan, N.G.S., Rose, S.A., Markham, A.F. & Robinson, P.A. (2001) Features of the Parkin/Ariadne-like ubiquitin ligase, HHARI, which regulate its interaction with the ubiquitin-conjugating enzyme, UbcH7. *J. Biol. Chem.* **276**, 19640–19647

16. Capili, A.D., Edghill, E.L., Wu, K. & Borden, K.L. (2004) Structure of the C-terminal RING finger from a RING-IBR-RING/TRIAD motif reveals a novel zinc-binding domain distinct from a RING. *J. Mol. Biol.* **340**, 1117–1129

17. Dikic, I. (2003) Mechanisms controlling EGF receptor endocytosis and degradation. *Biochem. Soc. Trans.* **31**, 1178–1181

18. Marmor, M.D. & Yarden, Y. (2004) Role of protein ubiquitination in regulating endocytosis of receptor tyrosine kinases. *Oncogene* **23**, 2057–2070

19. Courbard, J.R., Fiore, F., Adelaide, J., Borg, J.P., Birnbaum, D. & Ollendorff, V. (2002) Interaction between two ubiquitin-protein isopeptide ligases of different classes, CBLC and AIP4/ITCH. *J. Biol. Chem.* **277**, 45267–45275

20. Morett, E. & Bork, P. (1999) A novel transactivation domain in Parkin. *Trends Biochem. Sci.* **24**, 229–231

21. Marin, I., Lucas, J.I., Gradilla, A.C. & Ferrus, A. (2004) Parkin and relatives: the RBR family of ubiquitin ligases. *Physiol. Genomics* **17**, 253–263

22. Kitada, T., Asakawa, S., Hattori, N., Matsumine, H., Yamamura, Y., Minoshima, S., Yokochi, M., Mizuno, Y. & Shimizu, N. (1998) Mutations in the *parkin* gene cause autosomal recessive juvenile parkinsonism. *Nature (London)* **392**, 605–608

23. Shimura, H., Hattori, N., Kubo, S., Mizuno, Y., Asakawa, S., Minoshima, S., Shimizu, N., Iwai, K., Chiba, T., Tanaka, K. & Suzuki, T. (2000) Familial Parkinson disease gene product, parkin, is a ubiquitin-protein ligase. *Nat. Genet.* **25**, 302–305

24. Mizuno, Y., Hattori, N., Mori, H., Suzuki, T. & Tanaka, K. (2001) Parkin and Parkinson's disease. *Curr. Opin. Neurol.* **14**, 477–482

25. Chung, K.K.K., Zhang, Y., Lim, K.L., Tanaka, Y., Huang, H., Gao, J., Ross. C.A., Dawson, V.L. & Dawson, T.M. (2001) Parkin ubiquitinates the α-synuclein-interacting protein, synphilin-1: implications for Lewy-body formation in Parkinson disease. *Nat. Med.* **7**, 1144–1150

26. Huynh, D.P., Scoles, D.R., Nguyen, D. & Pulst, S.M. (2003) The autosomal recessive juvenile Parkinson disease gene product, parkin, interacts with and ubiquitinates synaptotagmin XI. *Hum. Mol. Genet.* **12**, 2587–2597

27. Imai, Y., Soda, M., Hatakeyama, S., Akagi, T., Hashikawa, T., Nakayama, K-I. & Takahashi, R. (2002) CHIP is associated with Parkin, a gene responsible for familial Parkinson's disease, and enhances its ubiquitin ligase activity. *Mol. Cell* **10**, 55–67

28. Staropoli, J.F., McDermott, C., Martinat, C., Schulman, B., Demireva, E. & Abeliovich, A. (2003) Parkin is a component of an SCF-like ubiquitin ligase complex and protects postmitotic neurons from kainite excitotoxicity. *Neuron* **37**, 735–749

29. Petroski, M.D. & Deshaies, R.J. (2005) Function and regulation of cullin-RING ubiquitin ligases. *Nat. Rev. Mol. Cell Biol.* **6**, 9–20

30. Vodermaier, H.C., Gieffers, C., Maurer-Stroh, S., Eisenhaber, F. & Peters, J.M. (2003) TPR sub-units of the anaphase-promoting complex mediate binding to the activator protein CDH1. *Curr. Biol.* **13**, 1459–1468

31. Passmore, L.A., McCormack, E.A., Au, S.W., Paul, A., Willison, K.R., Harper, J.W. & Barford, D. (2003) Doc1 mediates the activity of the anaphase-promoting complex by contributing to sub-strate recognition. *EMBO J.* **22**, 786–796

32. Cyr, D.M., Hohfeld, J. & Patterson, C. (2002) Protein quality control: U-box-containing E3 ubiquitin ligases join the fold. *Trends Biochem. Sci.* **27**, 368–375

33. Hatakeyama, S. & Nakayama, K.I. (2003) U-box proteins as a new family of ubiquitin ligases. *Biochem. Biophys. Res. Commun.* **302**, 635–645

34. Shirmura, H., Schwartz, D., Gygi, S.P. & Kisik, K.S. (2004) CHIP-Hsc70 complex ubiquitinates phosphorylated tau and enhances cell survival. *J. Biol. Chem.* **279**, 4869–4876

35. Hatakeyama, S., Matsumoto, M., Kamura, T., Murayama, M., Chui, D.-H., Planel, E., Takahashi, R., Nakayama, K.I. & Takshima, A. (2004) U-box protein carboxyl terminus of Hsc70-interacting protein (CHIP) mediates poly-ubiquitination preferentially on four-repeat Tau and is involved in neurodegeneration of tauopathy. *J. Neurochem.* **91**, 299–307

36. Hoppe, T., Cassata, G., Barral, J.M., Springer, W., Hutagalung, A.H., Epstein, H.F. & Baumeister, R. (2004) Regulation of the myosin-directed chaperone UNC-45 by a novel E3/E4-polyubiquitination complex in *C. elegans. Cell* **118**, 337–349

3

Proteasomes

Burkhardt Dahlmann[1]

*Institut für Biochemie, Charité Universitätsmedizin Berlin,
Monbijoustr. 2, 10117 Berlin, Germany*

Abstract

The major enzyme system catalysing the degradation of intracellular proteins is the proteasome system. A central inner chamber of the cylinder-shaped 20 S proteasome contains the active site, formed by N-terminal threonine residues. The 20 S proteasomes are extremely inefficient in degrading folded protein substrates and therefore one or two multisubunit 19 S regulatory particles bind to one or both ends of the 20 S proteasome cylinder, forming 26 S and 30 S proteasomes respectively. These regulatory complexes are able to bind proteins marked as proteasome substrates by prior conjugation with polyubiquitin chains, and initiate their unfolding and translocation into the proteolytic chamber of the 20 S proteasome, where they are broken down into peptides of 3–25 amino acids. The polyubiquitin tag is removed from the substrate protein by the deubiquitinating activity of the 19 S regulator complex. Under conditions of an intensified immune response, many eukaryotic cells adapt by replacing standard 20 S proteasomes with immuno-proteasomes and/or generating the proteasome activator complex, PA28. Both of these adaptations change the protein-breakdown process for optimized generation of antigenic peptide epitopes that are presented by the class I MHCs. Hybrid proteasomes (19 S regulator–20 S proteasome–PA28) may have a special function during the immune response. The functions of other proteasome accessory complexes, such as PA200 and PI31 are still under investigation.

[1]*Email burkhardt.dahlmann@charite.de*

Introduction

A prerequisite for cell viability is the presence of a set of thousands of precisely working proteins. Since there is no storage form of proteins, the synthesis of each protein is based on specific demands, depending on the developmental and environmental situation of a given cell. This implies that each protein is eliminated from a cell as soon as it is no longer needed, resulting in the phenomenon that each cellular protein has a specific half-life. While synthesis of all proteins is regulated on the level of gene transcription and mRNA translation, the mechanisms of their specific rate of degradation are less well understood; the discovery of the UPS (ubiquitin–proteasome system) as the major pathway for intracellular protein degradation was a big step forward. The UPS works almost hierarchically: the ubiquitinating enzymes select and mark the proteins committed for degradation, by conjugation with polyubiquitin chains; the proteasomes, generally designated 26 S proteasomes but appearing in various forms (such as proteasomes 26 S, 30 S and hybrid), fulfil this degradation. As protein degradation is irreversible, it is devastating to the cell if it proceeds in an uncontrolled manner. Therefore most proteolytic enzymes are regulated by protease inhibitors and activators, or are spatially separated from their potential substrates. With regard to proteasomes, both of these control mechanisms occur and enable all eukaryotic cells, as well as several archaeal and some eubacterial cells, to eliminate selectively proteins that are no longer needed to maintain cellular homoeostasis [1–4].

20 S, 26 S and 30 S proteasomes

The proteolytic enzyme that recognizes proteins committed for degradation by conjugation with polyubiquitin tags is called the 26 S proteasome. This high-molecular-mass complex is composed of a central cylindrical or barrel-shaped 11 nm × 15 nm core complex, the 20 S proteasome, which is built up by four stacked rings containing, in its inner hole, the active sites for catalysis of peptide-bond hydrolysis. The outer rings are composed of seven α-subunits, and the internal two rings each consists of seven β-subunits, resulting in an overall configuration of α1–α7/β1–β7/β1–β7/α1–α7 (Figure 1). Since the 20 S proteasome alone is unable to recognize and bind polyubiquitinated substrate proteins, 19 S Rps (19 S regulatory particles) bind to one or both α-rings of the 20 S proteasome and thus build up 26 S and 30 S proteasomes respectively (Figure 1). Whether 26 S proteasomes exist *in vivo*, or result from dissociation of one 19 S Rp from 30 S proteasomes during the purification process, is unknown. The mechanism of assembly of the 20 S proteasome and 19 S Rp is largely unknown; in addition to its ATP-dependency, the chaperone Hsp90 (heat-shock protein 90) seems to play a positive regulatory role, and PAAF-1 (proteasomal ATPase-associated factor-1) a negative role within this process [5,6]. The 19 S

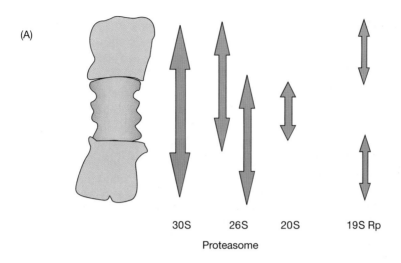

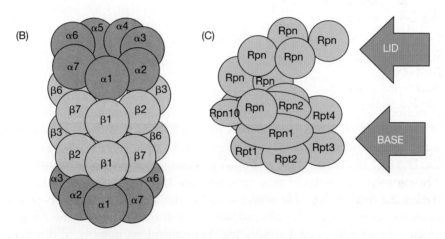

Figure 1. 30 S, 26 S and 20 S proteasomes and the 19 S Rp
(**A**) Representation of a 30 S proteasome based on electron micrographs, indicating its subcomponents. (**B**) Subunit arrangement in the 20 S proteasome. (**C**) The base subcomplex of the 19 S Rp consists of six AAA-ATPase subunits (Rpt1–Rpt6) and two non-ATPase subunits, Rpn1 and Rpn2. The lid is composed of eight non-ATPase subunits (Rpn), the exact arrangement of which is still unknown. Rpn10 may function as a hinge between the base and lid.

Rp has the ability to bind ubiquitinated as well as several non-ubiquitinated substrates and to pass them over to the 20 S proteasome for degradation [7].

The 19 S regulator complex

Molecular architecture

The 19 S regulator, also called cap, is composed of about 17 subunits, which assemble into a complex [8]. This is subdivided into two subcomplexes, one of which, the base, consists of six proteins with ATP-hydrolysing activity, designated Rpt1–Rpt6 (Figure 1). These proteins belong to a family of about 100 different cellular ATPases containing one or two copies of a conserved amino acid motif called AAA (ATPase associated with various cellular activities) [9]. Rpt1–Rpt6 are essential for the survival of yeast cells and form a hexameric ring that associates with the outer α-rings of the 20 S proteasome. Two additional components of the base are non-ATPase subunits, Rpn1 and Rpn2, the largest proteins of the 19 S Rp. The second subcomplex, called the lid, is added on top of the base. The lid is composed of eight different non-ATPase subunits (Rpn3, Rpn5–Rpn9, Rpn11 and Rpn12) and might be partly anchored to the base by Rpn10, because deletion of this subunit in yeast cells results in lability of the 19 S Rp. However, additional proteins seem to stabilize the lid–base interaction.

Substrate binding
Subunit Rpn10 has been found to bind polyubiquitin conjugates, but as it is not necessary for the survival of a yeast cell, recognition and binding of ubiquitinated substrates cannot be confined to this subunit. One would expect a protein escorting substrates to the proteasome to have two essential properties: on the one hand, it must be able to recognize the substrate, for instance by binding polyubiquitin via a UIM (ubiquitin-interacting motif) or a UBA (ubiquitin-associated) domain, and, on the other hand, it should be able to bind to the 19 S Rp, e.g. via a UBL (ubiquitin-like) domain. Several proteasome-interacting proteins (proteins that are non-essential components of the purified 26 S/30 S proteasomes but are known to interact transiently with them) have been found to contain both UBA and UBL domains, e.g. Rad23, Dsk2 and Ddi1. These and other proteins may carry polyubiquitinated substrates to the 19 S Rp by binding to subunit Rpn1 or Rpn2, or to both [10] (Figure 2). Another possible acceptor site in the 19 S Rp is Rpn6, as it was found to interact with the ubiquitinated pro-transcription factor NF-κB (nuclear factor κB)/p100. Considering the tremendous number of different substrate proteins that are degraded by proteasomes, multiple carriers [e.g. Cdc48 (cell-division cycle 48)/valosin, Bag1 and several other proteins] may work in parallel, delivering their cargos to different acceptor sites depending on the length of the conjugated polyubiquitin chain [11]. The ATPase subunit Rpt5 is also able to bind polyubiquitin chains, suggesting that all substrates are funnelled to a final gateway in the base [12]. The proteins that have been found to be degraded by 26 S proteasomes without being tagged by polyubiquitin chains seem to be recognized by the same elements in the 19 S Rp lid that recognize ubiquitin conjugates [13].

Substrate unfolding and translocation
Tethering of a protein–polyubiquitin conjugate at one or several acceptor sites of the 19 S Rp allows its further processing (Figure 2). Since final degradation of substrate proteins takes place in the innermost central chamber of the 20 S

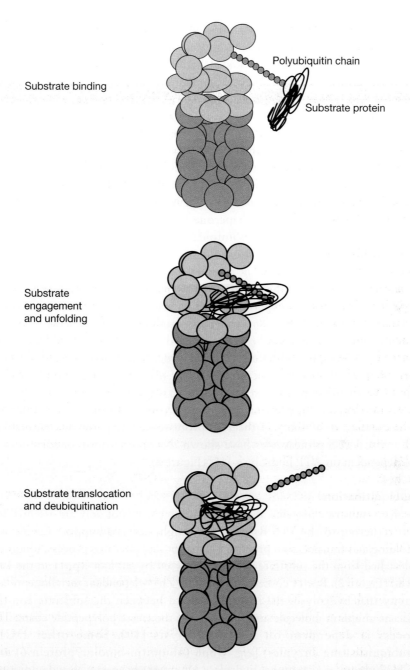

Figure 2. Functions of the 19 S Rp

A 19 S Rp added to a 20 S proteasome. Both complexes are partially sectioned longitudinally. A polyubiquitin–protein substrate is recognized by a lid-subunit of the 19 S Rp. The polyubiquitin chain is used to engage and tether the substrate protein and its unfolding by 19 S Rp base subunits begins at an unstructured initiation site. The N-termini of the α-subunits of the 20 S proteasome form a mesh, closing the central pore within the α-ring. Docking of the 19 S Rp complex has displaced these N-termini and caused opening of the pore. Thus, the unfolded part of the substrate protein is translocated from the 19 S Rp through the α-ring pore into the chambers of the 20 S proteasome. The polyubiquitin chain is then removed from the substrate.

proteasome, which is accessible only through a narrow pore in the outer α-ring and a channel leading through an antechamber between the α- and β-rings, substrate proteins have to be unfolded before they are transportable through this bottleneck [14]. This sequence of events was actually shown to take place when the ATP-dependent proteasomal degradation of a folded, globular protein was studied in the presence of an archaeal 19 S base-homologous complex, PAN (proteasome-activating nucleotidase) [15]. Unfolding is efficiently initiated when the substrate contains an unstructured sequence that is recognized as an engagement site by the 19 S Rp [16]. It has been suggested that solvent-exposed hydrophobic β-strands of subunits Rpn1 and Rpn2 act as a binding platform for unfolded proteins [8]. As the 19 S Rp, and especially the base, has been found to exert chaperone-like activity [17], the Rp may also work as a reverse chaperone or 'unfoldase', depending on how a protein is delivered and what happens subsequently to the unfolded protein. Since breaking of a hydrogen bond in a folded protein is energy-consuming, the unfolding process is probably one of the major ATP-dependent steps in proteolysis and there is experimental evidence to suggest that some of the ATPase subunits (Rpt1–Rpt6) co-operate to catalyse this process [18].

Although it has not yet been investigated in detail in eukaryotic proteasomes, it is conceivable that this unfolding process is closely connected to the mechanical translocation of the unfolded part of a substrate protein, from the base complex through a (presumptive) coaxial pore formed by the ATPase hexameric ring, and then through the central pore in the annulus, formed by the juxtaposed α-subunits of the 20 S proteasomes. Experiments with PAN and archaeal 20 S proteasomes have shown that translocation of substrates is also dependent on ATP hydrolysis [15] (Figure 2).

Deubiquitination

For many substrate proteins, the polyubiquitin chains not only are essential for their tethering to the 19 S Rp, but also might act as a support during the unfolding and translocation process. During or just after this process, ubiquitin is detached from the substrate protein, catalysed by subunit Rpn11 in the 19 S Rp lid (Figure 2). Rpn11 contains an intrinsic Zn^{2+}-dependent metallopeptidase activity that hydrolyses the isopeptide bond between the substrate and the adjacent ubiquitin molecule and thus releases the entire polypeptide chain. The process is dependent on ATP hydrolysis [19]. Some other DUBs (deubiquitinating enzymes) [e.g. Ubp6 (ubiquitin-binding protein 6) and UCH37(ubiquitin C-terminal hydrolase 37)] might have similar and additional functions; for example, deubiquitination of certain protein–ubiquitin conjugates to prevent their degradation, or depolymerization of the released polyubiquitin chain to fill up the free ubiquitin pool in the cell [20].

The 20 S proteasome

Molecular structure and gating of the proteolytic chamber

α- and β-subunits of the proteolytic core particle, the 20 S proteasome, evolved from the same predecessor. The most primitive archaeal proteasomes contain just one α- and one β-subunit and their subunit stoichiometry is therefore α7,β7,β7,α7. During evolution, each of these two subunits diverged into seven different α- and β-subunits, resulting in a stoichiometry of α1–α7/β1–β7/β1–β7/α1–α7 in eukaryotic 20 S proteasomes (Figure 1) [21]. In principle, the molecular structure of all 20 S proteasome subunits consists of two layers of five-stranded β-sheets sandwiched by two helices at either side (Figure 3). Within the cylinder-shaped complex, the helices mediate the interactions between α- and β- as well as between β- and β-subunits. A major structural difference between α- and β-subunits is found in their N-terminal parts. The N-termini of α-subunits form an extra helix that fills the cleft between the two layers of β-sheets. The extreme N-terminal amino acids of the α-subunits form a lattice that gates a central pore within the ring of α-subunits. Although in archaeal 20 S proteasomes this pore is wide enough to allow entry of small peptide substrates but not proteins [15], free uncapped eukaryotic 20 S proteasomes are latent with regard to their peptide- and protein-degrading activity. *In vitro*, their gate can be opened by low concentrations of SDS, long chain fatty acids, hydrophobic peptides and other compounds [7]. *In vivo*, the 19 S Rp unlocks this gate by docking to the 20 S proteasome in an ATP-dependent process (probably concurrent with phosphorylation of Rpt6) and thus putting the AAA-ATPase base-subunit Rpt2 in a position to replace the N-terminal tail of subunit α3, which interacts with the N-termini of all other α-subunits and forms the closing mesh [22,23]. Thus opened, the entryway allows passage of single-stranded unfolded proteins from either the C- or N-terminus as well as double-stranded stretched polypeptides [24]. Substrates can enter through both α-pores of a proteasome at the same time and degradation products are released the same way [25].

Mechanism of protein fragmentation

β-Subunits lack this N-terminal extra helix. Instead, their N-terminal threonine residue is positioned just at the open cleft between the two layers of β-sheets and is exposed to the inner surface of the central chamber (Figure 3). This single threonine residue forms the proteolytically active site, because its serves as the catalytic nucleophile and as a primary proton acceptor (Figure 4). Therefore proteasomes belong to the group of Ntn (N-terminal nucleophile) hydrolases.

To reach this proteolytic cavity, an unfolded substrate has to travel the 8 nm-long distance from the α-pore through the antechamber by a mechanism that is not yet understood. Small synthetic chromogenic peptide substrates

(A)

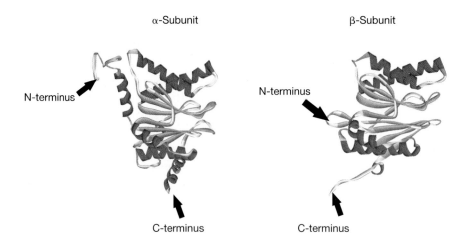

(B)

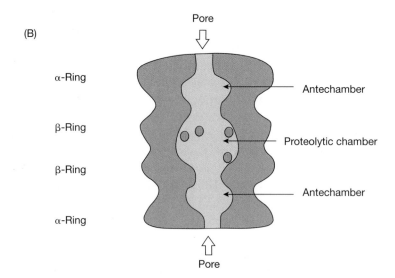

Figure 3. Structure of the 20 S proteasome
(**A**) Schematic drawing of an α- and β-subunit of eukaryotic 20 S proteasomes. Both have a sand-wich-like structure consisting of two layers of β-strands embedded between two helices at either side. The N-terminus of β-subunits is exposed within the cleft of β-strands and thus can form the catalytic site, whereas α-subunits contain an extra helix at their N-termini that fills the cleft. (**B**) Cartoon of a longitudinally sectioned 20 S proteasome. Between the ring of α- and β-subunits, the pores enlarge into antechambers that give access to the central chamber (volume approx. 84 nm³) where the N-terminal threonine residues (blue circles) of β-subunits are exposed for catalysis of peptide-bond hydrolysis. Substrates and products enter and leave the inner chambers through the α-ring pores.

easily cover this distance by diffusion, and by use of these substrates it has been found that archaebacterial proteasomes preferentially hydrolyse peptide bonds at the C-terminal side of large hydrophobic amino-acid residues, thus exhibiting chymotrypsin-like specificity. However, within protein substrates, peptide-bond cleavage occurs after almost every amino acid.

During evolution, the number of active sites was reduced from 14 in archaeal proteasomes to six in eukaryotic proteasomes, since only subunits β1, β2 and β5 still contain functional active sites. Although they all use their N-terminal threonine for the nucleophilic attack on peptide bonds, their substrate specificity is determined by different substrate-binding channels, containing binding sites for peptides with a length of 7–9 amino acids. Their cleavage-site specificity can be roughly characterized as chymotrypsin-like (catalysed by subunit β5), trypsin-like (by β2), and post-glutamylpeptide hydrolysing or caspase-like (by β1) [26]. When tested with protein or polypeptide substrates, proteasomes produce cleavage fragments with an average length of 7–8 amino acids, but their length ranges from 3 to 25 amino acids. These features are found in all proteasomes, independent of the content of their active sites. The length of the degradation products is most probably determined by the affinity of the substrate for the binding channels, the rate of peptide-bond cleavage, fragment release and its diffusion rate out of the complex. Many small products obtained in *in vitro* digestion experiments may result from re-processing of initial substrate fragments [23,27].

Proteasomes can be classified as endoproteases, since a double strand of an unfolded part of a protein that is threaded through the α-ring-gate into the proteolytic hole is attacked, via hydrolysis of an internal peptide bond, and cut into two fragments [24]. This property, and possibly stop-transfer mechanisms, enables proteasomes to process proteins by limited proteolysis. Among the few examples known, the most well-studied example is p105, the C-terminal part of which is cleaved off to release the N-terminal part, p50, which is a subunit of the transcription factor NF-κB [28]. Since it remains undigested, the N-terminal part leaves the proteasome at the same site as that where it entered. Degradation products have been found to take the same route, at least in 20 S proteasomes [25], a process possibly facilitated by the 19 S Rp-induced enlargement of the pores [23]. Results recently obtained with yeast cell extracts suggest that substrate degradation and fragment release by 26 S proteasomes triggers an ATP hydrolysis-dependent release of 19 S Rp from 20 S proteasomes as well as disassembly of 19 S Rp into sub-complexes and Rpn10 [29]. Whether this 'chew and spew' model, necessitating a continuous re-assembly of the 26 S complex, reflects the basic working mechanism of the 26 S proteasome awaits further experimental substantiation.

Biogenesis of 20 S proteasomes
Knowledge about the regulation of proteasome subunits at the level of transcription is relatively poor and confined only to yeast cells. The promoters

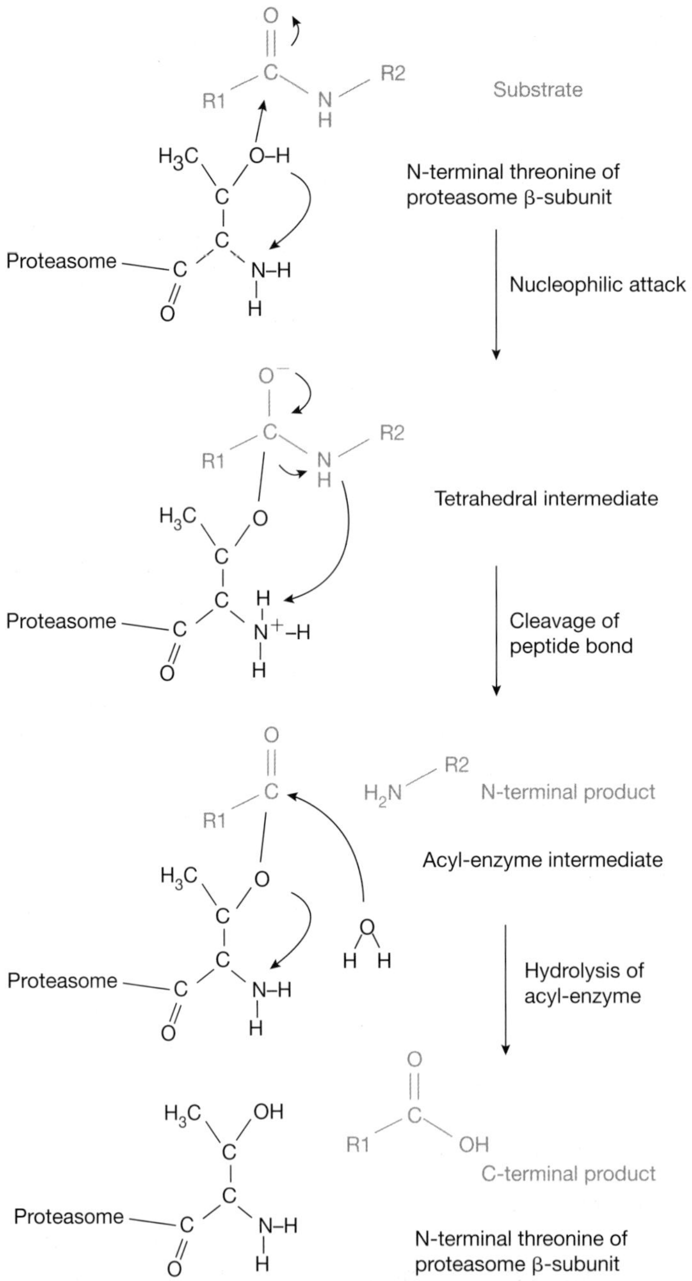

Figure 4. Mechanism of peptide-bond hydrolysis by the 20 S proteasome
The N-terminal threonine of a proteasome β-subunit exposed to the central chamber is the catalytically active nucleophile. The hydroxy group attacks the carbonyl group of the substrate peptide bond, while its proton is delocalized to the threonine amino group. This attack results in the
formation of a tetrahedral intermediate, followed by peptide-bond cleavage and release of the N-
terminal fragment of the substrate protein. Hydrolysis of the acyl-enzyme intermediate releases
the C-terminal substrate fragment.

of 26 out of 32 genes for subunits of the 20 S proteasome and 19 S Rp contain a PACE (proteasome-associated control element) sequence, to which Rpn4 binds and acts as a transcriptional activator. Because Rpn4 is degraded by the proteasome, a feedback regulation exists for transcription of most proteasomal genes [30]. Neither PACE sequences nor an Rpn4 homologue have been detected so far in mammalian cells.

Our present knowledge about the biogenesis of the 20 S proteasome is more precise, especially with regard to archaeal proteasomes. Co-expression of α- and β-subunits in an *Escherichia coli* protein-expression system yields complete, active 20 S proteasomes. Since archaeal proteasome α-subunits, but not β-subunits, have been found to contain the intrinsic property of self-formation of heptameric rings, immature β-subunits need the α-ring for autocatalytic processing of their N-terminal propeptides and ring formation [31].

Biogenesis of eubacterial 20 S proteasomes that are composed of either one or two species of α- and β-subunits probably proceeds via the formation of α/β-dimers that assemble to inactive half-proteasome precursors (α7,β7), followed by autocatalytic processing of the N-terminal pro-peptide of the β-subunits, unveiling the N-terminal threonine residue and yielding active holo-proteasomes. In contrast to biogenesis of archaeal proteasomes, the presence (either *cis* or *trans*) of the β-subunit pro-peptide is indispensable for formation of eubacterial proteasomes [8].

While complete 20 S archaeal and eubacterial proteasomes can be generated by means of an *E. coli* expression system, the generation of eukaryotic proteasomes requires a eukaryotic Ump1/POMP (proteasome-maturation protein, also known as proteassemblin) and chaperones (e.g. Hsc73) and thus cannot be performed successfully using bacterial protein expression systems. The earliest natural intermediate identified so far is an α-ring associated with subunits β2, β3 and β4. The next stable intermediate is a half-proteasome composed of an α-ring, a ring of all N-terminally unprocessed β-subunits and Ump1/POMP. Dimerization of two half-proteasomes results in encasement of Ump1/POMP, which thereupon interacts with the (pro-)subunit β5 and induces (auto)-catalytic processing of all pro-β-subunits. This processing step allows subsequent formation of the mature 20 S proteasome, the first substrate of which is Ump1/POMP [32].

Special proteasomes for special tasks

Immuno-proteasomes

As oligopeptides are the major reaction products of proteasome action, Nature has taken advantage of these degradation fragments by using them as a source of antigenic epitopes of cellular proteins, and presenting them (by class I MHCs) to T-cells for immune surveillance in higher eukaryotes. When cells present epitopes, which may result from the proteasomal breakdown of a foreign, e.g. virus-encoded, protein, these are recognized as non-self and the cell is eliminated by the T-lymphocyte. Although proteasomes that are constitutively expressed in most somatic cells are able to generate these antigenic peptides (or at least their precursor fragments), cytokines (especially interferon-γ), released by activated T-lymphocytes, induce the expression of three alternative active-site-containing 20 S proteasome subunits, designated β1i, β2i, and β5i, that replace the standard subunits in nascent proteasomes, resulting in the formation of 'immuno-proteasomes' (Figure 5). Biogenesis of immuno-proteasomes is faster than that of standard proteasomes owing to a favoured interaction between Ump1/POMP, the expression of which is also enhanced by interferon-γ, and subunit β5i (as compared with β5). Incorporation of β5i favours the subsequent integration of β2i and β1i, thus enabling an infected cell to process antigens in a rapid and efficient manner. Since immuno-proteasomes have a half-life of about 1 day and standard proteasomes one of about 5 days, interferon-γ might trigger a transient and limited change to the type of proteasomes within a cell [33]. Spleen cells and other cells involved 'professionally' in immune surveillance, however, constitutively express immuno-proteasomes. Although some of the cleavage preferences of immuno-proteasomes are the same as those of standard proteasomes, generation of certain virus-derived antigenic epitopes is improved or is even dependent on immuno-proteasomes. The substrate-binding sites of immuno-proteasomes probably facilitate a cleavage preference for certain peptide bonds that results in the production of a critical concentration of an antigenic epitope (and/or its precursor) that is high enough to induce a T-lymphocyte response. On the other hand, it has also been found that immuno-proteasomes fail to produce certain self-antigens that are more easily generated by standard proteasomes [34].

Proteasome-activator PA28

Although constitutively present in many mammalian cells, interferon-γ causes an intensified expression of another protein, called PA28 or 11 S regulator. This is an approx. 200 kDa complex of two different proteins, PA28α and PA28β, the expression of which can be differentially regulated owing to the presence of an NF-κB binding site that is present only in the promoter sequence of PA28β [35]. X-ray crystallographic studies with the homomer of PA28α revealed a heptameric barrel-shaped structure and the most likely composition of native PA28 is α4β3 or α3β4. The openings of the barrel are 2 and 3 nm in diameter. With the latter opening ahead, the complex docks on to one or both of the outer α-rings of the 20 S proteasome — a process executed without ATP consumption (Figure 5). This interaction presses the N-terminal tails of the proteasome α-subunits upwards, resulting in an opening of the pore. Thus, *in vitro* PA28 activates latent 20 S proteasomes by facilitating the entry of small peptide substrates and the release of products [36]. The *in vivo* function of PA28 is less clear. It has been shown that certain cells generate certain antigen epitope precursors only in the presence of PA28 [37]. Whether this results from a facilitated release of longer degradation products owing to

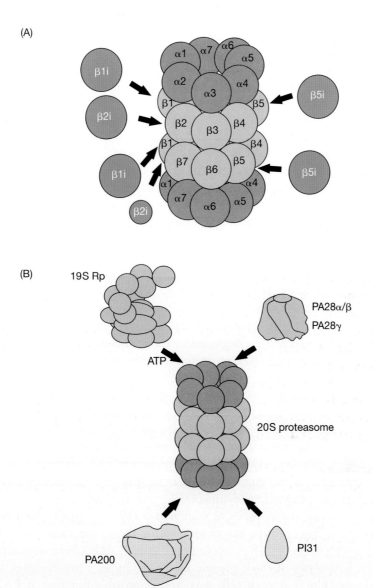

Figure 5. Proteasome accessory parts in eukaryotic cells
(**A**) Immuno-proteasomes are formed by incorporation of interferon-inducible subunits β1i, β2i, and β5i instead of β1, β2, and β5 respectively, in nascent 20 S proteasomes. (**B**) ATP-dependent docking of 19 S Rp to one or both ends of the 20 S proteasome cylinder leads to formation of 26 S and 30 S proteasomes respectively. Alternatively, one or two proteasome-activator complexes, PA28α/β, PA28γ or one or two PA200 molecules can attach to the α-rings of 20 S proteasomes. Complexes consisting of one 19 S Rp and one PA28 attached to a 20 S proteasome have been detected in mammalian cells. The interaction site of proteasome inhibitor PI31 with the 20 S proteasome has not yet been localized. The shapes of PA28 and PA200 are based on electron micrographs.

the opened α-pores, or whether PA28 induces allosteric changes within the proteasomes, allowing a co-ordinated dual- or singly-modified cleavage within a substrate protein, is still a matter requiring investigation [35].

Hybrid proteasomes

As determined in HeLa cells, a remarkable number (approx. 40%) of total cellular proteasomes are free 20 S proteasomes, which allow the binding of 19 S Rp (approx. 15%), PA28 (approx. 20%) or both (Figure 5). In fact, about a quarter of all proteasomes in these cells were calculated to have bound 19 S Rp at one side and PA28 at the other, and their cellular concentration increases when the cells are treated with interferon-γ, probably owing to the induction of PA28 expression. These enzymes are called hybrid proteasomes [38]. They degrade the protein ornithine decarboxylase in a ubiquitin-independent, but ATP-dependent, manner and generate a pattern of degradation fragments different from that generated by 26 S proteasomes [39]. The exact biological function of hybrid proteasomes is still unknown.

Additional accessory parts

Since proteasomes degrade substrates from almost all cellular compartments except mitochondria, they have been detected not only in the cytosolic compartment but also attached to the ER (endoplasmic reticulum) and within cell nuclei (except nucleoli) [40]. Even without being polyubiquitinated, several substrates seem to be degraded by the 26 S or 20 S proteasomes [41]. In certain organisms, e.g. *Ascidia*, proteasomes perform special, even extracellular, functions such as fertilization [42].

To fulfil all these diverse functions, proteasomes have acquired several additional attachments [43]. For example, a protein called PA28γ that seems to be the ancestor of PA28α and PA28β, but is not inducible by interferon-γ, forms homo-heptamers and binds to 20 S proteasomes, but activates predominantly the trypsin-like activity [44]. It is present in high concentrations in the nuclei of brain cells and might function as an adaptor of proteasomes to other complexes, e.g. apoptosis regulators [43].

Also present in the nuclei of mammalian cells is a single-chain protein, called PA200. This protein has an asymmetric dome-like shape and binds to one or both α-rings of 20 S proteasomes (Figure 5). It has been shown to activate the hydrolysis of small peptide substrates by 20 S proteasomes, but its homologue (Blm3) in yeast cells may not. A possible function of PA200 to recruit proteasomes to enzyme complexes catalysing DNA repair has been questioned [43].

A proline-rich 30 kDa molecule has been found *in vitro* to inhibit the chymotrypsin-like and caspase-like activities of 20 S proteasomes, but is less effective towards the trypsin-like activity. It is designated proteasome inhibitor PI31 (Figure 5). The inhibitor, which is not present in yeast cells, is located predominantly at the nuclear/ER membranes and was found not to impair the overall cellular ATP/ubiquitin-dependent protein breakdown, but was suggested to be involved in the biogenesis of immuno-proteasomes [43].

Whether other complexes, such as PC530 (found in starfish oocytes) [42] and COP9 signalosome [45], can replace the 19 S Rp or its lid-subcomplex respectively, to enable proteasomes to fulfil such special functions, is still under investigation.

Conclusion

Although only discovered about 20 years ago, intensive studies of proteasomes from archaeal, eubacteria and eukaryotes have lead to deep insights into the structure and function of these nano-machines. In particular, the fact that proteasomes, as the molecular 'mincers' of the UPS, are involved in the regulation of many basic cellular functions and pathological malfunctions has attracted the inquisitiveness of investigators from biomolecular, biomedical and pharmaceutical research areas. Nevertheless, detailed knowledge about the function of most of the 19 S regulator Rpt- and Rpn-subunits is still lacking, as are the detailed mechanisms of substrate unfolding and translocation. On the basis of results obtained by two-hybrid screens and other investigations, it is not unreasonable to suggest that a plethora of proteasome-interacting proteins deliver substrates to proteasomes and direct, as well as furnish, the machinery for special functions at various subcellular locations [29,46–48]. Even basic knowledge about the exact functions of PA28, PI31 and PA200 and the molecular mechanism of how immuno-subunits change the enzymatic properties of 20 S proteasomes have yet to be elucidated, not to mention the the co-operation of the proteasomal system with other parallel-working and post-proteasomal proteinases in the cell. These and many other questions will attract the interest of hosts of investigators to proteasomes in the future.

Summary

- *20 S proteasomes are intracellular, multi-subunit, cylinder-shaped complexes with an interior cave containing proteolytically active sites mechanistically belonging to the N-terminal threonine hydrolases.*
- *A major part, but not all, of their substrates are protein–polyubiquitin conjugates. These are trapped by the 19 S Rps, which are added to one or to both ends of the 20 S proteasome cylinder, to form 26 S and 30 S proteasomes respectively.*
- *Driven by the energy of ATP hydrolysis, 19 S Rps unfold, deubiquitinate and translocate substrate proteins into the proteolytic cavity of 20 S proteasomes.*
- *Proteolytic products of proteasomes are oligopeptides of 3–25 amino acids, a small fraction of which are used by higher eukaryotic cells as protein epitopes (or their precursors) for presentation to the immune surveillance system.*

- *For the generation of immuno-epitopes, cytokines can induce many eukaryotic cells to generate 20 S immuno-proteasomes that contain special subunits with optimized substrate-binding pockets. Additionally, and alternatively, docking of a proteasome activator, PA28, can affect the type and length of degradation fragments.*
- *Several other activating and inhibiting accessory molecule complexes modulate the action of proteasomes.*

The author thanks Dr. R. Preissner and Dr. A. Goede for preparing the schematic drawing of the structure of 20 S proteasome subunits. The author's own contributions to the exploration of proteasomes were, and still are, supported by grants (SFB 113; DA146/1-6; SFB 507) of the Deutsche Forschungsgemeinschaft (Bonn, Germany). I apologize for not citing many other relevant publications owing to publisher's limitations.

References

1. Zwickl, P. (2002) The 20 S proteasome. *Curr. Top. Microbiol. Immunol.* **268**, 23–41
2. Viestra, R.D. (2003) The ubiquitin/26 S proteasome pathway, the complex last chapter in life of many plant proteins. *Trends Plant Sci.* **8**, 135–142
3. Mykles, D.L. (1998) Intracellular proteinases of invertebrates: calcium-dependent and proteasome/ubiquitin-dependent systems. *Int. Rev. Cytol.* **184**, 157–289
4. Glickman, M.H. & Ciechanover, A. (2002) The ubiquitin–proteasome proteolytic pathway: destruction for the sake of construction. *Physiol. Rev.* **82**, 373–428
5. Imai, J., Maruya, M., Yashiroda, H., Yahara, I. & Tanaka, K. (2003) The molecular chaperone Hsp90 plays a role in the assembly and maintenance of the 26 S proteasome. *EMBO J.* **22**, 3557–3567
6. Park, Y., Hwang, Y.-P., Lee, J.-S., Seo, S.-H., Yoon, S.K. & Yoon, J.-B. (2005) Proteasomal ATPase-associated factor 1 negatively regulates proteasome activity by interacting with proteasomal ATPases. *Mol. Cell. Biol.* **25**, 3842–3853
7. Coux, O., Tanaka, K. & Goldberg, A.L. (1996) Structure and functions of the 20 S and 26 S proteasomes. *Annu. Rev. Biochem.* **65**, 801–847
8. Voges, D., Zwickl, P. & Baumeister, W. (1999) The 26 S proteasome: a molecular machine designed for controlled proteolysis. *Annu. Rev. Biochem.* **68**, 1015–1068
9. Patel, S. & Latterich, M. (1998) The AAA team: related ATPases with diverse functions. *Trend Cell Biol.* **8**, 65–71
10. Hartmann-Petersen, R., Seeger, M. & Gordon, C. (2003) Transferring substrates to the 26 S proteasome. *Trends Biochem. Sci.* **28**, 26–31
11. Richy, H., Rape, M., Braun, S., Rumpf, S., Hoege, C. & Jentsch, S. (2005) A series of ubiquitin binding factors connects CDC48/p97 to substrate multiubiquitylation and proteasomal targeting. *Cell* **120**, 73–84
12. Verma, R., Oania, R., Graumann, J. & Deshaies, R.J. (2004) Multiubiquitin chain receptors define a layer of substrate selectivity in the ubiquitin–proteasome-system. *Cell* **118**, 99–110
13. Zhang,M., Pickart, C.M. & Coffino, P. (2003) Determinants of proteasome recogniton of ornithine decarboxylase, a ubiquitin-independent substrate. *EMBO J.* **22**, 1488–1496
14. Förster, A. & Hill, C.P. (2003) Proteasome degradation: enter the substrate. *Trends Cell Biol.* **13**, 550–553
15. Benaroudj, N., Zwickl, P., Seemüller, E., Baumeister, W. & Goldberg, A.L. (2003) ATP hydrolysis by the proteasome regulatory PAN serves multiple functions in protein degradation. *Mol. Cell* **11**, 69–78

16. Prakash, S., Tian, L., Ratliff, K.S., Lehotzky, R.E. & Matouschek, A. (2004) An unstructured initiation site is required for efficient proteasome-mediated degradation. *Nat. Struct. Mol. Biol.* **11**, 830–837

17. Braun, B., Glickman, M., Kraft, R., Dahlmann, B., Kloetzel, P.-M., Finley, D. & Schmidt, M. (1999) The base of the proteasome regulatory particle exhibits chaperone-like activity. *Nat. Cell Biol.* **1**, 221–226

18. Rubin, D.M., Glickman, M.H., Larsen, C.N., Dhruvakumar, S., & Finley, D. (1998) Active site mutants in the six regulatory particle ATPases reveal multiple roles for ATP in the proteasome. *EMBO J.* **17**, 4909–4919

19. Yao, T. & Cohen R.E. (2002) A cryptic protease couples deubiquitination and degradation by the proteasome. *Nature (London)* **419**, 403–407

20. Amerik, A.Y. & Hochstrasser, M. (2004) Mechanism and function of deubiquitinating enzymes. *Biochim. Biophys. Acta* **1695**, 189–207

21. Bochtler, M., Ditzel, L., Groll, M., Hartmann, C. & Huber, R. (1999) The proteasome. *Annu. Rev. Biophys. Biomol. Struct.* **28**, 295–317

22. Groll, M., Bajorek, M., Köhler, A., Moroder, L., Ruber, D.M., Huber, R., Glickman, M.H. & Finley, D. (2000) A gated channel into the proteasome core particle. *Nat. Struct. Biol.* **7**, 1062–1067

23. Köhler, A., Cascio, P., Legett, D.S., Woo, K.M., Goldberg, A.L. & Finley, D. (2001) The axial channel of the proteasome core particle is gated by the Rpt2 ATPase and controls both substrate entry and product release. *Mol. Cell* **7**, 1143–1152

24. Liu, C.-W., Corboy, M.J., DeMartino,G.N. & Thomas, P.J. (2003) Endoproteolytic activity of the proteasome. *Science* **299**, 408–411

25. Hutschenreiter, S., Tinazli, A., Model, K. & Tampé, R. (2004) Two substrate association with the 20 S proteasome at single molecule level. *EMBO J.* **23**, 2488–2497

26. Groll, M., Bochtler, M., Brandstetter, H., Clausen, T. & Huber, R. (2005) Molecular machines for protein degradation. *ChemBioChem.* **6**, 222–256

27. Peters, B., Janek, K., Kuckelkorn, U. & Holzhütter, H.G. (2002) Assessment of proteasomal cleavage probabilities from kinetic analysis of time-dependent product formation. *J. Mol. Biol.* **318**, 847–862

28. Rape, M. & Jentsch, S. (2004) Productive RUPture: activation of transcription factors by proteasomal processing. *Biochim. Biophys. Acta* **1695**, 209–213

29. Babbitt, S.E., Kiss, A., Deffenbaugh, A.E., Chang, Y.-H., Bailly, E., Erdjument-Bromage, H., Tempst, P., Buranda, T., Sklar, L.A., Baumler, J. et al. (2005) ATP hydrolysis-dependent disassembly of the 26 S proteasomes is part of the catalytic cycle. *Cell* **121**, 553–585

30. Xie, Y. & Varshavsky, A. (2001) RPN4 is a ligand, substrate, and transcriptional reglator of the 26 S proteasomes: a negative feedback circuit. *Proc. Natl. Acad. Sci. U.S.A.* **98**, 3056–3061

31. Zwickl, P., Kleinz, J. & Baumeister, W. (1994) Critical elements in proteasome assembly. *Nat. Struct. Biol.* **1**, 765–770

32. Heinemeyer, W., Ramos, P.C. & Dohmen, R.J. (2004) The ultimate nanoscale mincer: assembly, structure and active sites of the 20 S proteasomes core. *Cell. Mol. Life Sci.* **61**, 1562–1578

33. Heink, S., Ludwig, D., Kloetzel, P.-M. & Krüger, E. (2005) IFNγ-induced immune adaptation of the proteasome system is an accelerated and transient response. *Proc. Natl. Acad. Sci. U.S.A.* **102**, 9241–9246

34. Krüger, E., Kuckelkorn, U., Sijts, A. & Kloetzel, P.-M. (2003) The components of the proteasome system and their role in MHC class I antigen processing. *Rev. Physiol. Biochem. Pharmacol.* **148**, 81–104

35. Ossendorp, F., Fu, N., Camps, M., Granucci, F., Gobin, S.J.P., van den Elsen, P.J., Schuurhuis, D., Adema, G.J., Lipford, G.B., Chiba, T. et al. (2005) Differential expression regulation of the α and β subunits of the PA2 proteasome activator in mature dendritic cells. *J. Immunol.* **174**, 7815–7822

36. Whitby, F.G., Masters, E.I., Kramer, L., Knowlton, J.R., Yao, Y., Wang, C.C. & Hill, C.P. (2000) Structural basis for the activation of 20S proteasomes by 11S regulators. *Nature (London)* **408**, 115–120

37. Sijts, A., Sun, Y., Janek, K., Kral, S., Paschen, A., Schadendorf, D. & Kloetzel, P.-M. (2002) The role of the proteasome activator PA28 in MHC class I antigen processing. Mol. Immunol. **39**, 165–169

38. Tanahashi, N., Murakami, Y., Minami, Y., Shimbara, N., Hendil, K.B. & Tanaka, K. (2000) Hybrid proteasomes. Induction by interferon-γ and contribution to ATP-dependent proteolysis. J. Biol. Chem. **275**, 14336–14345

39. Cascio, P., Call, M., Petre, B.M., Walz, T. & Goldberg, A.L. (2002) Properties of the hybrid form of the 26S proteasomes containing both 19S and PA28 complexes. EMBO J. **21**, 2636–2645

40. Wójcik, C. & DeMartino, G.N. (2003) Intracellular localization of proteasomes. Int. J. Biochem. Cell Biol. **35**, 579–589

41. Orlowski, M. & Wilk, S. (2003) Ubiquitin-independent proteolytic functions of the proteasome. Arch. Biochem. Biophys. **415**, 1–5

42. Sakai, N., Sawada, M.T. & Sawada, H. (2004) Non-traditional roles of ubiquitin–proteasome system in fertilization and gametogenesis. Int. J. Biochem. Cell Biol. **36**, 776–784

43. Rechsteiner, M. & Hill, C.P. (2005) Mobilizing the proteolytic machine: cell biological roles of proteasome activators and inhibitors. Trends Cell Biol. **15**, 27–33

44. Gao, X., Li, J., Pratt, G., Wilk, S. & Rechsteiner, M. (2004) Purification procedures determine the proteasome activation properties of REGγ (PA28γ). Arch. Biochem. Biophys. **425**, 158–164

45. Seeger, M., Gordon, C. & Dubiel, W. (2001) Protein stability: the COP9 signalosome gets in on the act. Curr. Biol. **11**, R643–R646

46. Cagney, G., Uetz, P. & Fields, S. (2001) Two-hybrid analysis of the Saccharomyces cerevisiae 26S proteasome. Physiol. Genomics **7**, 27–34

47. Davy, A., Bello, P., Thierry-Mieg, N., Vaglio, P., Hitti, J., Doucette-Stamm, L., Thierry-Mieg, D., Reboul, J., Boulton, S., Walhout, A.J.M. et al. (2001) A protein–protein interaction map of the Caenorhabditis elegans 26 S proteasome. EMBO Rep. **21**, 821–828

48. Gorbea, C., Goellner, G.M., Teter, K., Holmes, R.K. & Rechsteiner, M. (2004) Characterization of mammalian Ecm-29, a 26 S proteasome-associated protein that localizes to the nucleus and membrane vesicles. J. Biol. Chem. **279**, 54849–54861

4

Ubiquitin-binding proteins: similar, but different

Katrine M. Andersen*, Kay Hofmann† and Rasmus Hartmann-Petersen*[1]

Institute of Molecular Biology and Physiology, University of Copenhagen, Universitetsparken 13, Copenhagen Ø, Denmark DK-2100, and †Bioinformatics Group, Memorec Biotec GmbH, Stoeckheimer Weg 1, Köln D-50829, Germany

Abstract

Covalent modification of proteins with ubiquitin is a common regulatory mechanism in eukaryotic cells. Typically, ubiquitinated proteins are targeted for degradation by the 26 S proteasome. However, more recently the ubiquitin signal has also been connected with many other cell processes, including endocytosis, vesicle fusion, DNA repair and transcriptional silencing. Hence ubiquitination may be comparable with phosphorylation in its importance as an intracellular switch, controlling various signal-transduction pathways. Similar to the regulation of the extent of phosphorylation by kinases and phosphatases, specific sets of ubiquitinating/deubiquitinating enzymes control the degree of ubiquitination. A large number of ubiquitin-binding proteins act at different steps in the downstream pathways, followed by the ubiquitinated protein. Different families of ubiquitin-binding proteins have been described. UBA (ubiquitin-associated) domain-containing proteins is the largest family and includes members involved in different cell processes. The smaller groups of UIM (ubiquitin-interacting motif), GAT [GGA (Golgi-associated γ-adaptin homologous) and Tom1 (target of Myb 1)], CUE (coupling of ubiquitin conjugation to endoplasmic reticulum degradation), UEV [ubiquitin E2

[1]*To whom correspondence should be addressed (email rhpetersen@aki.ku.dk).*

(ubiquitin-conjugating enzyme) variant] and NZF (nuclear protein localization gene 4 zinc finger) domain-containing proteins appear to have more specialized functions. Here we discuss functional and structural properties of ubiquitin-binding proteins.

Introduction

An efficient and common way to alter protein function is by post-translational modifications, such as phosphorylation, glycosylation and acetylation, or through the addition of a ubiquitin molecule in a process called ubiquitination [1]. Typically, ubiquitination of a protein leads to its degradation in the 26 S proteasome. However, ubiquitination has also been linked to a number of other cellular activities, including endocytosis, vesicle fusion, DNA repair and gene silencing, to name a few [2].

The 26 S proteasome is an abundant protein complex found in the cytoplasm and nucleus of all eukaryotic cells. It is composed of two subcomplexes: a 20 S cylindrical core particle, which provides the proteolytic activity, and a 19 S regulatory complex, which mediates substrate recognition and substrate unfolding. The 19 S particle is itself composed of two smaller subcomplexes: the base complex, which binds the 20 S core particle and contains ATPase subunits, and the lid complex, which covers the base and is functionally not as well characterized [1].

Ubiquitin–substrate ligation is catalysed by the sequential action of three enzymes, E1 (ubiquitin-activating enzyme), E2 (ubiquitin-conjugating enzyme) and E3 (ubiquitin ligase) [3]. Ubiquitin is first activated by the E1 and then, in collaboration between an E2 and E3, transferred to a specific target protein, forming an isopeptide bond between the C-terminus of ubiquitin and a primary amino group in the target protein. In some cases, the ubiquitination process stops at this point [4]. However, many ubiquitinated proteins undergo several rounds of ubiquitination, so that a new ubiquitin moiety is conjugated to a lysine residue in the last ubiquitin moiety of the growing ubiquitin chain. Some proteins require the action of a ubiquitin-chain-elongation factor, E4 (polyubiquitin chain conjugation factor), to become polyubiquitinated efficiently [5]. Ubiquitin contains seven lysine residues, and chains connected through most of these residues have been detected *in vivo* [2,6]. Lys^{48}-linked chains are the most common signal for proteasomal degradation, while the other lysine-linkages are mostly involved in non-proteolytic functions. For instance, Lys^{63}-linked ubiquitin chains regulate tolerance to DNA damage [7].

In combination, the E2 and E3 enzymes determine the type of chain linkage and substrate specificity of the ubiquitination process, and human cells probably contain hundreds of different E3s. However, at least two other levels of regulation can be envisioned. Firstly, regulation may also occur by deubiquitination of substrates, a process catalysed by a large family of DUBs (deubiquitinating enzymes) [8]. Secondly, regulation may occur at the level of recognizing the ubiquitinated protein as a signal for inducing a downstream cellular event [6].

In this review, we describe certain ubiquitin-binding proteins. However, the number of potential and proven ubiquitin-binding proteins is steadily increasing. We have assembled a list of ubiquitin-binding proteins ordered according to function (Table 1), but this account is in no way comprehensive.

Families of ubiquitin-binding proteins

Several different families of ubiquitin-binding proteins have been described. The largest group, the UBA (ubiquitin-associated) domain-containing proteins, includes members involved in different cellular processes. The families of UIM (ubiquitin-interacting motif), CUE [coupling of ubiquitin conjugation to ER (endoplasmic reticulum) degradation], GAT [GGA (Golgi-associated γ-adaptin homologous) and Tom (target of Myb)], UEV (ubiquitin E2 variant) and NZF [Npl4 (nuclear protein localization gene 4) zinc finger] domain-containing proteins appear to some extent to be more specialized in their functions [6].

The structures of the ubiquitin-binding domains [9–15] have been determined for representative members of the families (Figure 1). Except for the somewhat similar UBA (Figure 1A) and CUE (Figure 1B) domains, their three-dimensional structures are disparate. However, in all cases, the domains appear to interact with a hydrophobic patch on ubiquitin, formed by residues Leu^8, Ile^{44} and Val^{70} [16].

UBA domains have been shown also to bind UBL (ubiquitin-like) domains [17], which show only limited sequence similarity with ubiquitin, but share the ubiquitin fold. The function of the UBL domain is also connected with the ubiquitin–proteasome system, since it interacts with the 26 S proteasome [18–20], but the significance of the interactions between ubiquitin-binding domains and UBL domains is yet unknown.

Ubiquitin-binding proteins in proteolysis

Ubiquitin binding by the 26 S proteasome

Two 26 S proteasome subunits, S6'/Rpt5 [21] and S5a/Rpn10/Pus1 [22], have been shown to interact directly with ubiquitin chains. The interaction with the ATPase subunit S6'/Rpt5 appears to be modulated by ATP hydrolysis [21]. However, the primary sequence within S6'/Rpt5, which is responsible for the interaction, has not yet been defined.

S5a/Rpn10/Pus1 was the first protein found to interact non-covalently with ubiquitin chains. In human S5a/Rpn10/Pus1, which contains two UIM domains (whereas the yeast orthologues contains only one), the ubiquitin-binding region was mapped to an approx. 20-amino-acid region near the C-terminus [22], now known as the UIM domain, which is found in several pro-

Table 1. Selected confirmed and putative human ubiquitin-binding proteins

Gene name	Accession no.	Class	Comment
UBA domain proteins			
UBC1	P61086	E2: UBC	Ubiquitin conjugating E2-25 kDa
EDD	O95071	E3: HECT	HECT-ligase, homologue of *Drosophila* 'Hyperplastic disc'
HERC2	O95714	E3: HECT	HECT-ligase HERC2 or RJS
UREB1	Q7Z6Z7	E3: HECT	HECT-ligase URE-B1
CBL	P22681	E3: RING	Proto-oncogene c-Cbl
CBLB	Q13191	E3: RING	Cbl-like protein Cbl-B
RNF31	Q96EP0	E3: RING	RING-finger protein 31
USP5	P45974	Ubiquitin protease	Deubiquitinating isopeptidase T
USP13	Q92995	Ubiquitin protease	Deubiquitinating isopeptidase T3
USP25	Q9UHP3	Ubiquitin protease	Ubiquitin-specific protease 25
USP28	Q96RU2	Ubiquitin protease	Ubiquitin-specific protease 28
RAD23A	P54725	Adaptor UBL/UBA	Rad23 homologue A
RAD23B	P54727	Adaptor UBL/UBA	Rad23 homologue B
UBQLN1	Q9UMX0	Adaptor UBL/UBA	Ubiquilin-1/PLIC1, Dsk2-homologue
UBQLN2	Q9UHD9	Adaptor UBL/UBA	Ubiquilin-2/PLIC2, Dsk2-homologue
UBQLN3	Q9H347	Adaptor UBL/UBA	Ubiquilin-3, Dsk2-homologue
UBQLN4	Q9NRR5	Adaptor UBL/UBA	Ubiquilin-4/A1U, Dsk2-homologue
GBDR1	O75500	Adaptor UBL/UBA	Glialblastoma cell-differentiation-related protein
NUB1	Q9Y5A7	Adaptor UBL/UBA	NEDD8 ultimate buster-1
SB132	Q96S82	Adaptor UBL/UBA	Bone marrow stromal cell-derived
NSFL1C	Q9UNZ2	Adaptor UBA/UBX	p97-cofactor p47
ETEA	Q9BVM7	Adaptor UBA/UBX	T-cell UBA/UBX protein

contd ☞

Gene	ID	Family	Description
U33K	Q04323	Adaptor UBA/UBX	UBA/UBX protein 33.3 kDa
FAF1	Q9UNN5	Adaptor UBA/UBX	Fas-associated factor 1
KIAA0794	O94888	Adaptor UBA/UBX	KIAA0794 protein
SQSTM1	Q13501	Adaptor PB1/UBA	Sequestosome 1
M17S2	Q14596	Adaptor PB1/UBA	Neighbour of BRCA1 (NBR1)
MARK1	Q5VTF9	SNF-1 like kinases	MAP/microtubule affinity-regulating kinase 1
MARK3	P27448	SNF-1 like kinases	MAP/microtubule affinity-regulating kinase 3
MARK4	Q96L34	SNF-1 like kinases	MAP/microtubule affinity-regulating kinase 4
SIK2	Q76N03	SNF-1 like kinases	SNF1-like kinase 2
SNF1LK	P57059	SNF-1 like kinases	SNF1-like kinase
SNRK	Q6IQ46	SNF-1 like kinases	SNF-1-related kinase
KIAA0999	Q9Y2K2	SNF-1 like kinases	SNF-1/MARK-like kinase KIAA0999
UBAP1	Q6FI75	Lingerer family	Uncharacterized UBA-protein UBAP1
UBAP2	Q9POH6	Lingerer family	Ubiquitin-associated protein 2
UBAP2L	Q14157	Lingerer family	Uncharacterized UBA-protein KIAA0144
OTTHUMP00000000473	Q5T6F2	Lingerer family	ORF, related to UBAP2 family
STS-1	Q96IG9	PGAM family	Cbl-interacting protein Sts-1
UBASH3A	P57075	PGAM family	T-cell ubiquitin ligand protein
LATS1	O95835	LATS kinases	Tumour suppressor kinase LATS1/WARTS
LATS2	Q9NRM7	LATS kinases	Tumor suppressor kinase LATS2
VPS13D	Q5THJ4	Other	UBA-containing homologue of yeast VPS13
C22orf3	Q9Y3P4	Other	Rhomboid-type protease
DHX57	Q6PI58	Other	DEAH box helicase 57
PHGDHL1	Q8NBM4	Other	Phosphoglycerate dehydrogenase-like 1
TDRD3	Q9H7E2	Other	Tudor domain containing protein 3

Table 1. (contd)

Gene name	Accession no.	Class	Comment
TNRC6C	Q9HCJ0	Other	Trinucleotide repeat containing 6C
CUE domain proteins			
AMFR	Q9UKV5	Cue-A	Autocrine motility factor receptor
AUP1	Q9Y679	Cue-A	Ancient ubiquitous protein 1
TOLLIP	Q9H0E2	Cue-ub	Toll interacting protein
CUEDC1	Q9NWM3	Cue-ub	CUE domain containing 1
N4BP2	Q86UW6	Cue-ub	Nedd4 binding protein 2
SMARCAD1	Q9H4L7	Cue-ub	SWI/SNF-related helicase
DMRT3/DMRTA3	Q9NQL9	Cue-dma	Doublesex/mab-3 transcription factor 3
DMRT4/DMRTA1	Q5VZB9	Cue-dma	Doublesex/mab-3 transcription factor 4
DMRT5/DMRTA2	Q96SC8	Cue-dma	Doublesex/mab-3 transcription factor 5
UIM domain proteins			
PSMD4	P55036	Proteasome	Proteasome subunit S5A, Rpn10-homologue
UREB1	Q7Z6Z7	E3: HECT	HECT-ligase URE-B1
ANKIB1	Q6P3S9	E3: RING	Ankyrin repeat Parkin triad protein
USP28	Q96RU2	Ubiquitin protease	Ubiquitin-specific protease 28
USP25	Q9UHP3	Ubiquitin protease	Ubiquitin-specific protease 25
USP37	Q86T82	Ubiquitin protease	Ubiquitin-specific protease 37
ATXN3	P54252	Ubiquitin protease	Ataxin-3 (MJD1)
ATNX3L	Q9H3M9	Ubiquitin protease	Ataxin-3-like protein
EPS15	P42566	EPS15	EGF receptor substrate 15
EPS15R	Q60902	EPS15	EGF receptor substrate 15 related protein
EPN1	Q9Y6I3	Epsin	Epsin 1

EPN2	O95208	Epsin	Epsin 2
EPN3	Q9H201	Epsin	Epsin 3
HGS/HRS	O14964	VHS	HGF receptor substrate
STAM	Q92783	VHS	Signal transducing adaptor molecule 1
STAM2/HBP	O75886	VHS	Signal transducing adaptor molecule 2 (HBP)
DNAJB2	P25686	Other	DnaJ homologue, subfamily B, member 2
ANKRD13	Q8IZ07	Other	Ankyrin repeat domain 13
RAP80	Q5XKQ1	Other	Retinoic X receptor interactor Rap80
FLJ25555	Q6P5X6	Other	Hypothetical protein FLJ25555
FLJ44474	Q6ZTN6	Other	Hypothetical protein LOC338692
LOC130617	Q8WV99	Other	Hypothetical protein BC018415
KIAA0794	O94888	Other	KIAA0794 protein

BRCA1, breast-cancer susceptibility gene 1; HECT, homologous to E6-associated protein C-terminus; HGF, hepatocyte growth factor; LATS, large tumour supressor; MAP, microtubule-associated protein; ORF, open reading frame; PGAM, phosphoglycerate mutase; UBAP, ubiquitin-associated protein; UBC, ubiquitin-conjugating enzyme.

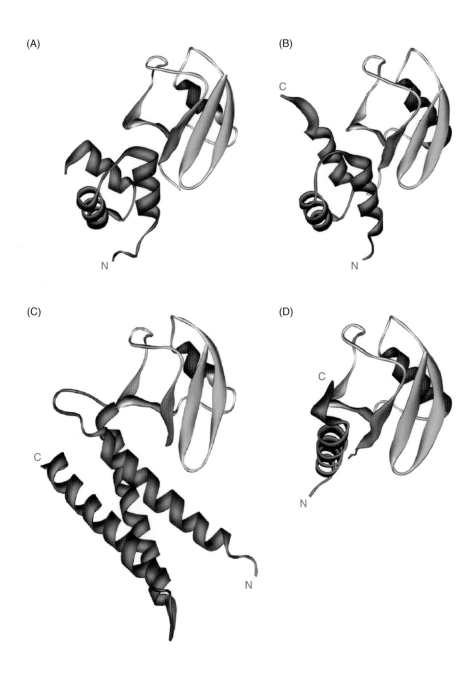

Figure 1. Structures of ubiquitin and ubiquitin-binding domains
Ribbon diagrams of the structures of (**A**) a UBA domain, (**B**) a CUE domain, (**C**) a GAT domain and (**D**) a UIM domain interacting with ubiquitin. The molecular models are derived from the PDB entries 1WR1, 1OTR, 1YD8 and 1Q0W, respectively. The binding domains are shown in dark blue. The N- and C-termini have been marked. Ubiquitin is shown in the same orientation; its sheets are coloured turquoise and its helix, red.

teins [23]. The UIM domain forms a helix (Figure 1D) [11] that is amphipathic and on one side engages the hydrophobic patch in ubiquitin.

Most proteasome subunits are essential, but curiously yeast deleted for the *RPN10/pus1+* gene proved viable [24,25]. More recent studies (described below) have clarified this initially surprising result.

In the N-terminus, S5a/Rpn10/Pus1 contains a VWA (von Willebrand factor A) domain, a domain found in cell adhesion molecules in higher eukaryotes [26] but encountered only rarely in intracellular proteins. The VWA domain in S5a/Rpn10/Pus1 interacts with PC (proteasome/cyclosome) repeats [20]. PC repeats are found exclusively in the S2/Rpn1/Mts4 and S1/Rpn2 subunits of the 26 S proteasome and in the Apc1/Cut4 subunit of the E3, called the APC/C (anaphase-promoting complex/cyclosome) [27]. Therefore an attractive model for the function of S5a/Rpn10/Pus1 is that it may shuttle from the APC/C to the proteasome to pick-up and deliver, respectively, ubiquitinated protein cargo for degradation [28]. This observation perhaps explains the finding that a substantial amount of S5a/Rpn10/Pus1 exists in a free form in yeast cells [24,25]. However, in HeLa cells, S5a/Rpn10/Pus1 is found exclusively in high molecular mass fractions, and proteasome-bound S5a/Rpn10/Pus1 does not appear to dissociate from the 26 S proteasome more readily than any other subunit [29]. Together, these data point to a functional difference between human and yeast S5a/Rpn10/Pus1.

The UBA domain is a widespread, approx. 50-residue, protein module, which structurally forms a bundle of three helices (Figure 1A) [9,30]. Even in the relatively small fission and budding yeast genomes, about 15 different UBA domain-containing proteins are encoded. Most of these genes have orthologues in higher eukaryotes, which, in addition, contain many other more specialized proteins with UBA domains. The most well-characterized UBA domain proteins are the UBL/UBA proteins Rad23/Rhp23 and Dsk2/Dph1.

Recruiting substrates to proteasomes via UBL/UBA adaptors

The first clues to the function of UBL/UBA proteins came from studies in yeast [18]. The UBL domain of Rad23/Rhp23 was found to associate with S2/Rpn1/Mts4 of the 26 S proteasome [19,20].

The UBA domain interacts with ubiquitin chains, and the UBL/UBA proteins therefore link ubiquitinated substrates to the 26 S proteasome [31]. Single knock-out strains proved viable. However, a triple mutant in Rhp23, Dph1 and Pus1 was inviable, indicating that the UBL/UBA proteins function in parallel to the proteasome's substrate-receptor subunit S5a/Rpn10/Pus1 [31]. Thus, Rad23/Rhp23 and Dsk2/Dph1 may function as the 26 S proteasome's substrate receptors, or by carrying ubiquitinated proteins from the E3 enzymes to the proteasome [28].

The first attempt to verify this 'substrate shuttle model' by biochemical assays was unsuccessful, but revealed that UBA domains protect ubiquitin chains from disassembly by DUBs, and as chain disassembly is coupled to proteasomal degradation, UBA domains were inhibitory for proteasomal degradation *in vivo* [32]. Recently, however, an elegant cell-free system was developed, which provided direct evidence that the UBL/UBA domain proteins actually fulfil the role of *bona fide* substrate receptors/carriers [33].

The human genome encodes two Rad23/Rhp23 orthologues, hHR23a and hHR23b. The mammalian orthologues of yeast Dsk2/Dph1 are known as ubiquilins or PLICs. The protein Nub1 [Nedd8 (neural precursor cell expressed developmentally down-regulated 8) ultimate buster-1] has a domain organization similar to that of Rad23/Rhp23, but has not been linked to degradation of ubiquitinated proteins, but rather to the degradation of proteins conjugated to the small ubiquitin-like modifier Nedd8 [34]. This is a controversial observation, as Nedd8-conjugated proteins are not normally targeted for degradation. More recently, Nub1 was also shown to mediate the degradation of another ubiquitin-like modifier, FAT10 [35].

Ubiquitin-binding adaptors of the Cdc48 ATPase

A subfamily of UBA-domain proteins contains both UBA and UBX (ubiquitin regulatory X) domains [36]. The UBX domain is a general Cdc48-interacting module [37–39]. Cdc48, also known as VCP (valosin-containing protein) and p97, is a hexameric ATPase complex thought to unfold proteins and is involved in fusion of ER and Golgi membranes, but also in spindle disassembly, DNA synthesis, and degradation of ubiquitinated proteins [40]. The question of how Cdc48 is involved in such a diverse set of cellular processes remains open, but it is probably connected with a host of Cdc48 cofactors, including the UBA/UBX domain proteins.

The UBA/UBX domain protein p47 (Ubx3 in *Schizosaccharomyces pombe* and Shp1 in *Saccharomyces cerevisiae*) interacts with ubiquitin chains via its N-terminal UBA domain [41], a binding required for its function in Golgi-membrane fusion. As proteasome activity is not required for membrane fusion, the recruitment of certain ubiquitinated proteins to Cdc48 by p47 is not connected with proteasomal degradation [42]. However, the recruitment of ubiquitinated substrates to Cdc48 via p47 is, in at least some cases, an important step, upstream of proteasome degradation [38,39,43]. Like the *rhp23 dph1* double mutant, an *shp1/ubx3* null mutant is synthetically lethal with null mutants in *RPN10/pus1⁺* [38,39]. Also, *shp1/ubx3* null mutants display slowed turnover of certain proteasomal substrates, and increased levels of ubiquitinated proteins are found when p47 is knocked down with RNAi (RNA interference) [43]. Hence, it appears that p47 can recruit ubiquitinated proteins to Cdc48 for both proteolytic and non-proteolytic purposes.

A null mutant in budding yeast Ubx2, another UBA/UBX domain protein, also displays retarded protein degradation [38]. However, *Sacch. cerevisiae* Ubx5 null mutant, which corresponds to *Schiz. pombe* Ubx2 null mutant, does not display any obvious defects in the ubiquitin–proteasome pathway [38,39].

Human Npl4 is another ubiquitin-binding Cdc48 cofactor. It interacts with ubiquitin via an NZF domain [41], which is not conserved in yeast. The NZF domain is composed of four β-strands stabilized by a Zn^{2+} ion [14]. Similar to the UBA domain, the NZF domain also interacts with the hydrophobic patch on ubiquitin. Although another NZF domain protein, Vps36 (vacuolar protein sorting 36), also binds ubiquitin, the NZF domain is not a general ubiquitin-binding domain, as the NZF domain from RanBP2 (Ran-binding protein 2) does not interact with ubiquitin [14].

If proteins that are to be secreted are unable to attain a proper structure within the ER, these proteins are transported back into the cytoplasm, where they are ubiquitinated and degraded. Together with another protein, Ufd1 (ubiquitin fusion degradation protein-1), Npl4 interacts with Cdc48, and the Cdc48–Ufd1–Npl4 complex is involved in this ERAD (ER-associated degradation) pathway [44], presumably pulling the proteins through a channel in the ER membrane. However, the Cdc48–Ufd1–Npl4 complex is involved not only in degrading ERAD substrates; certain membrane bound transcription factor precursors are also processed via the Cdc48–Ufd1–Npl4 complex. Recently, it was shown that the complex prevents excessive formation of ubiquitin chains and works upstream from, but in co-operation with, the UBL/UBA proteins Rad23/Rhp23 and Dsk2/Dph1 [45].

Ubiquitin binding in ubiquitination and deubiquitination

Although they bind ubiquitin, only a modest subset of ubiquitinating enzymes and DUBs contain recognizable ubiquitin-binding domains.

Gp78 and c-Cbl are ubiquitinating enzymes. The c-Cbl proto-oncoprotein is an E3 of the RING (really interesting new gene) finger family which recognizes activated RTKs (receptor tyrosine kinases), and terminates their signalling by promoting their destruction. Gp78 is an E3 enzyme in the ER membrane, where it is involved in the ERAD pathway [46]. The gp78 enzyme contains a CUE domain near the C-terminus. As no mammalian orthologue of the yeast ERAD component called Cue1 has been found, gp78 perhaps also carries out the function of Cue1 in mammalian cells.

Usp5 (ubiquitin-specific protease 5), or isopeptidase T-1, is a DUB enzyme which cleaves Lys^{48}-linked ubiquitin chains released from target proteins [47], but it also shows affinity for Lys^{29}-linked chains and for the ubiquitin-like protein ISG (interferon-stimulated gene)-15 [48]. Hence, isopeptidase T probably utilizes its UBA domains to grasp the ubiquitin chains prior to catalysis. In yeast, isopeptidase T is not essential, but in accordance with its role in ubiquitin recycling, a null mutant accumulates free ubiquitin chains [47]. No other yeast DUBs contain UBA domains, so they must interact with their substrates in a different manner. In humans, a close homologue of isopeptidase T-1, Usp13 (isopeptidase T-3), also contains a UBA domain, but Usp13 largely remains to be functionally characterized.

Usp25 and Usp28 are two related human DUBs, which both contain UIM domains.

Ubiquitin-binding proteins in membrane events

Ubiquitin also works as a signal for endosomal sorting of many receptors. At least some targeted proteins carry ubiquitin chains, but monoubiquitination is often sufficient to promote lysosomal protein targeting. In many, but not all, cases, UIM-domain proteins both bind ubiquitin and promote their own mono- and poly-ubiquitination. However, UIM-dependent ubiquitination does not lead to degradation of the protein, and since the ubiquitination of UIM-domain proteins inhibits their interaction with other ubiquitinated proteins, it appears that their ubiquitination may be a regulatory mechanism [49,50].

During endocytosis of the EGFR (epidermal growth factor receptor), it becomes ubiquitinated by the UBA domain-containing c-Cbl E3 enzyme, enabling the protein Eps15 (EGFR pathway substrate 15) to recruit the EGFR to clathrin-coated pits [51]. Epsins and Eps15 are UIM-domain proteins involved in endocytosis. Their role in this process is critical and derives from their capacity to bind ubiquitin and to undergo ubiquitination.

Generally, ubiquitin-tagged substrate proteins are sorted into the interior of MVBs (multi-vesicular bodies). These MVBs subsequently fuse with lysosomes, thereby delivering both hydrolytic enzymes and substrate proteins to the lysosome/vacuole. The biogenesis of MVBs requires the activity of Vps proteins, some of which are subunits of the ESCRT (endosomal sorting complexes required for transport) [52]. The ESCRT complexes are recruited to the endosome membranes, where ubiquitinated proteins are sorted and vesicles are formed. Several of the proteins involved in these events are ubiquitin-binding proteins [49].

The ubiquitin signal is recognized by the protein Hrs (hepatocyte growth factor-regulated tyrosine kinase substrate; Vps27 in yeast), which also recruits the ESCRT complex to endosomes through an interaction with TSG101 (tumour susceptibility gene 101; Vps23 in yeast) [53]. When Hrs/Vps27 is recruited to the endosome, it is in a complex with the protein STAM (signal transducing adaptor molecule; Hse1 in yeast). At the endosome, it is localized to clathrin-coated areas and interacts directly with clathrin. It is thought that Hrs/Vps27 serves to concentrate receptors modified with ubiquitin prior to inward vesiculation [54]. Hrs, TSG101 and STAM are all ubiquitin-binding proteins, albeit utilizing different protein modules for the interaction. Hrs and STAM contain UIM domains, whereas TSG101 interacts with ubiquitin via a UEV domain.

Vps9 is a guanine nucleotide exchange factor for the yeast Rab5 ortho-logue Vps21 [12] and is necessary for the delivery of proteins to the vacuole. Mis-sorting is seen when Vps9 is absent, and the CUE domain in Vps9 is required for its monoubiquitination [55]. Vps9 binds ubiquitin via its CUE domains and this interaction is necessary for Vps9's endocytotic activity.

Interestingly, the human neuronal protein HSJ1 contains both a UIM domain and a DnaJ domain, the latter being a module present in cofactors of Hsp70 (heat-shock protein 70)-type chaperones. The role of the UIM domain in HSJ1 is unknown but HSJ1 has been linked to the processing of rhodopsin and in clathrin uncoating [56], which are both processes where ubiquitin plays a role. Hence it is possible that HSJ1 also functions in endocytosis, perhaps in analogy to another chaperone-binding protein, Swa2. The yeast protein Swa2 contains a C-terminal auxillin-type DnaJ domain, and, like auxillin, Swa2 is able to activate the ATPase activity of Hsc70 (heat-shock cognate 70 stress protein) and stimulate the uncoating of clathrin-coated vesicles [57]. The structure of the Swa2 UBA domain has been determined, and it has been confirmed that Swa2 interacts with ubiquitin chains [58]. This indicates either that Swa2 is a multifunctional protein involved in other processes related to ubiquitin, or that ubiquitin-binding is part of Swa2's function in clathrin-uncoating.

The human protein called Tom1 is another ubiquitin-binding protein. Tom1 binds ubiquitin via a GAT domain, which in a mutually exclusive manner also interacts with another ubiquitin-binding protein, called tollip (toll-interacting protein) [59]. Tollip contains a C2-like domain, and a CUE domain. C2 domains are typically associated with various phospholipids. Tollip localizes to early endosomes and can recruit Tom1 [59], suggesting that Tom1 and tollip are involved in endosome trafficking of ubiquitinated proteins.

Other ubiquitin-binding proteins

Snf1-like kinases
The budding yeast protein Snf1 is a serine/threonine kinase, which mediates glucose repression of several genes and is involved in the cellular response to various forms of stress [60]. Snf1 interacts with ubiquitin [61]. However, the physiological significance of this interaction is presently unknown. The Snf1 orthologue in humans is the AMP-activated protein kinase, which is one of at least 13 related kinases, of which some contain UBA domains [62]. The functional relevance of the UBA domains in these kinases is still unknown.

Other putative ubiquitin-binding proteins
NAC (nascent polypeptide-associated complex) α-subunit is an abundant UBA domain protein which interacts with nascent polypeptide chains emerging from the ribosome. NAC has been proposed to protect the nascent chains from premature interaction with other cell proteins [63]. It is therefore attractive to speculate whether NAC is involved in directing nascent chains with folding defects to the 26 S proteasome. However, the presence of a UBA domain in archaeal orthologues of NAC makes this hypothesis less attractive,

since archaea lack a ubiquitin system. Since this UBA domain seems more ancient than ubiquitin, its function is intriguing also from an evolutionary perspective. Recently, the structure of the NAC UBA domain was determined, revealing that the hydrophobic ubiquitin-binding area is structurally conserved in archaea [64].

The activation of the transcription factor NF-κB (nuclear factor κB) is highly complex and is regulated on several levels by the ubiquitin system. NF-κB activation requires a complex consisting of the kinase TAK1 [TGF (trans-forming growth factor)-β activated kinase] and the regulatory proteins TAB1, TAB2 or TAB3 (TAK1-binding protein-1, -2 and -3 respectively). The activity of TAK1 is regulated by the E3 enzyme, TRAF (tumour-necrosis-factor-receptor-associated factor)-6. When TRAF-6 ubiquitinates TAK1 with a chain of Lys^{63}-linked ubiquitin moieties, the kinase is activated [65]. Structurally, Lys^{63}-linked ubiquitin chains have a different conformation from Lys^{48}-linked chains [66]. The N-termini in both TAB2 and TAB3 contain CUE domains, whereas in their C-termini, they contain highly conserved Zn-finger domains. The TAB2 and TAB3 proteins interact with ubiquitinated TAK1. However, as with the NZF domain, the interactions appear to be mediated by the Zn-finger domains, while the CUE domains may co-operate with the Zn-finger domains in providing specificity for Lys^{63}-linked ubiquitin chains [67]. The ubiquitin-binding Zn-finger domains in TAB2 and TAB3 are essential for activation of TAK1, revealing a striking example of how the ubiquitin signal may be involved in signal transduction via a non-proteolytic mechanism.

Ubiquitin-binding proteins in disease

Paget's disease of bone is a disorder affecting about 3% of individuals in their mid-fifties. It is caused by mutation in the UBA domain of the p62 protein, also known as sequestosome 1 and SQSTM1. Among other functions, p62 regulates NF-κB signalling and localizes, along with ubiquitin, to intracellular protein aggregates typical of Alzheimer's and Parkinson's diseases [68]. Interestingly, the N-terminus of p62 contains a PB1 (Phox and Bem1)-domain that has a ubiquitin-like fold. Hence, p62 may be somewhat analogous to the UBL/UBA domain proteins.

Aggregates are also found in MJD (Machado–Joseph disease) and Huntington's disease, where they contain molecular chaperones, ubiquitin and ubiquitin-binding proteins, including tollip and ubiquilin/Dsk2/Dph1 [69]. MJD is caused by the expansion of a polyglutamine (polyQ) stretch in the pro-tein ataxin-3. Ataxin-3 contains a Josephin domain with deubiquitinating activity [70], and two UIM domains besides the polyQ region [71]. Ataxin-3 is alternatively spliced, and a splicing variant contains a third UIM domain at the C-terminus. Ataxin-3 is conserved in higher eukaryotes, including plants, but no orthologue is present in yeast.

The UIM domains in ataxin-3 bind ubiquitin chains, ubiquitinated proteins and Rad23/Rhp23 [72]. Interestingly, ataxin-3 also binds to Cdc48 [73], and

Cdc48 contributes to the formation of vacuoles in polyQ-associated disorders [73]. Presumably, ataxin-3 plays an important role in the ubiquitin–proteasome system, but its substrates and its precise role remains to be determined.

Conclusion

This review is only a brief account of the increasing amount of literature on ubiquitin-binding proteins, and although the ubiquitin field is progressing at a rapid pace, it is clear that there are still fundamental problems to address.

Much remains to be learned about how poly- and mono-ubiquitin chains are recognized within the cell and how the cell distinguishes between the different types of chains. Biochemical studies have uncovered some detailed aspects of ubiquitin-binding proteins, but more physiological studies on the *in vivo* function of the different proteins are still needed.

The diversity of the ubiquitin-binding proteins indicates that the ubiquitin–proteasome pathway is more versatile than previously acknowledged, but also reveals how many other cellular functions may require and interplay with the ubiquitin signal.

Summary

- *Several families of ubiquitin-binding proteins have been characterized and their three-dimensional structures reveal that they are a heterogeneous group of proteins.*
- *The UBL/UBA domain proteins are involved in targeting ubiquitinated substrates to the 26 S proteasome for destruction.*
- *The UBA/UBX proteins are involved in targeting ubiquitinated proteins to Cdc48.*
- *An array of ubiquitin-binding proteins is involved at several levels in the regulation of endocytosis and vesicle fusion.*
- *Some ubiquitin-binding proteins are connected to hereditary human diseases: most notable are p62 and ataxin-3.*

We thank Dr Colin Gordon, Dr Klavs B. Hendil and Dr Peter S. Walmod for critical comments on the manuscript and apologise to those whose work we were unable to include due to space constraints. R.H.-P. is supported by a grant from the Danish Natural Science Council.

References

1. Glickman, M.H. & Ciechanover, A. (2002) The ubiquitin–proteasome proteolytic pathway: destruction for the sake of construction. *Physiol. Rev.* **82**, 373–428
2. Weissman, A.M. (2001) Themes and variations on ubiquitylation. *Nat. Rev. Mol. Cell Biol.* **2**, 169–178
3. Pickart, C.M. (2001) Mechanisms underlying ubiquitination. *Annu. Rev. Biochem.* **70**, 503–533

4.   Hicke, L. (2001) Protein regulation by monoubiquitin. *Nat. Rev. Mol. Cell Biol.* **2**, 195–201
5.   Koegl, M., Hoppe, T., Schlenker, S., Ulrich, H.D., Mayer, T.U. & Jentsch, S. (1999) A novel
     ubiquitination factor, E4, is involved in multiubiquitin chain assembly. *Cell* **96**, 635–644
6.   Pickart, C.M. & Fushman, D. (2004) Polyubiquitin chains: polymeric protein signals. *Curr. Opin.
     Chem. Biol.* **8**, 610–616
7.   Spence, J., Sadis, S., Haas, A.L. & Finley, D. (1995) A ubiquitin mutant with specific defects in DNA
     repair and multiubiquitination. *Mol. Cell. Biol.* **15**, 1265–1273
8.   Wilkinson, K.D. (2000) Ubiquitination and deubiquitination: targeting of proteins for degradation
     by the proteasome. *Semin. Cell Dev. Biol.* **11**, 141–148
9.   Mueller, T.D. & Feigon, J. (2002) Solution structures of UBA domains reveal a conserved
     hydrophobic surface for protein protein interactions. *J. Mol. Biol.* **319**, 1243 1255
10. Pornillos, O., Alam, S.L., Rich, R.L., Myszka, D.G., Davis, D.R. & Sundquist, W.I. (2002) Structure
     and functional interactions of the Tsg101 UEV domain. *EMBO J.* **21**, 2397–2406
11. Fisher, R.D., Wang, B., Alam, S.L., Higginson, D.S., Robinson, H., Sundquist, W.I. & Hill, C.P.
     (2003) Structure and ubiquitin binding of the ubiquitin-interacting motif. *J. Biol. Chem.* **278**,
     28976–28984
12. Prag, G., Misra, S., Jones, E.A., Ghirlando, R., Davies, B.A., Horazdovsky, B.F. & Hurley, J.H. (2003)
     Mechanism of ubiquitin recognition by the CUE domain of Vps9p. *Cell* **113**, 609–620
13. Wang, B., Alam, S.L., Meyer, H.H., Payne, M., Stemmler, T.L., Davis, D.R. & Sundquist, W.I. (2003)
     Structure and ubiquitin interactions of the conserved zinc finger domain of Npl4. *J. Biol. Chem.*
     278, 20225–20234
14. Alam, S.L., Sun, J., Payne, M., Welch, B.D., Blake, B.K., Davis, D.R., Meyer, H.H., Emr, S.D. &
     Sundquist, W.I. (2004) Ubiquitin interactions of NZF zinc fingers. *EMBO J.* **23**, 1411–1421
15. Prag, G., Lee, S., Mattera, R., Arighi, C. N, Beach, B.M., Bonifacino, J.S. & Hurley, J.H. (2005)
     Structural mechanism for ubiquitinated-cargo recognition by the Golgi-localized, gamma-ear-con-
     taining, ADP-ribosylation-factor-binding proteins. *Proc. Natl. Acad. Sci. U.S.A.* **102**, 2334–2339
16. Piotrowski, J., Beal, R., Hoffman, L., Wilkinson, K.D., Cohen, R.E. & Pickart, C.M. (1997) Inhibition
     of the 26 S proteasome by polyubiquitin chains synthesized to have defined lengths. *J. Biol. Chem.*
     272, 23712–23721
17. Ryu, K.S., Lee, K.J., Bae, S.H., Kim, B.K., Kim, K.A. & Choi, B.S. (2003) Binding surface mapping of
     intra- and interdomain interactions among hHR23B, ubiquitin, and polyubiquitin binding site 2 of
     S5a. *J. Biol. Chem.* **278**, 36621–36627
18. Schauber, C., Chen, L., Tongaonkar, P., Vega, I., Lambertson, D., Potts, W. & Madura, K. (1998)
     Rad23 links DNA repair to the ubiquitin/proteasome pathway. *Nature (London)* **391**, 715–718
19. Elsasser, S., Gali, R.R., Schwickart, M., Larsen, C.N., Leggett, D.S., Muller, B., Feng, M.T., Tubing,
     F., Dittmar, G.A. & Finley, D. (2002) Proteasome subunit Rpn1 binds ubiquitin-like protein
     domains. *Nat. Cell Biol.* **4**, 725–730
20. Seeger, M., Hartmann-Petersen, R., Wilkinson, C.R., Wallace, M., Samejima, I., Taylor, M.S. &
     Gordon, C. (2003) Interaction of the anaphase-promoting complex/cyclosome and proteasome
     protein complexes with multiubiquitin chain-binding proteins. *J. Biol. Chem.* **278**, 16791–16796
21. Lam, Y.A., Lawson, T.G., Velayutham, M., Zweier, J.L. & Pickart, C.M. (2002) A proteasomal
     ATPase subunit recognizes the polyubiquitin degradation signal. *Nature (London)* **416**, 763–767
22. Deveraux, Q., Ustrell, V., Pickart, C. & Rechsteiner, M. (1994) A 26 S protease subunit that binds
     ubiquitin conjugates. *J. Biol. Chem.* **269**, 7059–7061
23. Hofmann, K. & Falquet, L. (2001) A ubiquitin-interacting motif conserved in components of the
     proteasomal and lysosomal protein degradation systems. *Trends Biochem. Sci.* **26**, 347–350
24. van Nocker, S., Sadis, S., Rubin, D.M., Glickman, M., Fu, H., Coux, O., Wefes, I., Finley, D. &
     Vierstra, R.D. (1996) The multiubiquitin-chain-binding protein Mcb1 is a component of the 26 S
     proteasome in *Saccharomyces cerevisiae* and plays a nonessential, substrate-specific role in protein
     turnover. *Mol. Cell. Biol.* **16**, 6020–6028
25. Wilkinson, C.R., Ferrell, K., Penney, M., Wallace, M., Dubiel, W. & Gordon, C. (2000) Analysis of
     a gene encoding Rpn10 of the fission yeast proteasome reveals that the polyubiquitin-binding site

of this subunit is essential when Rpn12/Mts3 activity is compromised. *J. Biol. Chem.* **275**, 15182–15192

26. Whittaker, C.A. & Hynes, R.O. (2002) Distribution and evolution of von Willebrand/integrin A domains: widely dispersed domains with roles in cell adhesion and elsewhere. *Mol. Biol. Cell* **13**, 3369–3387

27. Lupas, A., Baumeister, W. & Hofmann, K. (1997) A repetitive sequence in subunits of the 26 S proteasome and 20 S cyclosome (anaphase-promoting complex). *Trends Biochem. Sci.* **22**, 195–196

28. Hartmann-Petersen, R., Seeger, M. & Gordon, C. (2003) Transferring substrates to the 26 S proteasome. *Trends Biochem. Sci.* **28**, 26–31

29. Hendil, K.B., Hartmann-Petersen, R. & Tanaka, K. (2002) 26 S proteasomes function as stable entities. *J. Mol. Biol.* **315**, 627–636

30. Hofmann, K. & Bucher, P. (1996) The UBA domain: a sequence motif present in multiple enzyme classes of the ubiquitination pathway. *Trends Biochem. Sci.* **21**, 172–173

31. Wilkinson, C.R., Seeger, M., Hartmann-Petersen, R., Stone, M., Wallace, M., Semple, C. & Gordon, C. (2001) Proteins containing the UBA domain are able to bind to multi-ubiquitin chains. *Nat. Cell Biol.* **3**, 939–943

32. Raasi, S. & Pickart, C.M. (2003) Rad23 ubiquitin-associated domains (UBA) inhibit 26 S proteasome-catalyzed proteolysis by sequestering lysine 48-linked polyubiquitin chains. *J. Biol. Chem.* **278**, 8951–8959

33. Verma, R., Oania, R., Graumann, J. & Deshaies, R.J. (2004) Multiubiquitin chain receptors define a layer of substrate selectivity in the ubiquitin–proteasome system. *Cell* **118**, 99–110

34. Kamitani, T., Kito, K., Fukuda-Kamitani, T. & Yeh, E.T. (2001) Targeting of NEDD8 and its conjugates for proteasomal degradation by NUB1. *J. Biol. Chem.* **276**, 46655–46660

35. Hipp, M.S., Raasi, S., Groettrup, M. & Schmidtke, G. (2004) NEDD8 ultimate buster-1L interacts with the ubiquitin-like protein FAT10 and accelerates its degradation. *J. Biol. Chem.* **279**, 16503–16510

36. Buchberger, A. (2002) From UBA to UBX: new words in the ubiquitin vocabulary. *Trends Cell Biol.* **12**, 216–221

37. Decottignies, A., Evain, A. & Ghislain, M. (2004) Binding of Cdc48p to a ubiquitin-related UBX domain from novel yeast proteins involved in intracellular proteolysis and sporulation. *Yeast* **21**, 127–139

38. Schuberth, C., Richly, H., Rumpf, S. & Buchberger, A. (2004) Shp1 and Ubx2 are adaptors of Cdc48 involved in ubiquitin-dependent protein degradation. *EMBO Rep.* **5**, 818–824

39. Hartmann-Petersen, R., Wallace, M., Hofmann, K., Koch, G., Johnsen, A.H., Hendil, K.B. & Gordon, C. (2004) The Ubx2 and Ubx3 cofactors direct Cdc48 activity to proteolytic and non-proteolytic ubiquitin-dependent processes. *Curr. Biol.* **14**, 824–828

40. Woodman, P.G. (2003) p97, a protein coping with multiple identities. *J. Cell Sci.* **116**, 4283–4290

41. Meyer, H.H., Wang, Y. & Warren, G. (2002) Direct binding of ubiquitin conjugates by the mammalian p97 adaptor complexes, p47 and Ufd1-Npl4. *EMBO J.* **21**, 5645–5652

42. Wang, Y., Satoh, A., Warren, G. & Meyer, H.H. (2004) VCIP135 acts as a deubiquitinating enzyme during p97-p47-mediated reassembly of mitotic Golgi fragments. *J. Cell Biol.* **164**, 973–978

43. Wojcik, C., Yano, M. & DeMartino, G.N. (2004) RNA interference of valosin-containing protein (VCP/p97) reveals multiple cellular roles linked to ubiquitin/proteasome-dependent proteolysis. *J. Cell Sci.* **117**, 281–292

44. Kostova, Z. & Wolf, D.H. (2003) For whom the bell tolls: protein quality control of the endoplasmic reticulum and the ubiquitin–proteasome connection. *EMBO J.* **22**, 2309–2317

45. Richly, M., Rape, M., Braun, S., Rumpf, S., Hoege, C. & Jentsch, S. (2005) A series of ubiquitin binding factors connects CDC48/p97 to substrate multiubiquitylation and proteasomal targeting. *Cell* **120**, 73–84

46. Fang, S., Ferrone, M., Yang, C., Jensen, J.P., Tiwari, S. & Weissman, A.M. (2001) The tumor autocrine motility factor receptor, gp78, is a ubiquitin protein ligase implicated in degradation from the endoplasmic reticulum. *Proc. Natl. Acad. Sci. U.S.A.* **98**, 14422–14427

47. Amerik, A.Yu. Swaminathan, S., Krantz, B.A., Wilkinson, K.D. & Hochstrasser, M. (1997) In vivo disassembly of free polyubiquitin chains by yeast Ubp14 modulates rates of protein degradation by the proteasome. *EMBO J.* **16**, 4826–4838

48. Hemelaar, J., Borodovsky, A., Kessler, B.M., Reverter, D., Cook, J., Kolli, N., Gan-Erdene, T., Wilkinson, K.D., Gill, G., Lima, C.D. et al. (2004) Specific and covalent targeting of conjugating and deconjugating enzymes of ubiquitin-like proteins. *Mol. Cell. Biol.* **24**, 84–95

49. Di Fiore, P.P., Polo, S. & Hofmann, K. (2003) When ubiquitin meets ubiquitin receptors: a signalling connection. *Nat. Rev. Mol. Cell Biol.* **4**, 491–497

50. Miller, S.L., Malotky, E. & O'Bryan, J.P. (2004) Analysis of the role of ubiquitin-interacting motifs in ubiquitin binding and ubiquitylation. *J. Biol. Chem.* **279**, 33528–33537

51. de Melker, A.A., van der Horst, G. & Borst, J. (2004) Ubiquitin ligase activity of c-Cbl guides the EGF receptor into clathrin-coated pits by two distinct modes of Eps15 recruitment. *J. Biol. Chem.* **279**, 55465–55473

52. Raiborg, C., Rusten, T.E. & Stenmark, H. (2003) Protein sorting into multivesicular endosomes. *Curr. Opin. Cell Biol.* **15**, 446–455

53. Bache K.G., Brech, A., Mehlum, A. & Stenmark, H. (2003) Hrs regulates multivesicular body formation via ESCRT recruitment to endosomes. *J. Cell Biol.* **162**, 435–442

54. Clague, M.J. & Urbe, S. (2003) Hrs function: viruses provide the clue. *Trends Cell Biol.* **13**, 603–606

55. Shih, S.C., Prag, G., Francis, S.A., Sutanto, M.A., Hurley, J.H. & Hicke, L. (2003) A ubiquitin-binding motif required for intramolecular monoubiquitylation, the CUE domain. *EMBO J.* **22**, 1273–1281

56. Chapple, J.P., van der Spuy, J., Poopalasundaram, S. & Cheetham, M.E. (2004) Neuronal DnaJ proteins HSJ1a and HSJ1b: a role in linking the Hsp70 chaperone machine to the ubiquitin–proteasome system? *Biochem. Soc. Trans.* **32**, 640–642

57. Gall, W.E., Higginbotham, M.A., Chen, C., Ingram, M.F., Cyr, D.M. & Graham, T.R. (2000) The auxilin-like phosphoprotein Swa2p is required for clathrin function in yeast. *Curr. Biol.* **10**, 1349–1358

58. Chim, N., Gall, W.E., Xiao, J., Harris, M.P., Graham, T.R. & Krezel, A.M. (2004) Solution structure of the ubiquitin-binding domain in Swa2p from *Saccharomyces cerevisiae*. *Proteins* **54**, 784–793

59. Katoh, Y., Shiba, Y., Mitsuhashi, H., Yanagida, Y., Takatsu, H. & Nakayama, K. (2004) Tollip and Tom1 form a complex and recruit ubiquitin-conjugated proteins onto early endosomes. *J. Biol. Chem.* **279**, 24435–24443

60. Hardie, D.G., Carling, D. & Carlson, M. (1998) The AMP-activated/SNF1 protein kinase subfamily: metabolic sensors of the eukaryotic cell? *Annu. Rev. Biochem.* **67**, 821–855

61. Ho, Y., Gruhler, A., Heilbut, A., Bader, G.D., Moore, L., Adams, S.L., Millar, A., Taylor, P., Bennett, K., Boutilier, K. et al. (2002) Systematic identification of protein complexes in *Saccharomyces cerevisiae* by mass spectrometry. *Nature (London)* **415**, 180–183

62. Lizcano, J.M., Goransson, O., Toth, R., Deak, M., Morrice, N.A., Boudeau, J., Hawley, S.A., Udd, L., Makela, T.P., Hardie, D.G. & Alessi, D.R. (2004) LKB1 is a master kinase that activates 13 kinases of the AMPK subfamily, including MARK/PAR-1. *EMBO J.* **23**, 833–843

63. Shi, X., Parthun, M.R. & Jaehning, J.A. (1995) The yeast EGD2 gene encodes a homologue of the alpha NAC subunit of the human nascent-polypeptide-associated complex. *Gene* **165**, 199–202

64. Spreter, T., Pech, M. & Beatrix, B. (2005) The crystal structure of archaeal nascent polypeptide-associated complex (NAC) reveals a unique fold and the presence of a ubiquitin-associated domain. *J. Biol. Chem.* **280**, 15849–15854

65. Deng, L., Wang, C., Spencer, E., Yang, L., Braun, A., You, J., Slaughter, C., Pickart, C. & Chen, Z.J. (2000) Activation of the IκB kinase complex by TRAF6 requires a dimeric ubiquitin-conjugating enzyme complex and a unique polyubiquitin chain. *Cell* **103**, 351–361

66. Varadan, R., Assfalg, M., Haririnia, A., Raasi, S., Pickart, C. & Fushman, D. (2004) Solution conformation of Lys63-linked di-ubiquitin chain provides clues to functional diversity of polyubiquitin signaling. *J. Biol. Chem.* **279**, 7055–7063

67. Kanayama, A., Seth, R.B., Sun, L., Ea, C.K., Hong, M., Shaito, A., Chiu, Y.H., Deng, L. & Chen, Z.J. (2004) TAB2 and TAB3 activate the NF-κB pathway through binding to polyubiquitin chains. *Mol. Cell* **15**, 535–548

68. Layfield, R. & Hocking, L.J. (2004) SQSTM1 and Paget's disease of bone. *Calcif. Tissue Int.* **75**, 347–357

69. Doi, H., Mitsui, K., Kurosawa, M., Machida, Y., Kuroiwa, Y. & Nukina, N. (2004) Identification of ubiquitin-interacting proteins in purified polyglutamine aggregates. *FEBS Lett.* **571**, 171–176

70. Burnett, B., Li, F. & Pittman, R.N. (2003) The polyglutamine neurodegenerative protein ataxin-3 binds polyubiquitylated proteins and has ubiquitin protease activity. *Hum. Mol. Genet.* **12**, 3195–3205

71. Scheel, H., Tomiuk, S. & Hofmann, K. (2003) Elucidation of ataxin-3 and ataxin-7 function by integrative bioinformatics. *Hum. Mol. Genet.* **12**, 2845–2852

72. Wang, G., Sawai, N., Kotliarova, S., Kanazawa, I. & Nukina, N. (2000) Ataxin-3, the MJD1 gene product, interacts with the two human homologs of yeast DNA repair protein RAD23, HHR23A and HHR23B. *Hum. Mol. Genet.* **9**, 1795–1803

73. Hirabayashi, M., Inoue, K., Tanaka, K., Nakadate, K., Ohsawa, Y., Kamei, Y., Popiel, A.H., Sinohara, A., Iwamatsu, A., Kimura, Y. et al. (2001) VCP/p97 in abnormal protein aggregates, cytoplasmic vacuoles, and cell death, phenotypes relevant to neurodegeneration. *Cell Death Differ.* **8**, 977–984

5

Ubiquitin and control of transcription

Sarath C. Dhananjayan, Ayesha Ismail and Zafar Nawaz[1]

Department of Biochemistry and Molecular Biology, University of Miami Miller School of Medicine, 1580 NW 10 Avenue, Miami, FL 33136, U.S.A.

Abstract

Eukaryotic transcription is one of the most complex cellular processes and constitutes the first step in protein synthesis. Ubiquitination and subsequent degradation by the 26 S proteasome, on the other hand, represents the final chapter in the life of a protein. Intriguingly, ubiquitin and the ubiquitin–proteasome system play vital roles in the regulation of transcription. Ubiquitin has dual *modus operandi*: firstly, ubiquitin functions via the 26 S proteasome — it is tagged to components of the transcription machinery, marking them for degradation via the proteasome, which results in the proper exchange of complexes during transcription and the prompt removal of activators after each round of transcription; and secondly, ubiquitin can function independently of the proteasome — histone ubiquitination results in heterochromatin relaxation and assembly of transcription complexes on the promoter, and ubiquitination of transcription factors enhances their transcriptional-activation function. Although ubiquitin and the ubiquitin–proteasome system were initially perceived as a graveyard for proteins, recent advances in molecular biological techniques have redefined their role as a regulatory system that influences the fate of many cellular processes, such as apoptosis, transcription and cell cycle progression.

[1]*To whom correspondence should be addressed (email znawaz@med.miami.edu).*

Introduction

Ubiquitination is a post-translational protein modification resulting in the covalent linkage of a 76-amino-acid polypeptide, ubiquitin, to lysine residues of substrate proteins. Ubiquitination of a substrate protein is a multi-step process and requires three different sets of enzymes that facilitate the transfer of ubiquitin to the substrate. These are the ubiquitin-activating (E1), ubiquitin-conjugating (E2) and ubiquitin-ligase (E3) enzymes. A combination of specific E2–E3 or E3 alone confers substrate specificity. Recent evidence suggests the existence of an additional factor, E4 (polyubiquitin chain conjugation factor), that could contribute to polyubiquitination of the substrate protein targeted for degradation [1–3]. The ubiquitination process is involved in the regulation of many cellular processes, such as cell-cycle progression, signal transduction, differentiation, apoptosis and transcription [4].

Eukaryotic transcription is a co-ordinated process that requires the assembly of RNA polymerase II (RNA pol II) and a multitude of protein cofactors on the promoter of a target gene [5–7]. These cofactors are transcriptional activators, chromatin-modifying enzymes, transcriptional co-activators and GTFs (general transcription factors). GTFs are multi-protein complexes that assemble at the gene promoter and facilitate transcription. These complexes comprise RNA pol II, TBP (TATA-box binding protein), TFIIB (transcription factor IIB) and TFIID [8,9]. It has been suggested that TFIID contains multiple activities associated with the formation of the pre-initiation complex. Of these various factors, transcriptional activators are vital because they interact directly with DNA sequences and are essential for the subsequent assembly of other factors for transcription. Transcriptional activators generally contain two distinct domains: a DNA-binding domain that tethers the protein to the specific DNA sequences and a TAD (transcriptional activation domain) that mediates interaction with GTFs and recruitment of transcriptional co-activators. Although these transcriptional proteins, together with the RNA pol II, are necessary and sufficient for transcription, research in recent years has shown that a functional interplay exists between the protein-making (transcription and translation) and the protein-degrading [ubiquitin–proteasome system (UPS)] machinery. In this review, we discuss the role of ubiquitination in the regulation of eukaryotic transcription.

Proteasome-dependent ubiquitin functions

Regulation of levels of transcription factors

The most well-understood characteristic of the UPS is its ability to target proteins for degradation via the 26 S proteasome [2]. This provides a high level of control because the majority of proteins, including transcription factors that are synthesized in the cell, are destined for destruction by this pathway. Transcription factors are especially vulnerable to rapid degradation because a potent transcription factor, when active, can sequester the limited pool of transcription machinery, which is deleterious to the cell. In this section, we discuss a few examples of transcription factors that are regulated by ubiquitin and the UPS.

Regulation of β-catenin is one of the most well-understood examples of UPS-mediated regulation of a transcription factor. β-Catenin is involved in Wnt and other signalling pathways that result in the activation of p53 by genotoxic stress. In the absence of Wnt signalling, β-catenin is phosphorylated by GSK3β (glycogen synthase kinase 3β) [10]. Phosphorylated β-catenin is then ubiquitinated by a SCF$^{\beta TrCP}$ [Skp1(S-phase associated protein-1)–Cdc(cell-division cycle)53/Cullin-1–F-box β-transducin repeat-containing protein] complex, which specifically targets phosphorylated β-catenin for ubiquitination [11]. Wnt signalling leads to rapid inactivation of GSK3β, and consequently β-catenin stabilizes and enters the nucleus, where it dimerizes with the TCF/LEF (T-cell factor/lymphoid enhancer factor) family of transcription factors and activates its transcription programme [12]. β-Catenin has also been shown to be ubiquitinated and degraded in a GSK3β-independent mechanism by RING (really interesting new gene)-finger E3 Siah-1, which is also implicated in the degradation of oncogenic transcription factor c-myb [13]. Interestingly, Siah-1 protein expression is triggered by p53 signalling, thus allowing both Wnt and p53 signalling pathways to converge on the regulation of β-catenin via the UPS [14].

Oncogenic transcription factor *c-myc* is a prominent regulator of cancer as it can collaborate with other oncogenes to transform normal cells into cancerous cells. The UPS is implicated in the modulation of protein levels of *c-myc*. It is aberrantly expressed in many cancers (adenocarcinomas, colon, breast etc.) and approx. 30% of all human cancers have dysregulated *c-myc* signalling. Skp2, an F-box protein with E3 activity, promotes *c-myc*'s ubiquitination and degradation. Skp2 has also been shown to be a transcriptional co-activator of *c-myc* signalling. It is perceived that during S-phase transformation, Skp2 levels are increased, which results in the ubiquitination and activation of *c-myc* [15,16].

The other major group of transcription factors that is regulated by the UPS is NHRs (nuclear hormone receptors). This transcription-factor super-family includes steroid hormone receptors such as androgen, progesterone, oestrogen, glucocorticoid and mineralocorticoid receptors. The NHR family also contains receptors for thyroid hormone, vitamin D and retinoids, and some orphan receptors with unknown ligands [17]. All members of the NHR family have similarities in structure and signalling. NHRs have a global effect on gene transcription, from cell-cycle progression to inflammation and apoptosis. Their activity is finely tuned and regulated by a limited pool of proteins called co-activators. These co-activators consist of an array of proteins with various enzymatic activities, and are known to provide the link between NHRs and GTFs.

The UPS regulates the functions of NHRs by modulating the receptor, as well as the co-activator, protein levels. For certain NHRs, UPS-mediated degradation is essential for their transcriptional activities [18–23]. It has also been shown that NHRs cycle their responsive promoters on and off and this cycling is essential for the proper functioning of NHR. The UPS is a critical component of this cycling process [24,25]. These observations suggest that the UPS plays a vital role in the regulation of eukaryotic transcription by modulating the protein levels of many transcription factors in the cell.

Ubiquitin-mediated cofactor exchange

Transcription factors can be repressive or transactivating, depending on the type of cofactor that it interacts with. In this way, cofactor exchange can cause the activity state of transcription factors to change. This type of regulation is observed in the LIM-HD (LIM homeodomain) transcription factor and NHRs. LIM-HD can interact with its repressor, RLIM (RING-finger LIM domain-binding protein), and with its cofactor, CLIM (cofactor of LIM-HD proteins). Interaction of LIM-HD with RLIM represses its activity, whereas interaction with CLIM results in its activation. The UPS controls LIM-HD's transcriptional activity by exchanging CLIM with RLIM (which is also an E3 that targets CLIM for degradation by the 26 S proteasome) [26]. In the case of NHRs, the UPS modulates their transcriptional activity by the recruitment of the components of the ubiquitin–proteasome pathway to the promoter. These components regulate receptor function by exchanging co-repressors and co-activators [24]. Taken together, a clear-cut relationship emerges between transcription activation and protein ubiquitination and degradation.

Ubiquitin–proteasome-pathway enzymes and components as co-regulators

The UPS can also regulate the transactivation function of the transcription factors because components of the UPS function as transcriptional co-activators. It has been shown that E3s, such as Rsp5 and its human homologue RPF1 (receptor potentiation factor 1)/NEDD4 (neural precursor cell expressed developmentally down-regulated 4) [27] and E6-AP (E6-associated protein) [23], act as transcriptional co-activators of NHRs. E6-AP is also implicated in the congenital human disease, Angelman syndrome, and is essential for p53 degradation in HPV (human papillomavirus)-induced carcinogenesis [23]. Interestingly, the E3 activity of both proteins is not necessary for their co-activation function. A well-characterized co-activator, p300, has been shown to catalyse the polyubiquitination of p53, suggesting that p300 is a dual-functioning protein that modulates gene transcription and ubiquitination [28,29]. In addition to E3, the E2 UbcH7 has also been shown to act as a co-activator; however, its enzymatic activity is required for its co-activation function [30].

It has been demonstrated that UPS enzymes as well as the proteasome sub-units are recruited to the promoter region of target genes during transcription. SUG1 (supressor of Gal4D lesions1) is an ATPase subunit of the proteasome and is involved in the unfolding of protein while proteins are entering the pro-teasome. SUG-1 has also been characterized as a co-activator of NHRs [22]. Similarly, other ATPase subunits, TRIP1 (thyroid-hormone-receptor-interact-ing protein 1) and TBP1 (TATA-box-binding protein 1), have been shown to interact with NHRs and regulate their function [31]. Although the precise mol-ecular role of the ATPase subunits is not fully understood, it is fascinating to comprehend that the proteasome is physically present on the promoter [32], where various modifications and exchange of cofactor proteins occurs. The proximity of the proteasome to the promoter is also critical for the timely removal of transcriptional repressors during pre-initiation-complex formation and the degradation of activators after initiation, followed by the rapid recy-cling of the RNA pol II itself, upon completion of transcription (Figure 1). This

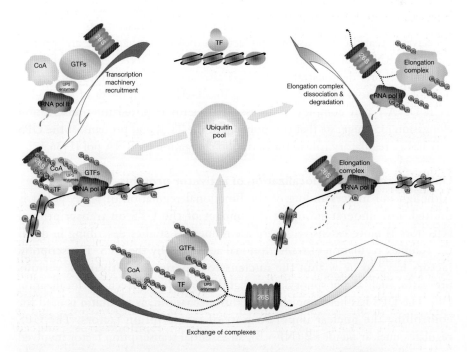

Figure 1. The role of ubiquitin and the UPS in eukaryotic transcription
In this model, ubiquitin (Ub), together with the UPS, regulates transcription at different stages. UPS enzymes and the 26 S proteasome are recruited by transcription factors (TF) during pre-ini-tiation complex formation. These UPS enzymes then promote ubiquitination of the pre-initiation complex components, tagging them for degradation via the 26 S proteasome. Exchange of com-plexes takes place and the pre-initiation complex is replaced by the elongation complex. Upon transcription termination, the elongation complex and the polymerase are also degraded by the proteasome. These ubiquitination events regulate transcription by facilitating cofactor exchange and prompt degradation of exiting protein complexes.

interesting scenario, if true, will facilitate the recycling and regulation of all the factors involved in the transcription process after each round of transcription, making the process more processive and precise.

Proteasome-independent ubiquitin functions

Regulation of RNA pol II by ubiquitination

One of the profound mechanisms of transcription control is the control of RNA pol II recruitment and subsequent degradation, which influences the transcriptional outcome. Our current understanding of this control mechanism is limited to TCR (transcription-coupled repair), a process by which transcriptionally active genes are preferentially repaired following DNA damage [33]. DNA lesions in the strand that is being transcribed can arrest movement of the transcription complex. Evidence from normal cells, as well as cells from xeroderma pigmentosum patients, indicate that the ubiquitinated form of RNA pol II is hyperphosphorylated at the C-terminal domain of its largest subunit that is involved in transcription elongation [34]. The yeast E3 Rsp5 ubiquitinates RNA pol II's C-terminal domain but is not required for TCR. This does not preclude a role for the 26 S proteasome in TCR; it is conceivable that the proteasome may act as a molecular chaperone and protect the stalled RNA pol II, leading to the assembly of the DNA-repair machinery. Previous reports demonstrate that Rsp5 also acts as a co-activator of steroid hormone receptors [27] and the finding that Def1, a component of the Rad26 TCR DNA-repair complex, is an essential factor required for transcription elongation [35] suggests that components of the TCR and proteins of the UPS may have a regulatory role in transcription elongation by RNA pol II [36,37].

Ubiquitin controls the localization of activator proteins

Although our understanding of the functional regulation of RNA pol II is limited, our understanding of the impact of the UPS on transcriptional activators is more extensive. There are numerous studies describing in detail the complex regulation of transcriptional activators by the UPS. Transcription factors have to be within the nucleus to function as activators; various processes, such as phosphorylation, tightly regulate their cellular localization [38]. The UPS has been implicated in this mechanism, as ubiquitin is used for controlling the nuclear import/export of transcription factors. The UPS regulates nuclear factor κB (NF-κB), an essential transcription factor involved in the inflammatory response. NF-κB, under unstimulated conditions, is held in the cytoplasm by an inhibitory κB (IκB) protein. During inflammation, IκB is rapidly degraded via the 26 S proteasome, which releases NF-κB to translocate into the nucleus, which is essential for NF-κB function [39].

Oncoprotein Mdm2 (murine double minute clone 2 oncoprotein) is an E3 involved in the regulation of the tumour suppressor p53. It has long been known that p53 is ubiquitinated and degraded via the UPS and that Mdm2 is the specific E3 that is involved in this process. Recently, it has been suggested that p53 exists in two different states of ubiquitination (mono and poly), depending on the expression level of Mdm2. Mdm2 at low levels preferentially monoubqinates p53, which leads to its nuclear exclusion, whereas at high levels of Mdm2, p53 is polyubiquitinated and marked for degradation by the 26 S proteasome [40,41].

A ubiquitin-mediated regulatory mechanism is also observed in the control of the yeast transcriptional activator Spt23, which is involved in fatty acid biosynthesis. Spt23 is synthesized as an endoplasmic reticulum outer-membrane protein following a reduction of fatty acid levels in the cell. It is then clipped precisely by the UPS and moves into the nucleus, accompanied by a ubiquitin-specific chaperone.

These ubiquitin-mediated mechanisms are just a few examples of how ubiquitin and the UPS regulate activator function by modifying their cellular localization [42,43].

Ubiquitin regulates the activities of activator proteins

Apart from controlling activator localization in the cell, the UPS also modulates the activator function of transcriptional activators. One of the best examples available is the ubiquitin-mediated regulation of VP16, a potent viral transcriptional activator. Work by Salghetti et al. [44] suggests a link between the UPS and transcription activation. They showed that the VP16 TAD signals for ubiquitination via SCF/Met30 (an E3) and that ubiquitination is essential for its transcriptional activation [44]. This process of ubiquitin-mediated activation is also shared by other activators, such as HIV-1 Tat protein. HIV-1 codes for a potent transcriptional activator Tat that hijacks cellular transcriptional co-activators, such as p300, PCAF [p300/CREB(cAMP/Ca^{2+}-responsive element-binding protein)-binding protein-associated factor] and P-TEFb (positive transcription elongation factor b), to promote viral gene expression. Since Tat binds to a short leader RNA, known as the transactivation responsive element, its regulation is critical for HIV-1. Hdm2 (human homologue of Mdm2) is a RING-finger E3 that has been shown to interact with Tat, and this interaction leads to Tat ubiquitination. Interestingly, Tat ubiquitination by Hdm2 positively stimulates its transcriptional activation function [45–47]. Taken together, this suggests a fundamental link between activator potency and protein degradation [44].

Although this mechanism of TAD regulation is simple, there are more complex and intriguing aspects to this process, as observed in the case of the yeast methionine/cysteine biosynthesis gene activator Met4. SCF/Met30 is an E3 that specifically oligo-ubiquitinates Met4. This ubiquitination event results in dual regulation of Met4: one degradation-dependent and the other degradation-independent [48]. In the degradation-dependent mechanism, Met4 ubiquitination by SCF/Met30 leads to its degradation via the 26 S proteasome only in minimal nutrient conditions. In the degradation-independent mechanism, however, regulation of Met4 occurs in nutrient-rich media, and Met4 is excluded from the *MET* gene promoters via a ubiquitin-dependent, but unknown, mechanism. A plausible explanation for this degradation-independent mechanism of Met4 regulation is that the SWI/SNF chromatin-remodelling machinery specifically depresses *MET* genes in rich, but not minimal, nutrient conditions and that this excludes oligo-ubiquitinated Met4 from the promoter region [18].

Ubiquitin promotes chromatin remodelling by modifying histones

Eukaryotic chromatin consists of individual nucleosomes, comprising DNA wound around histone proteins H2A, H2B, H3 and H4; histone H1 is the linker that sits between two adjacent nucleosomes [49]. There are two classes of chomatin-modifying enzymes: the ATP-dependent nucleosome-remodelling enzymes, such as SW1/SNF, RCS, NURF etc. [50]; and histone-modifying enzymes, such as histone acetyletransferase, histone deacetylase and methylases. These chromatin modifications lead to the unwinding of the DNA, which aids the assembly of the general transcription machinery that is required for transcription [51].

Histone proteins undergo multiple post-translational changes (methylation, acetylation, phosphorylation and ubiquitination) that regulate their function by relaxing or condensing chromatin. The UPS has been linked to histone modifications (H2A was the first ubiquitinated protein to be described). Later publications have shown that H2A and H2B ubiquitination is closely linked to actively transcribed genes. Ubiquitination of H2B by Rad6 has been demonstrated to control H3 methylation at Lys^4, which leads to gene silencing in *Saccharomyces cerevisiae* [52]. Furthermore, Dot1-mediated methylation of H3 at Lys^{79} is also regulated by ubiquitination of H2B by Rad6 [53]; however, RAD6-deleted strains failed to methylate Lys^4 and Lys^{79} but could methylate Lys^{36} [54]. Taken together, these studies show that ubiquitination of H2B acts as a master controller of gene silencing, because it regulates the methylation of Lys^4 and Lys^{79} (which leads to gene silencing) but not Lys^{36}, even though these lysine residues are methylated by different enzymes [55]. Recently, histone H1 (linker histone) was shown to be monoubiquitinated by $TAF_{II}250$; it was shown that H1s have ubiquitin-activating and -conjugating activities [56]. One school of thought is that monoubiquitination of H1 may result in the destabilization of the higher-order folding of nucleosomes that is mediated by H1 [57]. Considering all the observations described above, a clear relationship emerges between transcription activation and protein ubiquitination and degradation. Although the molecular role played by the ubiquitin modification is not yet clear, a model is definitely appearing. By the judicious use of ubiquitin, the UPS is able to regulate transcription activators at three levels: by regulating activator location within the cell, by activating the transcriptional activators, and, ultimately, by limiting the protein level and stability.

Conclusion

Ubiquitin, until recently, was thought to act solely as a tag for proteins destined to be degraded by the UPS. Research in the last two decades has led us to appreciate its profound influence, directly or indirectly, on one of the most critically regulated cellular processes, transcription. In this review, we have discussed the different modes by which ubiquitin and the UPS regulate transcription, both with and without their closely related signalling partner, the proteasome. Taken together, these observations seem to present the UPS as a complex, yet flexible, system that the cell utilizes to regulate transcription at different stages, such as: pre-initiation complex formation; activator availability; assembly and exchange of co-regulators; transcription elongation; and ultimately, degradation of the entire transcription machinery. Even with the vast amount of literature available about the regulation of transcription by the UPS, we have barely explored the complexity of gene regulation and the functions of the UPS in this regulation; compared with what we know so far, there is much more to learn.

Summary

- *Transcription is tightly regulated from initiation to termination. Ubiquitin and the UPS play critical roles in this process.*
- *Ubiquitination and subsequent degradation is essential for transcription-factor function and activity, as well as the exchange of complexes during transcription that is essential for transcription efficiency.*
- *Regulation of transcription-factor function and translocation are classic examples of ubiquitin-mediated control of transcription via the UPS.*
- *Ubiquitin–proteasome components and enzymes have additional roles as co-activators, facilitating the assembly and turnover of the transcription machinery.*
- *Ubiquitination of histone proteins leads to other modifications, such as methylation, which increases the heterochromatin-facilitating assembly of transcription complexes.*
- *The UPS represents an ultimate tool for the regulation and control of eukaryotic transcription.*

This work was supported by a grant from the National Institutes of Health (DK56833) to Z.N.

References

1. Ciechanover, A., Orian, A. & Schwartz, A.L. (2000) The ubiquitin-mediated proteolytic pathway: mode of action and clinical implications. *J. Cell. Biochem. Suppl.* **34**, 40–51

2. Hershko, A. & Ciechanover, A. (1998) The ubiquitin system. *Annu. Rev. Biochem.* **67**, 425–479

3. Koegl, M., Hoppe, T., Schlenker, S., Ulrich, H.D., Mayer, T.U. & Jentsch, S. (1999) A novel ubiquitination factor, E4, is involved in multiubiquitin chain assembly. *Cell* **96**, 635–644

4. Molinari, E., Gilman, M. & Natesan, S. (1999) Proteasome-mediated degradation of transcriptional activators correlates with activation domain potency *in vivo*. *EMBO J.* **18**, 6439–6447

5. Choy, B. & Green, M.R. (1993) Eukaryotic activators function during multiple steps of preinitiation complex assembly. *Nature (London)* **366**, 531–536

6. Struhl, K. (1996) Chromatin structure and RNA polymerase II connection: implications for transcription. *Cell* **84**, 179–182

7. Tjian, R. & Maniatis, T. (1994) Transcriptional activation: a complex puzzle with few easy pieces. *Cell* **77**, 5–8

8. Krebs, J.E., Kuo, M.H., Allis, C.D. & Peterson, C.L. (1999) Cell cycle-regulated histone acetylation required for expression of the yeast HO gene. *Genes Dev.* **13**, 1412–1421

9. Lagrange, T., Kapanidis, A.N., Tang, H., Reinberg, D. & Ebright, R.H. (1998) New core promoter element in RNA polymerase II-dependent transcription: sequence-specific DNA binding by transcription factor IIB. *Genes Dev.* **12**, 34–44

10. Salic, A., Lee, E., Mayer, L. & Kirschner, M.W. (2000) Control of beta-catenin stability: reconstitution of the cytoplasmic steps of the wnt pathway in *Xenopus* egg extracts. *Mol. Cell* **5**, 523–532

11. Aberle, H., Bauer, A., Stappert, J., Kispert, A. & Kemler, R. (1997) Beta-catenin is a target for the ubiquitin–proteasome pathway. *EMBO J.* **16**, 3797–3804

12. Yost, C., Torres, M., Miller, J.R., Huang, E., Kimelman, D. & Moon, R.T. (1996) The axis-inducing activity, stability, and subcellular distribution of beta-catenin is regulated in *Xenopus* embryos by glycogen synthase kinase 3. *Genes Dev.* **10**, 1443–1454

13. Tanikawa, J., Ichikawa-Iwata, E., Kanei-Ishii, C., Nakai, A., Matsuzawa, S., Reed, J.C. & Ishii, S. (2000) p53 suppresses the c-Myb-induced activation of heat shock transcription factor 3. *J. Biol. Chem.* **275**, 15578–15585

14. Conaway, R.C., Brower, C.S. & Conaway, J.W. (2002) Emerging roles of ubiquitin in transcription regulation. *Science* **296**, 1254–1258

15. Kim, S.Y., Herbst, A., Tworkowski, K.A., Salghetti, S.E. & Tansey, W.P. (2003) Skp2 regulates Myc protein stability and activity. *Mol. Cell* **11**, 1177–1188

16. Salghetti, S.E., Muratani, M., Wijnen, H., Futcher, B. & Tansey, W.P. (2000) Functional overlap of sequences that activate transcription and signal ubiquitin-mediated proteolysis. *Proc. Natl. Acad. Sci. U.S.A.* **97**, 3118–3123

17. Tsai, M.J. & O'Malley, B.W. (1994) Molecular mechanisms of action of steroid/thyroid receptor superfamily members. *Annu. Rev. Biochem.* **63**, 451–486

18. Kuras, L., Rouillon, A., Lee, T., Barbey, R., Tyers, M. & Thomas, D. (2002) Dual regulation of the met4 transcription factor by ubiquitin-dependent degradation and inhibition of promoter recruitment. *Mol. Cell* **10**, 69–80

19. Lin, H.K., Altuwaijri, S., Lin, W.J., Kan, P.Y., Collins, L.L. & Chang, C. (2002) Proteasome activity is required for androgen receptor transcriptional activity via regulation of androgen receptor nuclear translocation and interaction with coregulators in prostate cancer cells. *J. Biol. Chem.* **277**, 36570–36576

20. Lin, H.K., Wang, L., Hu, Y.C., Altuwaijri, S. & Chang, C. (2002) Phosphorylation-dependent ubiquitylation and degradation of androgen receptor by Akt require Mdm2 E3 ligase. *EMBO J.* **21**, 4037–4048

21. Lonard, D.M., Nawaz, Z., Smith, C.L. & O'Malley, B.W. (2000) The 26 S proteasome is required for estrogen receptor-alpha and coactivator turnover and for efficient estrogen receptor-alpha transactivation. *Mol. Cell* **5**, 939–948

22. Masuyama, H. & MacDonald, P.N. (1998) Proteasome-mediated degradation of the vitamin D receptor (VDR) and a putative role for SUG1 interaction with the AF-2 domain of VDR. *J. Cell. Biochem.* **71**, 429–440

23. Nawaz, Z., Lonard, D.M., Smith, C.L., Lev-Lehman, E., Tsai, S.Y., Tsai, M.J. & O'Malley, B.W. (1999) The Angelman syndrome-associated protein, E6-AP, is a coactivator for the nuclear hormone receptor superfamily. *Mol. Cell. Biol.* **19**, 1182–1189

24. Nawaz, Z. & O'Malley, B.W. (2004) Urban renewal in the nucleus: is protein turnover by proteasomes absolutely required for nuclear receptor-regulated transcription? *Mol. Endocrinol.* **18**, 493–499

25. Reid, G., Hubner, M.R., Metivier, R., Brand, H., Denger, S., Manu, D., Beaudouin, J., Ellenberg, J. & Gannon, F. (2003) Cyclic, proteasome-mediated turnover of unliganded and liganded ERalpha on responsive promoters is an integral feature of estrogen signaling. *Mol. Cell* **11**, 695–707

26. Ostendorff, H.P., Peirano, R.I., Peters, M.A., Schluter, A., Bossenz, M., Scheffner, M. & Bach, I. (2002) Ubiquitination-dependent cofactor exchange on LIM homeodomain transcription factors. *Nature (London)* **416**, 99–103

27. Imhof, M.O. & McDonnell, D.P. (1996) Yeast RSP5 and its human homolog hRPF1 potentiate hormone-dependent activation of transcription by human progesterone and glucocorticoid receptors. *Mol. Cell. Biol.* **16**, 2594–2605

28. Grossman, S.R., Deato, M.E., Brignone, C., Chan, H.M., Kung, A.L., Tagami, H., Nakatani, Y. & Livingston, D.M. (2003) Polyubiquitination of p53 by a ubiquitin ligase activity of p300. *Science* **300**, 342–344

29. Grossman, S.R., Perez, M., Kung, A.L., Joseph, M., Mansur, C., Xiao, Z.X., Kumar, S., Howley, P.M. & Livingston, D.M. (1998) p300/MDM2 complexes participate in MDM2-mediated p53 degradation. *Mol. Cell* **2**, 405–415

30. Verma, S., Ismail, A., Gao, X., Fu, G., Li, X., O'Malley, B.W. & Nawaz, Z. (2004) The ubiquitin-conjugating enzyme UBCH7 acts as a coactivator for steroid hormone receptors. *Mol. Cell. Biol.* **24**, 8716–8726

31. Lee, J.W., Ryan, F., Swaffield, J.C., Johnston, S.A. & Moore, D.D. (1995) Interaction of thyroid-hormone receptor with a conserved transcriptional mediator. *Nature (London)* **374**, 91–94

32. Gonzalez, F., Delahodde, A., Kodadek, T. & Johnston, S.A. (2002) Recruitment of a 19 S proteasome subcomplex to an activated promoter. *Science* **296**, 548–550

33. Svejstrup, J.Q. (2002) Mechanisms of transcription-coupled DNA repair. *Nat. Rev. Mol. Cell Biol.* **3**, 21–29

34. Ratner, J.N., Balasubramanian, B., Corden, J., Warren, S.L. & Bregman, D.B. (1998) Ultraviolet radiation-induced ubiquitination and proteasomal degradation of the large subunit of RNA polymerase II. Implications for transcription-coupled DNA repair. *J. Biol. Chem.* **273**, 5184–5189

35. Woudstra, E.C., Gilbert, C., Fellows, J., Jansen, L., Brouwer, J., Erdjument-Bromage, H., Tempst, P. & Svejstrup, J.Q. (2002) A Rad26-Def1 complex coordinates repair and RNA pol II proteolysis in response to DNA damage. *Nature (London)* **415**, 929–933

36. Lee, K.B., Wang, D., Lippard, S.J. & Sharp, P.A. (2002) Transcription-coupled and DNA damage-dependent ubiquitination of RNA polymerase II in vitro. *Proc. Natl. Acad. Sci. U.S.A.* **99**, 4239–4244

37. Sweder, K. & Madura, K. (2002) Regulation of repair by the 26 S proteasome. *J. Biomed. Biotechnol.* **2**, 94–105

38. Muratani, M. & Tansey, W.P. (2003) How the ubiquitin–proteasome system controls transcription. *Nat. Rev. Mol. Cell Biol.* **4**, 192–201

39. Palombella, V.J., Rando, O.J., Goldberg, A.L. & Maniatis, T. (1994) The ubiquitin–proteasome pathway is required for processing the NF-κB1 precursor protein and the activation of NF-κB. *Cell* **78**, 773–785

40. Brooks, C.L., Li, M. & Gu, W. (2004) Monoubiquitination: the signal for p53 nuclear export? *Cell Cycle* **3**, 436–438

41. Li, M., Brooks, C.L., Wu-Baer, F., Chen, D., Baer, R. & Gu, W. (2003) Mono- versus polyubiquitination: differential control of p53 fate by Mdm2. *Science* **302**, 1972–1975

42. Hoppe, T., Matuschewski, K., Rape, M., Schlenker, S., Ulrich, H.D. & Jentsch, S. (2000) Activation of a membrane-bound transcription factor by regulated ubiquitin/proteasome-dependent processing. *Cell* **102**, 577–586

43. Tansey, W.P. (2000) Transcriptional regulation: RUPture in the ER. *Nat. Cell Biol.* **2**, E175–E177

44. Salghetti, S.E., Caudy, A.A., Chenoweth, J.G. & Tansey, W.P. (2001) Regulation of transcriptional activation domain function by ubiquitin. *Science* **293**, 1651–1653

45. Bres, V., Kiernan, R.E., Linares, L.K., Chable-Bessia, C., Plechakova, O., Treand, C., Emiliani, S., Peloponese, J.M., Jeang, K.T., Coux, O. et al. (2003) A non-proteolytic role for ubiquitin in Tat-mediated transactivation of the HIV-1 promoter. *Nat. Cell Biol.* **5**, 754–761

46. Fujinaga, K., Irwin, D., Huang, Y., Taube, R., Kurosu, T. & Peterlin, B.M. (2004) Dynamics of human Immunodeficiency virus transcription: P-TEFb phosphorylates RD and dissociates negative effectors from the transactivation response element. *Mol. Cell. Biol.* **24**, 787–795

47. Ishizuka, T., Satoh, T., Monden, T., Shibusawa, N., Hashida, T., Yamada, M. & Mori, M. (2001) Human immunodeficiency virus type 1 Tat binding protein-1 is a transcriptional coactivator specific for TR. *Mol. Endocrinol.* **15**, 1329–1343

48. Kaiser, P., Flick, K., Wittenberg, C. & Reed, S.I. (2000) Regulation of transcription by ubiquitina-tion without proteolysis: Cdc34/SCF(Met30)-mediated inactivation of the transcription factor Met4. *Cell* **102**, 303–314

49. Kornberg, R.D. & Lorch, Y. (1999) Twenty-five years of the nucleosome, fundamental particle of the eukaryote chromosome. *Cell* **98**, 285–294

50. Vignali, M., Hassan, A.H., Neely, K.E. & Workman, J.L. (2000) ATP-dependent chromatin-remodeling complexes. *Mol. Cell. Biol.* **20**, 1899–1910

51. Kornberg, R.D. & Lorch, Y. (1999) Chromatin-modifying and -remodeling complexes. *Curr. Opin. Genet. Dev.* **9**, 148–151

52. Sun, Z.W. & Allis, C.D. (2002) Ubiquitination of histone H2B regulates H3 methylation and gene silencing in yeast. *Nature (London)* **418**, 104–108

53. van Leeuwen, F., Gafken, P.R. & Gottschling, D.E. (2002) Dot1p modulates silencing in yeast by methylation of the nucleosome core. *Cell* **109**, 745–756

54. Robzyk, K., Recht, J. & Osley, M.A. (2000) Rad6-dependent ubiquitination of histone H2B in yeast. *Science* **287**, 501–504

55. Briggs, S.D., Xiao, T., Sun, Z.W., Caldwell, J.A., Shabanowitz, J., Hunt, D.F., Allis, C.D. & Strahl, B.D. (2002) Gene silencing: trans-histone regulatory pathway in chromatin. *Nature (London)* **418**, 498

56. Metivier, R., Penot, G., Hubner, M.R., Reid, G., Brand, H., Kos, M. & Gannon, F. (2003) Estrogen receptor-alpha directs ordered, cyclical, and combinatorial recruitment of cofactors on a natural target promoter. *Cell* **115**, 751–763

57. Crane-Robinson, C. (1999) How do linker histones mediate differential gene expression? *Bioessays* **21**, 367–371

6

Ubiquitin and endocytic protein sorting

Sylvie Urbé[1]

Physiological Laboratory, University of Liverpool, Crown St., Liverpool L69 3BX, U.K.

Abstract

Ubiquitin plays a fundamental role not only in proteasome-mediated protein degradation but also in the targeting of membrane proteins for degradation inside the lysosome. Ubiquitination provides a key signal for endosomal sorting of membrane proteins into the MVB (multi-vesicular body), which delivers its cargo to the proteolytic interior of the lysosome. Attachment of single ubiquitin molecules, rather than ubiquitin chains, to one or multiple lysines of the cytoplasmic domains of many growth factor receptors, ion channels and other membrane transporters is sufficient to target these proteins to a complex sorting apparatus on the endosome. This machinery selects ubiquitinated proteins for lysosomal sorting through consecutive interactions with a variety of ubiquitin-binding domains. The major ubiquitin ligase (E3) responsible for ubiquitination in this pathway in yeast is the HECT [homologous to E6-AP (E6-associated protein) C-terminus]-ligase, Rsp5, whereas in mammalian cells the RING (really interesting new gene)-ligase Cbl has been implicated in the down-regulation of several RTKs (receptor tyrosine kinases). Ubiquitinated receptors can be rescued from degradation by the activity of DUBs (deubiquitinating enzymes), which may provide a proofreading mechanism that enhances the fidelity of this sorting and degradation process. DUBs also allow for recycling of the ubiquitin moieties from proteins prior to their final commitment to the MVB and lysosome interior.

[1]email urbe@liv.ac.uk

Introduction

Protein degradation plays a critical role in the maintenance of cell structure and function. Eukaryotic cells have developed two major systems controlling this process: lysosomal and proteasomal protein turnover (Figure 1). The lysosome, a membrane-bound organelle filled with proteolytic enzymes, was discovered in the 1950s by de Duve and colleagues, and first thought to be the major site of protein degradation [1]. This hypothesis held true for exogenous proteins that are taken up through endocytosis into lysosomes, and broken down by acid-activated hydrolases. However, experiments using weak bases

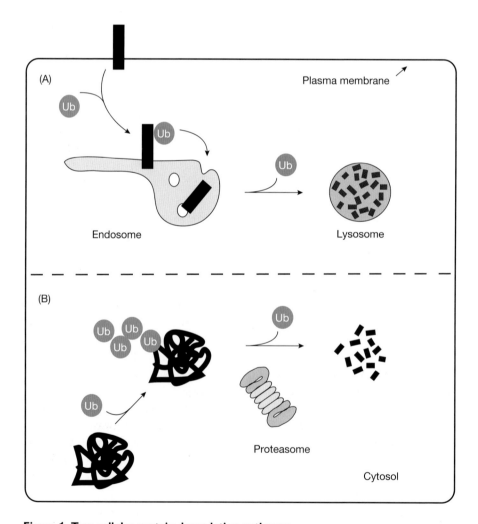

Figure 1. Two cellular protein degradation pathways
Many plasma membrane proteins are internalized and transported to the endosome, from where they are sorted for degradation in the lumen of the lysosome (**A**). The majority of cellular proteins are turned over in the cytosol by a multi-enzyme complex, the proteasome (**B**). Both degradation pathways use Ub (ubiquitin) as a targeting signal.

(e.g. ammonium chloride) to interfere with the acidification of the lysosome showed that the turnover of the bulk of endogenous, cellular proteins was not affected by the disruption of lysosomal proteolysis. The discovery, in 1974, of ubiquitin as a destruction tag and, in 1986, of the proteasome, provided the widely sought-after pathway for the degradation of cellular proteins (reviewed in [2]). This pathway is based on the covalent attachment of ubiquitin to proteins that are targeted to a cytosolic multi-enzyme complex, the proteasome. It is therefore rather ironic that recent work has revealed ubiquitin as a major player in the sorting of membrane proteins to the lysosome.

Proteasomal targeting requires the attachment of a chain of at least four ubiquitin moieties that are linked to each other through Lys^{48} in ubiquitin. In contrast, ubiquitination of proteins that are targeted to the lysosome is restricted to the attachment of ubiquitin monomers or, in some cases, to short chains of Lys^{63}-linked ubiquitin. In this case, ubiquitin acts as a sorting signal for membrane-trafficking events and this is most readily illustrated for the trafficking of growth factor receptors in mammalian cells [3].

Activated growth factor receptors are generally recruited into clathrin-coated pits and enter the endocytic pathway via CCVs (clathrin-coated vesicles), which deliver their content to a tubulo-vesicular compartment referred to as the early (or sorting) endosome (Figure 2). Here, receptors can either recycle back to the plasma membrane for another round of stimulation or travel onwards to the lysosome (reviewed in [4]). Ubiquitin-mediated sorting plays a role in both the initial internalization process at the plasma membrane and the lysosome-directed sorting at the early endosome. In both cases, the key to the mechanism of ubiquitin-mediated sorting lies in the recruitment of specific ubiquitin-binding proteins to the ubiquitinated cargo (reviewed in [5–7]).

Sorting to the lysosome involves the incorporation of the receptor into internal vesicles of MVBs (multi-vesicular bodies), also referred to as late endosomes. These organelles gradually accumulate lysosomal acidic hydrolases (proteases) and fuse with lysosomes. It should be noted that growth-factor receptors continue to signal within the endocytic pathway until they are sequestered into lumenal vesicles of the MVB [8].

Much of our detailed biochemical understanding about the molecular mechanisms governing protein sorting in the endocytic pathway is based on studies in yeast. Although the yeast endocytic pathway may be lacking in morphologically distinguishable sub-compartments, many of the fundamental mechanisms are conserved and the yeast vacuole is functionally equivalent to the mammalian lysosome.

This essay briefly reviews the work that led to the realization of the importance of ubiquitin in endocytic protein sorting and discusses the complex endocytic machinery that mediates the sorting process. Finally, the regulation of ubiquitination on this pathway is examined by considering the various E3s (ubiquitin ligases) and DUBs (deubiquitinating enzymes) that have been implicated to date.

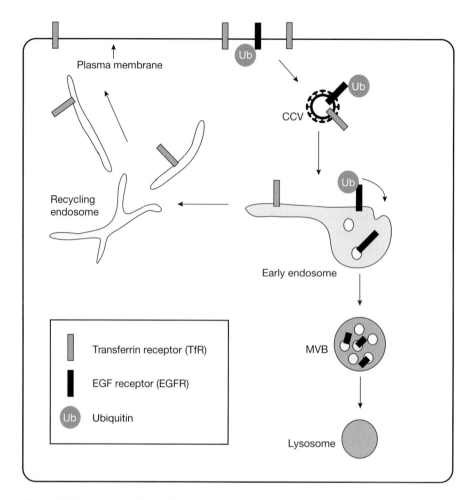

Figure 2. The mammalian endocytic pathway
Activated growth factor receptors (e.g. EGFR) are internalized via CCVs and transported to the tubulo-vesicular early endosome. Here, ubiquitinated receptors are sequestered into the lumenal vesicles of the MVB, which delivers its content to the lysosome. Other plasma-membrane proteins that are not ubiquitinated (e.g. TfR) enter the pathway via the same route, but return to the plasma membrane via the tubular recycling endosome.

Ubiquitin as a sorting signal for endocytic trafficking in yeast and mammalian cells

A role for ubiquitin in endocytic trafficking
The first observations that indicated a link between receptor endocytosis and ubiquitination were made in the mid-1980s and early 1990s, when it was shown that several RTKs (receptor tyrosine kinases), including PDGFR (platelet derived growth factor receptor) and GHR (growth hormone receptor), were ubiquitin-

ated. Furthermore, in the case of the T-cell receptor, this ubiquitination could be directly linked to ligand activation of the receptor [9].

The formal connection between ubiquitin and endocytosis came from studies in yeast on Ste6p, an ABC (ATP-binding cassette) transporter, which accumulates in a ubiquitinated form in *end* (endocytosis-defective) mutant cells (reviewed in [5,6]). This observation was later confirmed by analysis of the yeast α-factor (Ste2p) and a-factor (Ste3p) pheromone receptors. In addition, both proteins failed to internalize in mutant yeast strains that had defective ubiquitination machinery. In parallel to these studies, a genetic screen, aimed at the identification of genes involved in the down-regulation of amino-acid permeases, identified a gene called *npiI*, which was later shown to encode the HECT [homologous to E6-AP (E6-associated protein) C-terminus] E3-ligase Rsp5, which is responsible for the ubiquitination of plasma membrane proteins in yeast.

Mono-ubiquitination is sufficient for most endosomal sorting events

In contrast to the well-described role for polyubiquitin chains in targeting proteins to the proteasome, internalization of yeast plasma-membrane proteins like Ste2p is not inhibited by expression of mutant ubiquitin, which cannot form polyubiquitin chains. Furthermore, fusion of a single ubiquitin in-frame to many plasma-membrane proteins is sufficient for their internalization, although, in some cases, short-chain linkages formed through Lys^{63} may enhance the kinetics (reviewed in [5,6]). In mammalian cells, many plasma-membrane proteins are ubiquitinated in response to ligand binding. These include the RTKs EGFR [EGF (epidermal growth factor) receptor], PDGFR, FGF (fibroblast growth factor) receptor and Met [HGF (hepatocyte growth factor) receptor] [3]. In addition, some ion channels, such as the ENaC (epithelial Na^+ channel), are also known to be ubiquitinated.

The rather smeared appearance of ubiquitin signals associated with these proteins was interpreted as reflecting heterogeneous polyubiquitination. How then do polyubiquitinated receptors escape proteasomal targeting? Experiments based on the use of a panel of anti-ubiquitin antibodies discriminating between mono- and poly-ubiquitin showed that EGFR, PDGFR and Met are in fact mono-ubiquitinated at multiple lysine residues [3,10]. In addition, in-frame fusion of a single ubiquitin to the C-terminus of EGFR induces ligand-independent receptor internalization, suggesting that mono-ubiquitin is the endocytic sorting signal used in both yeast and mammalian cells.

The issue was further confused by the fact that the down-regulation of many, but not all, growth factor receptors (e.g. GHR, Met) is sensitive to proteasome inhibitors. Further experiments using inhibitors of the lysosomal pathway (inhibitors of vacuolar acidification or lysosomal enzymes) have shown that in all cases so far studied, degradation of these receptors is contingent on their sorting to the lysosome, and is most likely to take place there

[11]. Thus in these particular cases, proteasome activity is permissive for lyso-somal degradation.

Ubiquitin-dependent internalization

As discussed above, ubiquitin can promote internalization of plasma-membrane proteins both in yeast and mammalian cells. The vast majority of yeast proteins are strictly dependent upon ubiquitination for their endocytosis, and ubiquitin constitutes the major internalization signal in yeast [5,6].

In contrast, in mammalian cells, endocytosis relies on a variety of redun-dant signals. Many mammalian plasma-membrane proteins encode di-leucine- and tyrosine-based cytoplasmic sorting signals that recruit specific endocytic adaptor proteins in the form of AP-2 (adaptor protein 2), amphiphysin, clathrin and dynamin [12]. Hence, although mono-ubiquitination may be suf-ficient as an internalization signal in mammalian cells (see above), it is not essential. This is most commonly seen in cells in which the main E3 mediating RTK ubiquitination, Cbl, has been knocked out [13]. Although these cells show a clear defect in EGFR down-regulation, the initial internalization pro-ceeds with unaltered kinetics.

The ubiquitin internalization signal does not conform to a classical linear amino-acid sequence, but is encoded in its three-dimensional structure. The key residues (Phe[4], Ile[44]) for the recognition of ubiquitin by the sorting machinery contribute to two hydrophobic patches on the surface of the mole-cule. These hydrophobic patches are recognized not by a single ubiquitin

Table 1. Ubiquitin-binding motifs in endocytic proteins

Name	Length	Examples	K_d (μM)	Structure
UIM	~20	Hrs/Vps27	Hrs: ~300	α-Helix
		STAM/Hsel	Vps27: ~100–300	
		Eps15/Ent1/2	STAM: ~200	
		Epsin		
UEV	~60	Tsg101/Vps23	Tsg101: ~500	α-Helix/β-sheets
NZF	~25–30	Vps36	Vps36: ~200	Zn-finger
UBA	~40	Cbl-b	n.d.	Triple α-helix
		Ede1		
CUE	~45–50	Tollip	Vps9: 20	Triple α-helix
		Vps9		
GAT	Various	GGA3	yGGA:100–400	Triple α-helix

Ubiquitin binding of endocytic proteins is mediated by a large variety of ubiquitin-binding motifs. The average length of the motif is given in amino-acid residues. CUE, coupling of ubiquitin conjugation to endoplasmic reticulum degradation; n.d., not determined; GAT, GGA and Tom. K_d values correspond to measured affinities for mono-ubiquitin.

receptor, but by multiple sorting adaptors that bind to ubiquitin via a wide variety of ubiquitin-binding motifs (Table 1, reviewed in [14]).

Two examples of ubiquitin-binding proteins implicated in internalization, both in yeast and in mammalian cells, are Eps15/Eps15R (Ede1 in yeast) and Epsin (Ent1 and Ent2 in yeast), which bind ubiquitinated proteins through UIM (ubiquitin-interacting motif) and UBA (ubiquitin-associated) domains.

Ubiquitination of the endocytic sorting machinery

It should be noted that in some cases, ubiquitination of the receptor itself is dispensable for its internalization and/or down-regulation (e.g. GHR), although a functional ubiquitin proteasome system is required (reviewed in [11]). This suggests that, in these cases at least, the ubiquitination of a component of the sorting machinery may be key.

Many of the ubiquitin-binding proteins involved in endocytic sorting processes are themselves transiently ubiquitinated. This mono-ubiquitination of endocytic adaptor proteins may perform a regulatory function, by switching the proteins into an 'inactive' or 'closed' conformation, in which the ubiquitin-binding motif is occupied by an intramolecular ubiquitin interaction and therefore no longer available for recruiting ubiquitinated cargo (Figure 3A) [5,14].

Ubiquitination of the sorting machinery may also contribute to the establishment of large protein-interaction networks, which could enhance the fidelity of the system by relying on the coincident detection of many weak binding interactions (Figure 3B). Ubiquitin-binding motifs generally bind with very low affinity (K_d 100–500 μM) to ubiquitin (Table 1), a fact that is necessitated by the high concentration of free ubiquitin in mammalian cells (estimated at 10 μM [15]). Higher affinities for ubiquitin would result in a high degree of occupancy by free ubiquitin and effectively neutralize these adaptors.

Ubiquitin-mediated sorting at the endosome: the MVB sorting machinery

The most stringent requirement for ubiquitin in the sorting process is at the point of MVB sorting. Many plasma-membrane proteins (unoccupied receptors and transporters) flow through the endosome [4]. This is the case for TfR (transferrin receptor), which constitutively enters the cell to release its Fe^{3+} cargo from transferrin and then recycles back to the plasma membrane (Figure 2). An in-frame fusion of ubiquitin to TfR perturbs this itinerary by retaining the TfR at the sorting endosome and promoting its sorting into MVBs [16].

How is this ubiquitin signal recognized at the early/sorting endosome? Much of our knowledge comes from a genetic screen in yeast, which identified mutations that led to defects in the trafficking of vacuolar proteins {vps (vacuolar protein sorting) mutants [17]}. Among these, the class E mutants display a swollen prevacuolar compartment that corresponds to a defect in MVB formation. Each of these vps class E genes has been shown to have a mam-

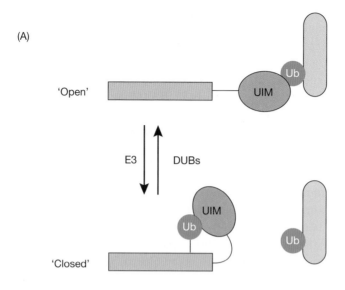

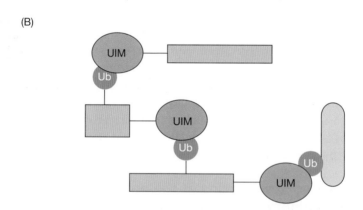

Figure 3. Putative roles for mono-ubiquitination of the endocytic sorting machinery
Many endocytic proteins that encode a ubiquitin-binding motif (e.g. UIM) are themselves ubiquitinated by E3s. (**A**) This mono-ubiquitination may perform a regulatory function by promoting a
conformational switch from an 'open' conformation, in which the UIM can bind to ubiquitinated
cargo, to a 'closed' conformation, in which the UIM is 'blocked' by an intramolecular ubiquitin
interaction. Deubiquitination by DUBs may revert the protein into an 'open' conformation. (**B**)
Mono-ubiquitination of the endocytic machinery may also contribute to a large ubiquitin-dependent interaction network.

malian counterpart [18]. The sorting of receptors into the internal vesicles of
the MVB is now thought to involve the sequential engagement of several
multi-protein complexes that are composed of class E Vps proteins (Figure 4):
the Hrs (hepatocyte growth factor-regulated tyrosine kinase substrate, also
referred to as Hgs)–STAM (signal-transducing adaptor molecule, also called
Hbp for Hrs binding protein) complex and ESCRT (endosomal sorting com-

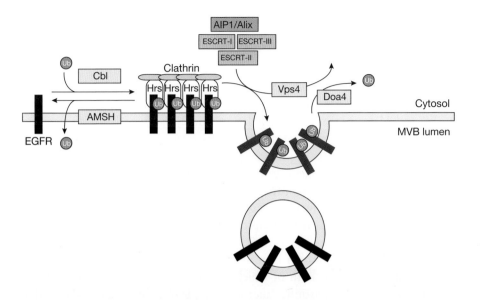

Figure 4. The MVB sorting machinery
Ubiquitination of membrane proteins (e.g. EGFR) by an E3 (e.g. Cbl) promotes their interaction with Hrs in a clathrin-coated microdomain. DUBs (e.g. AMSH) may counteract Cbl activity and oppose the MVB sorting process. Hrs recruits the ESCRT-I machinery, which, in concert with AIPI/Alix, activates and assembles ESCRT-II and -III. This induces the translocation of the ubiqui-tinated receptor into internal vesicles of the MVB. Ubiquitin itself is recycled by a DUB (e.g. Doa4) just before, or in parallel with, the disassembly of the ESCRT-machinery by the AAA-ATPase Vps4, which irreversibly seals the sorting process. Note that this illustration combines elements from yeast and mammalian cells.

plex required for transport)-I, -II, and -III. At least the first three of these complexes have the ability to bind ubiquitin, and the ubiquitinated receptors may be passed along from one complex to another. A fifth component, essential for this process, is an ATPase of the AAA (ATPase associated with various cellular activities) family called Vps4 or SKD1 [7].

The Hrs–STAM complex
Initial engagement of ubiquitinated receptors with the sorting machinery is mediated through interaction with a complex comprising the proteins Hrs and STAM. Their yeast orthologues are called Vps27 and Hse1, and all four proteins contain one or multiple UIM domains, which are required for their sorting function. Hrs binds directly to clathrin and contains a FYVE domain that allows it to bind to PtdIns3P, a lipid that is enriched on early endosomes [16]. Hrs and STAM are thought to act as a dimeric adaptor complex, by recruiting ubiquitinated receptors into a specialized area of the early endosome that is decorated by a flat clathrin coat. This clathrin coat is not thought to promote vesicle budding, but instead may provide a concentration device in

which ubiquitinated receptors are trapped, whereas recycling receptors diffuse freely through this microdomain [16].

Hrs plays a central role in MVB formation, in both yeast and mammalian cells: Vps27 is a class E *vps* mutant, and defects in MVB formation have also been reported in Hrs knock-out mice and *Drosophila* [19,20]. Hrs depletion by siRNA (small interfering RNA)-interference in human cells partially inhibits EGFR and Met receptor down-regulation [21,22]. Both receptor-sorting and internal vesicle formation are also inhibited by overexpression of Hrs, suggesting that the two processes are tightly coupled [23]. This inhibition of internal vesicle formation is contingent on an intact Hrs UIM domain, which therefore may play both positive (receptor-sorting) and negative (vesicle formation) roles in the pathway leading to lumenal vesicle budding.

Recently, several alternative adaptor complexes that may function in parallel, or in concert, with Hrs and STAM, have been identified. These include GGA (Golgi-associated γ-adaptin homologous) proteins and the Tom1(L1)–Tollip–Endofin complex, both of which have the ability to bind ubiquitin and clathrin. Whether this constitutes another example of redundancy in the sorting machinery, or whether selectivity allows for a higher degree of cargo, remains to be shown.

The ESCRT machinery

A major breakthrough came with the description of three distinct multimeric Vps protein complexes, named ESCRT-I, -II and -III, which have been proposed to be sequentially recruited to and activated at the endosome. These proteins constitute the core of the MVB-formation machinery downstream of the Hrs–STAM complex [7].

Hrs, and its yeast orthologue Vps27, also serve to recruit the ESCRT-I complex (Tsg101/Vps23, Vps28 and Vps37) to the endosome through interaction of a four-amino-acid motif [PS(T)AP] with TSG101/Vps23 (reviewed in [24]). The ubiquitin-binding site of this complex is found in TSG101/Vps23 in the form of a UEV (ubiquitin E2 variant) domain, which also provides the PS(T)AP binding site. TSG101 itself contains a PTAP motif, which may interact with its own UEV domain. It is possible that competitive binding by Hrs may then release TSG101 into a relaxed conformation that could be permissive for ESCRT-II recruitment, thereby imparting processivity to the sorting pathway.

ESCRT-II was described as a cytosolic complex, (approx. 155 kDa) consisting of the class E Vps proteins Vps22, Vps25 and Vps36 [called Eap30 (ELL-associated protein), Eap25 and Eap45 in mammalian cells], that transiently associates with endosomal membranes in an ESCRT-I-dependent manner. Crystal structures at 3.6 Å resolution of a yeast ESCRT-II complex containing one molecule of Vps22, the C-terminal domain of Vps36 and two molecules of Vps25, appear in the shape of a capital 'Y', of which the sub-complex Vps22 and Vps36 form one branch each. A flexible linker extending from the tip of the Vps36 branch would lead to two consecutive NZF [Npl4 (nuclear protein localization 4) zinc finger] motifs, the second of which is believed to bind ubiquitinated cargo. It has been suggested that this structure could provide a 'long swinging arm' for transfer of cargo over substantial distances [25]. The NZF motif is lacking in Eap45, the mammalian orthologue of Vps36, but this is compensated for by inclusion of a GLUE [GRAM (glucosyl transferase Rab-like GTPase activator and myolubularins)-like ubiquitin-binding in Eap45] domain, which has also been shown to have ubiquitin-binding properties [26].

The ESCRT-II complex is required for the membrane recruitment of the Snf7/Vps20 ESCRT-III sub-complex via an interaction between Vps25 and Vps20 [18], and this is a prerequisite for the recruitment of the other two ESCRT-III proteins, Vps24 and Vps2, to the membranes [7]. These last four class E Vps proteins belong to a structurally related 'family' of small, highly charged, coiled-coil proteins that in mammalian cells are referred to as CHMPs (charged multivesicular proteins). Although the initial functional genetic studies in yeast suggested a neat vectorial recruitment and association of these three complexes, further yeast two-hybrid interaction data indicate a much more complex interaction network [18]. One highly connected protein is AIP1 [ALG2 (apoptosis-linked gene 2)-interacting protein 1] or Alix (ALG2-interacting protein X), previously implicated in apoptosis, that has a yeast orthologue called Bro1. AIP1 shows interactions with both ESCRT-I (Tsg101) and ESCRT-III (Snf7/CHMP4b) complexes and may therefore act as a bridge between these two [18].

Vps4/SKD1 (suppressor of potassium transport growth defect 1)

The ESCRT-III component Snf7 recruits a class E Vps protein belonging to the AAA-ATPase family, called Vps4 in yeast and humans, and SKD1 in mouse cells [7]. The last resolved step in the MVB formation cascade is the dissociation of the ESCRT-machinery powered by Vps4/SKD1 hydrolysis of ATP. This is inferred from the dramatic phenotype of ATPase-defective Vps4/SKD1 mutants in yeast and mammalian cells. *Vps4* yeast deletion strains show a typical class E swollen pre-vacuolar compartment on which the entire upstream sorting machinery accumulates. Overexpression of a catalytically inactive Vps4 mutant in mammalian cells recapitulates this phenotype. These observations suggest that dissociation of the sorting machinery and the formation of internal vesicles are tightly coupled to allow efficient recycling of ESCRT proteins.

Viral hijack of the ESCRT machinery

One observation that has heightened interest in this pathway is the finding that a number of RNA viruses, most notably HIV-1, utilize the ESCRT machinery to elicit their escape through budding from the plasma membrane of the host cells [27]. Note that both viral and MVB budding have the same topology, in the sense that they are both budding away from the cytosol [24]. It has long been known that mutations in late domains of viral structural proteins arrest viral particle release from the plasma membrane, at a stage beyond which buds have formed, but prior to particle scission. In the case of HIV, the late domain is found in the p6 protein, which is produced upon proteolytic cleavage of the *gag* gene product. Morita and Sundquist uncovered an association between the p6 late domain of HIV-1 Gag and the ESCRT-I component TSG101 [27]. Furthermore, knock-down of TSG101 or expression of a dominant negative ATPase-deficient Vps4 inhibited budding of wild-type HIV-1. Thus a simple recruitment of the ESCRT machinery through p6 completes the release of viral-like particles.

How is the ESCRT machinery redirected to the plasma membrane? Effectively p6 mimics Hrs by virtue of its own PTAP sequence and therefore provides an ESCRT-I docking-site at the plasma membrane [24]. Other viruses use the same trick, or alternatively plug into other components of the ESCRT network [27].

Ubiquitin ligases and DUBs: the ying and yang of ubiquitination

Ubiquitination involves the sequential action of three classes of enzymes: the E1 (ubiquitin-activating enzyme), the E2 (ubiquitin-conjugating enzyme) and the E3 (ubiquitin ligase), which is responsible for substrate specificity [28]. Ubiquitination is a dynamic, reversible modification, in many ways similar to phosphorylation (Figure 5). The role of the kinase is played by the E3 and the DUBs take up the role of the phosphatases. In addition, an analogy can be drawn between ubiquitin-binding domains that allow recruitment to ubiquitinated proteins and phospho-residue-binding, granted by SH (Src homology) 2 domains.

E3s

E3s are generally split into two major classes: the RING (really interesting new gene) ligases, which have a catalytic domain based on a double zinc-finger, and the HECT ligases, which contain a 350-amino-acid long C-terminal domain with similarity to E6-AP, within which lies a conserved catalytic cysteine. The main functional difference between these two groups lies in the fact that HECT-ligases form a thiolester intermediate with ubiquitin, whereas RING-ligases promote the direct transfer of ubiquitin from the E2 to the substrate [6].

As mentioned earlier, the major E3 responsible for ubiquitination of plasma-membrane proteins in yeast is the HECT E3, Rsp5. HECT-ligases recognize their substrate via WW domains (protein–protein interaction domains containing two conserved tryptophan residues) that interact with various proline-rich sequences.

(A)   Ubiquitination

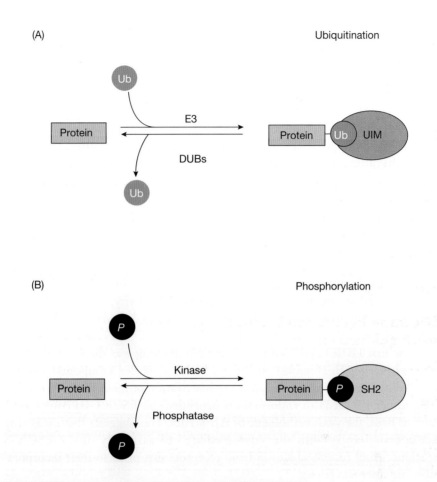

(B)   Phosphorylation

Figure 5. Comparison of ubiquitination with phosphorylation
Ubiquitination is a reversible post-translational modification akin to protein phosphorylation.
P, phosphate.

In mammalian cells, the major E3 implicated in endocytic trafficking of
RTKs is the cellular proto-oncogene Cbl [29]. Cbl is responsible for the ubiquitination of the majority of growth factor receptors that have been studied
and is recruited via its SH2 domain to activated, phosphorylated RTKs. Cbl
also acts as a multivalent adaptor for at least 40 proteins and some of its effects
may be owing to this adaptor function rather than its ligase activity.

The discovery of Cbl and its subsequent identification as a ubiquitin ligase
was an important landmark in the history of the role of ubiquitination in protein trafficking. The importance of Cbl-mediated ubiquitination is exemplified
by the viral oncogene v-cbl, which lacks the RING-finger motif and displaces
endogenous Cbl to allow growth factor receptors to escape from down-regulation. In addition, several EGF and Met receptor mutants that have been isolated from tumours are defective in their ability to bind Cbl [30].

Several HECT-ligases, including Nedd4 (neural precursor cell expressed developmentally down-regulated 4) and AIP4, have also been implicated in endocytic trafficking. However, in most cases, with the exception of Nedd4-mediated ubiquitination of ENaC, the salient substrate may well be a component of the endocytic machinery rather than the receptor itself. Eps15 (EGRF pathway substrate 15) and Hrs ubiquitination are thought to be mediated by Nedd4 or by AIP4. Ubiquitination of these proteins depends on their UIM and it is thought that the HECT ligase is partially recruited through a UIM–ubiquitin interaction. Once the protein is ubiquitinated, its UIM is occupied by its own ubiquitin and is no longer able to recruit another HECT-ligase. In this way, polyubiquitination, and subsequent targeting of the endocytic machinery to the proteasome, may be prevented [14].

DUBs

DUBs have the potential to fulfil two major functions on the endocytic pathway: firstly, they may regulate the ubiquitin status of endosomal proteins (receptors and sorting machinery) by opposing E3 activity, and secondly, they recycle ubiquitin from receptors that are committed to degradation in lysosomes and thereby maintain the free pool of ubiquitin necessary for endocytic sorting.

The first DUB implicated in endocytic trafficking was the yeast ubiquitin protease Doa4. In common with the ESCRT complex components, Doa4 accumulates on the endosome following inactivation of the ATPase, Vps4 [31]. Recruitment of Doa4 to endosomes is dependent on ESCRT-III components and on BroI, the yeast orthologue of AIP1/Alix. This suggests that Doa4 may act concomitantly with the Vps4-mediated disassembly of the ESCRT-machinery and recycle ubiquitin from receptors just prior to their incorporation into internal vesicles.

Endocytic cargo that is normally targeted to the vacuole lumen is mis-sorted to the limiting membrane of the vacuole in *doa4* mutant yeast [32]. However, deubiquitination may not be an absolute requirement for cargo-sorting into internal vesicles, since chimaeric proteins with in-frame fusions of ubiquitin are sorted efficiently [33]. In addition, the *doa4* block on vacuolar protein sorting can be overcome by overexpression of ubiquitin, suggesting that the requirement lies in the maintenance of ubiquitin homoeostasis [32]. Doa4 function may thus be analogous to that of the DUB Rpn11, which recycles ubiquitin from proteins that are degraded by the proteasome [34].

The most likely orthologue of Doa4 in mammalian cells, UBPY (ubiquitin-binding protein Y), also called USP8 (ubiquitin-specific protease 8), was originally described as a growth-regulated DUB, as it accumulates upon growth-stimulation of starved human fibroblasts, and its levels decrease in response to growth-arrest induced by cell–cell contact [35]. Although no functional data are yet available, a link to endosomal protein sorting has been suggested, as UBPY was identified as an interaction partner of the SH3 domain of STAM [36].

Intriguingly, the STAM SH3 domain also interacts with another DUB called AMSH (associated molecule with the SH3 domain of STAM) [37]. AMSH shares with UBPY a non-canonical SH3-domain binding motif PX(V/I)(D/N)RXXKP [36], which is required in both cases for STAM-binding. AMSH and UBPY may therefore be expected to compete with each other for binding to STAM *in vivo*.

In contrast to UBPY and Doa4, AMSH is not a cysteine protease, but belongs to the JAMM (JAB1/MPN/Mov34) metallo-enzyme family of DUBs, which includes the Rpn11/POH1 subunit of the 19 S proteasome lid [38]. AMSH is able to convert ubiquitin chains and is so far the only ubiquitin isopeptidase that shows specificity for Lys[63]- over Lys[48]-linked chains *in vitro* [39]. While the *in vivo* substrate of AMSH remains to be identified, *in vitro* assays also show that it is capable of removing mono-ubiquitin from EGFR. Overexpression of a catalytically inactive form of AMSH promotes the accumulation of ubiquitin on early endosomes, whereas depletion of cellular AMSH levels by siRNA treatment markedly enhances EGFR down-regulation. This suggests that AMSH may counteract E3 activity on endosomes and promote recycling, either by acting directly on the ubiquitinated receptors or by modulating the ubiquitination status of the sorting machinery. A similar role in promoting the recycling of the plasma-membrane proteins Ste2 and Ste6 has also been suggested by studies on the yeast DUB Ubp1 [40].

Conclusion

Over the last decade, ubiquitination has emerged as a major regulatory mechanism controlling protein trafficking through the endocytic pathway and thus influencing the cell-surface levels of many plasma-membrane proteins, including RTKs like EGFR and c-Met. Defects in ubiquitin-mediated sorting, as seen in v-*cbl*-transformed cells, lead to uncontrolled proliferation that is the hallmark of cancer. The fact that many retroviruses have hijacked components of the endocytic sorting machinery provides a further strong incentive to widen our understanding of the interplay between ubiquitination and endocytic trafficking. Now that most of the core components of this pathway have been identified, the challenge lies in elucidating the choreography underlying this complex process.

Summary

- *There are two main protein degradation pathways in eukaryotic cells: proteasomal and lysosomal. Both use ubiquitin as a targeting signal.*
- *Membrane proteins that are sorted to lysosomes are either multi-mono-ubiquitinated or have short Lys[63]-linked ubiquitin chains attached to them.*

- *Monoubiquitination can act as a sorting signal at multiple steps in the endocytic pathway: at the plasma membrane, for internalization, and at the early endosome, for the sorting of proteins into the internal vesicles of MVBs, which deliver their content to lysosomes.*

- *The ubiquitin attached to membrane proteins is recognized by multiple components of the endocytic sorting machinery, which bear a variety of ubiquitin-interacting domains.*

- *Proteins involved in ubiquitin-mediated sorting at the plasma membrane include Eps15 and Epsin. The sorting machinery at the early endosome comprises the Hrs–STAM complex and three multimolecular complexes called ESCRT-I, -II and -III that mediate the translocation of receptors into the internal vesicles of the MVB.*

- *Ubiquitination is a reversible dynamic modification under the control of E3s and DUBs. The main E3 responsible for the ubiquitination of growth factor receptors in mammalian cells is the proto-oncogene Cbl. Other ubiquitin ligases implicated in endocytic trafficking are AIP4, Nedd4 and its yeast-orthologue Rsp5.*

- *Endosomal DUBs may act to counterbalance E3 activity either before receptors are committed to enter internal vesicles of the MVB, thereby rescuing them from degradation (e.g. AMSH), or after commitment to entering the MVB pathway, in which case their main role is to recycle ubiquitin from doomed receptors (e.g. Doa4).*

I would like to thank Michael Clague for critically reading this manuscript.

References

1. De Duve, C. & Wattiaux, R. (1966) Functions of lysosomes. *Annu. Rev. Physiol.* **28**, 435–492
2. Ciechanover, A. (2005) Proteolysis: from the lysosome to ubiquitin and the proteasome. *Nat. Rev. Mol. Cell Biol.* **6**, 79–86
3. Marmor, M.D. & Yarden, Y. (2004) Role of protein ubiquitylation in regulating endocytosis of receptor tyrosine kinases. *Oncogene* **23**, 2057–2070
4. Clague, M.J. (1998) Molecular aspects of the endocytic pathway. *Biochem. J.* **336**, 271–282
5. Hicke, L. & Dunn, R. (2003) Regulation of membrane protein transport by ubiquitin and ubiquitin-binding proteins. *Annu. Rev. Cell Dev. Biol.* **19**, 141–172
6. Dupre, S., Urban-Grimal, D. & Haguenauer-Tsapis, R. (2004) Ubiquitin and endocytic internalization in yeast and animal cells. *Biochim. Biophys. Acta* **1695**, 89–111
7. Katzmann, D.J., Odorizzi, G. & Emr, S.D. (2002) Receptor downregulation and multivesicular-body sorting. *Nat. Rev. Mol. Cell Biol.* **3**, 893–905
8. Clague, M.J. & Urbe, S. (2001) The interface of receptor trafficking and signalling. *J. Cell Sci.* **114**, 3075–3081
9. Bonifacino, J.S. & Weissman, A. (1998) Ubiquitin and the control of protein fate in the secretory and endocytic pathways. *Annu. Rev. Cell Dev. Biol.* **14**, 19–57
10. Carter, S., Urbe, S. & Clague, M.J. (2004) The met receptor degradation pathway: requirement for K48-linked polyubiquitin independent of proteasome activity. *J. Biol. Chem.* **279**, 52835–52839
11. Hammond, D.E., Carter, S. & Clague, M.J. (2004) Met receptor dynamics and signalling. *Curr. Top. Immunol. Microbiol.* **286**, 21–44

12. Traub, L.M. (2003) Sorting it out: AP-2 and alternate clathrin adaptors in endocytic cargo selection. *J. Cell Biol.* **163**, 203–208

13. Duan, L., Miura, Y., Dimri, M., Majumder, B., Dodge, I.L., Reddi, A.L., Ghosh, A., Fernandes, N., Zhou, P., Mullane-Robinson, K., et al. (2003) Cbl-mediated ubiquitinylation is required for lysosomal sorting of epidermal growth factor receptor but is dispensable for endocytosis. *J. Biol. Chem.* **278**, 28950–28960

14. Di Fiore, P.P., Polo, S. & Hofmann, K. (2003) When ubiquitin meets ubiquitin receptors: a signalling connection. *Nat. Rev. Mol. Cell Biol.* **4**, 491–497

15. Haas, A.L. & Bright, P.M. (1987) The dynamics of ubiquitin pools within cultured human lung fibroblasts. *J. Biol. Chem.* **262**, 345–351

16. Clague, M.J. (2002) Membrane transport: a coat for ubiquitin. *Curr. Biol.* **12**, R529–R531

17. Bankaitis, V.A., Johnson, L.M. & Emr, S.D. (1986) Isolation of yeast mutants defective in protein targeting to the vacuole. *Proc. Natl. Acad. Sci. U.S.A.* **83**, 9075–9079

18. von Schwedler, U.K., Stuchell, M., Muller, B., Ward, D.M., Chung, H.Y., Morita, E., Wang, H.E., Davis, T., He, G.P., Cimbora, D.M. et al. (2003) The protein network of HIV budding. *Cell* **114**, 701–713

19. Komada, M. & Soriano, P. (1999) Hrs, a FYVE finger protein localized to early endosomes is implicated in vesicular traffic and required for ventral folding morphogenisis. *Genes Dev.* **13**, 1475–1485

20. Lloyd, T.E., Atkinson, R., Wu, M.N., Zhou, Y., Pennetta, G. & Bellen, H.J. (2002) Hrs regulates endosome membrane invagination and tyrosine kinase receptor signaling in *Drosophila*. *Cell* **108**, 261–269

21. Hammond, D.E., Carter, S., McCullough, J., Urbe, S., Vande Woude, G. & Clague, M.J. (2003) Endosomal dynamics of met determine signaling output. *Mol. Biol. Cell* **14**, 1346–1354

22. Bache, K.G., Raiborg, C., Mehlum, A. & Stenmark, H. (2003) STAM and Hrs are subunits of a multivalent ubiquitin-binding complex on early endosomes. *J. Biol. Chem.* **278**, 12513–12521

23. Urbé, S., Sachse, M., Row, P.E., Preisinger, C., Barr, F.A., Strous, G., Klumperman, J. & Clague, M.J. (2003) The UIM domain of Hrs couples receptor sorting to vesicle formation. *J. Cell Sci.* **116**, 4169–4179

24. Clague, M.J. & Urbe, S. (2003) Hrs function: viruses provide the clue. *Trends Cell Biol.* **13**, 603–606

25. Slagsvold, T. & Stenmark, H. (2004) The structure of an endosomal protein sorter. *Dev. Cell* **7**, 457–458

26. Slagsvold, T., Aasland, R., Hirano, S., Bache, K.G., Raiborg, C., Trambaiano, D., Wakatsuki, S. & Stenmark, H. (2005) Eap45 in mammalian ESCRT-II binds ubiquitin via a phosphoinositide-interacting GLUE domain. *J. Biol. Chem.* **280**, 19600–19606

27. Morita, E. & Sundquist, W.I. (2004) Retrovirus budding. *Annu. Rev. Cell Dev. Biol.* **20**, 395–425

28. Hershko, A. & Ciechanover, A. (1998) The ubiquitin system. *Annu. Rev. Biochem.* **67**, 425–479

29. Thien, C.B.F. & Langdon, W.Y. (2001) Cbl: many adaptions to regulate protein tyrosine kinases. *Nat. Rev. Mol. Cell Biol.* **2**, 294–305

30. Peschard, P. & Park, M. (2003) Escape from Cbl-mediated downregulation: a recurrent theme for oncogenic deregulation of receptor tyrosine kinases. *Cancer Cell* **3**, 519–523

31. Amerik, A.Y., Nowak, J., Swaminathan, S. & Hochstrasser, M. (2000) The DoA4 deubiquitinating enzyme is functionally linked to the vacuolar protein-sorting and endocytic pathways. *Mol. Biol. Cell* **11**, 3365–3380

32. Losko, S., Kopp, F., Kranz, A. & Kolling, R. (2001) Uptake of the ATP-binding cassette (ABC) transporter Ste6 into the yeast vacuole is blocked in the doa4 mutant. *Mol. Biol. Cell* **12**, 1047–1059

33. Reggiori, F. & Pelham, H.R. (2001) Sorting of proteins into multivesicular bodies: ubiquitin-dependent and -independent targeting. *EMBO J.* **20**, 5176–5186

34. Yao, T. & Cohen, R.E. (2002) A cryptic protease couples deubiquitination and degradation by the proteasome. *Nature (London)* **419**, 403–407

35. Naviglio, S., Mattecucci, C., Matoskova, B., Nagase, T., Nomura, N., Di Fiore, P.P. & Draetta, G.F. (1998) UBPY: a growth-regulated human ubiquitin isopeptidase. *EMBO J.* **17**, 3241–3250

36. Kato, M., Miyazawa, K. & Kitamura, N. (2000) A de-ubiquitinating enzyme UBPY interacts with the SH3 domain of Hrs binding protein via a novel binding motif Px(V/I)(D/N)RxxKP. *J. Biol. Chem.* **275**, 37481–37487

37. Tanaka, N., Kaneko, K., Asao, H., Kasai, H., Endo, Y., Fujita, T., Takeshita, T. & Sugamura, K. (1999) Possible involvement of a novel STAM-associated molecule 'AMSH' in intracellular signal transduction mediated by cytokines. *J. Biol. Chem.* **274**, 19129–19135

38. Maytal-Kivity, V., Reis, N., Hofmann, K. & Glickman, M.H. (2002) MPN+, a putative catalytic motif found in a subset of MPN domain proteins from eukaryotes and prokaryotes, is critical for Rpn11 function. *B.M.C. Biochem.* **3**, 28

39. McCullough, J., Clague, M.J. & Urbe, S. (2004) AMSH is an endosome-associated ubiquitin isopeptidase. *J. Cell Biol.* **166**, 487–492

40. Schmitz, C., Kinner, A. & Kolling, R. (2005) The deubiquitinating enzyme Ubp1 affects sorting of the ATP-binding cassette-transporter Ste6 in the endocytic pathway. *Mol. Biol. Cell* **16**, 1319–1329

7

The role of the ubiquitin–proteasome system in ER quality control

Yihong Ye[1]

Laboratory of Molecular Biology, National Institute of Diabetes and Digestive and Kidney Diseases, National Institutes of Health, Bethesda, MD 20892-0540, U.S.A.

Abstract

Misfolded endoplasmic reticulum (ER) proteins are eliminated by the retrotranslocation pathway in eukaryotes, which is an important physiological adaptation to ER stress. This pathway can be hijacked by certain viruses to destroy folded cellular proteins, such as MHC class I heavy chain. Recent studies have highlighted the importance of the ubiquitin–proteasome system (UPS) in this process.

Introduction

The endoplasmic reticulum (ER) is the major site of protein biosynthesis in eukaryotes. It receives newly synthesized polypeptides from the cytosol via a narrow channel formed by the Sec61 complex. An elaborate system of ER chaperones subsequently catalyses the folding and assembly of these polypeptides, allowing them to acquire folded, native conformations. However, polypeptides may adopt aberrant conformations, resulting in aggregation-prone, misfolded proteins. The accumulation of misfolded proteins represents a form of ER stress, which has been implicated in the pathogenesis of many human diseases [1]. To preserve ER homoeostasis,

[1]email yihongy@mail.nih.gov

eukaryotes have evolved a conserved ER quality-control pathway, termed retrotranslocation or dislocation, which efficiently eliminates unwanted ER proteins by exporting them into the cytosol [2,3]. Polypeptides undergoing retrotranslocation are disposed of by the proteasome in the cytosol. Thus, this pathway is also called ERAD (ER-associated degradation) [4]. The retrotranslocation pathway may be hijacked by certain viruses to destroy folded cellular proteins required for immune defence, allowing the virus to evade host immune surveillance. For example, the human cytomegalovirus (HCMV) encodes two proteins, US2 and US11, each of which can efficiently target newly synthesized MHC class I heavy chain for retrotranslocation and proteasomal degradation. The Vpu protein of human HIV also utilizes this pathway to remove the CD4 receptor selectively from the ER membrane [5].

Retrotranslocation first requires the recognition of polypeptides and their subsequent targeting to the site of translocation in the ER membrane. Misfolded or unassembled polypeptides are selected by ER chaperones to enter the pathway, whereas viral factors associate with their specific 'clients' (e.g. US2 and US11 are ER-localized membrane proteins that specifically bind MHC class I heavy chain), 'abducting' them to the translocation site. Polypeptides are then transferred across the membrane, presumably through a protein-conducting channel. Substrates emerging from the ER are polyubiquitinated on the cytosolic face of the ER membrane, and the modified polypeptides are then dislocated into the cytosol and degraded by the proteasome (Figure 1).

ER proteins are degraded in the cytosol by the ubiquitin–proteasome system (UPS)

Ubiquitin is a small polypeptide that can be covalently linked to either the ε-amino group of a lysine residue or the N-terminal amino group on a substrate. This process requires three types of enzymes: ubiquitin-activating enzyme (E1), ubiquitin-conjugating enzyme (E2), and ubiquitin ligase (E3). Either a single ubiquitin (mono-) or a chain linked by one of the lysines on ubiquitin itself (poly-) can be attached to a substrate. Chains linked by Lys^{48} specifically target the modified substrates to the proteasome for degradation, while other chain linkages and mono-ubiquitination mediate different cellular processes. Although it was known for many years that misfolded cytosolic proteins are degraded by the UPS, its role in ER protein degradation was not appreciated for a long time. It was initially thought that ER proteins are destroyed in the ER lumen, which lacks the UPS components, such as ubiquitin and the proteasome. However, genetic and biochemical studies in *Saccharomyces cerevisiae* and in mammalian cells have since convincingly demonstrated the involvement of the UPS in ER protein degradation [2–4]. For example, many misfolded ER proteins were found to undergo polyubiquitination. If polyubiquitination is prevented by the expression of a mutant ubiquitin with

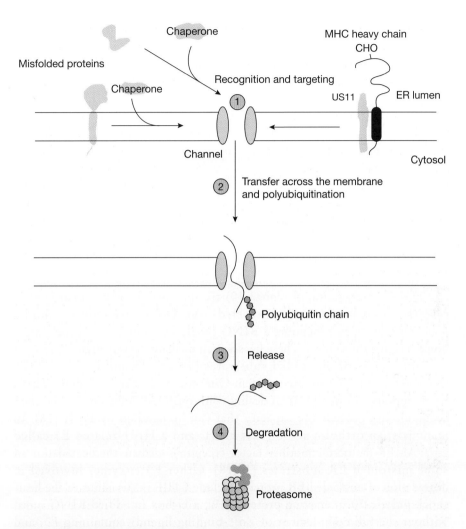

Figure 1. The retrotranslocation pathway
The retrotranslocation pathway can be divided into four steps. In step 1, misfolded proteins, both lumenal and transmembrane, are recognized by ER chaperones and targeted to the translocation channel in the ER membrane. The viral protein US11 delivers the associated MHC class I heavy chain to the same translocation site. In step 2, substrates are transferred across the membrane and modified by polyubiquitination. In step 3, polyubiquitinated proteins are dislocated into the cytosol. In step 4, the released polypeptides are degraded by the proteasome in the cytosol.

Lys^{48} changed to Ala, the degradation of many substrates is inhibited. In yeast, mutations in many components of the UPS stabilize misfolded ER proteins. Similarly, in mammalian cells expressing a temperature-sensitive mutant of the E1 enzyme, the degradation of ER proteins is blocked at non-permissive temperatures. Finally, inhibitors of the proteasome also affect the degradation of ER proteins, both in yeast and in mammalian cells. Together, these experiments establish a new model in which misfolded ER proteins, both lumenal and transmembrane, are disposed of by the UPS in the cytosol.

Obviously, the ER substrates must first be retrotranslocated into the cytosol before encountering the UPS.

The ubiquitination machinery for retrotranslocation

Many components of the ubiquitination system implicated in retrotranslocation were initially identified in yeast and later studied in mammalian cells. As expected, many of these enzymes are associated with the ER membrane. In yeast, the relevant E2s include Ubc7 (ubiquitin-conjugating enzyme 7), Ubc6, and Ubc1 [6–8]. Ubc7 is bound to the ER membrane by association with its partner Cue1 (coupling of ubiquitin conjugation to ER degradation 1) [9], and Ubc6 is an ER-localized transmembrane protein [6]. Deletion of these genes individually or in combination prevents the ubiquitination and degradation of many misfolded ER proteins [8,10,11]. The mammalian homologues of Ubc6 and Ubc7 appear to play a similar role [12,13]. In yeast, Hrd1 (hydroxymethylglutaryl-CoA reductase degradation) and Doa10 (degradation of alpha2-10) are the two major E3s dedicated to retrotranslocation [11,14]. Both Hrd1 and Doa10 are multi-spanning membrane proteins containing a RING (really interesting new gene)-finger domain facing the cytosol. These ligases each mediate the retrotranslocation of a distinct class of misfolded substrates [14,15]. In addition, a HECT (homologous to E6-associated protein C-terminus) domain-containing ligase, Rsp5, appears to assist Hrd1 in dealing with misfolded substrates when their accumulation exceeds the capacity that can be handled by Hrd1 [16]. In mammals, an orthologue of yeast Hrd1, and a Hrd1-related E3 called gp78/AMFR (autocrine motility factor receptor), mediate the degradation of some misfolded ER substrates [17,18]. Other E3 enzymes involved in degradation of misfolded ER proteins include CHIP (C-terminus of the heat-shock-protein-70-interacting protein) [19], a U-box (modified RING motif without the full complement of Zn^{2+}-binding ligand)-containing E3, and Parkin, a RING-finger E3 linked to the juvenile Parkinson's disease [20]. Two F-box-containing proteins, Fbs1 (F-box protein 2) and Fbs2 (F-box protein 6), each of which is part of a multi-subunit SCF [Skp1 (S-phase associated protein-1)–Cdc53 (cell-division cycle 53)/Cul1 (Cullin homologue 1)–F-box protein] ubiquitin ligase, can both recognize carbohydrate chains. The corresponding E3 ligase may be specific for the retrotranslocation of glycoproteins [21,22]. CHIP, Parkin, Fbs1 and Fbs2 are not membrane proteins, and must be recruited to the translocation site by association with a membrane partner.

The role of polyubiquitination in protein retrotranslocation

Polyubiquitination is required for retrotranslocation

When polyubiquitination is prevented, substrates cannot be moved into the cytosol; instead, they accumulate in the ER lumen. Thus, polyubiquitination not only is required for guiding substrates to the proteasome, but also participates in transferring polypeptides across the ER membrane [2]. However, because polyubiquitination occurs at the cytosolic face of the ER membrane, before substrates are completely exported into the cytosol, it cannot account for the initiation of retrotranslocation for lumenal proteins. It is currently unclear how these substrates are inserted into the membrane to initiate the translocation process.

What is the precise role of polyubiquitination in retrotranslocation? Studies on the US11-dependent retrotranslocation of MHC class I heavy chains in a permeabilized cell system have provided some clues. When membranes containing MHC class I heavy chains are incubated with cytosol in the presence of AMPPNP (adenosine 5′-(β,γ-imino)triphosphate), an ATP analogue that supports the polyubiquitination reaction but not other ATP-dependent processes, heavy chains can partially exit the ER and undergo polyubiquitination, but the modified substrates cannot be moved into the cytosol. These membrane-associated retrotranslocation intermediates can be released into the cytosol upon addition of ATP. These experiments indicate that polyubiquitination on its own is insufficient to move substrates from the ER membrane into the cytosol; it probably serves as a recognition signal for a cytosolic ATPase, which utilizes ATP hydrolysis to extract polyubiquitinated substrates and release them into the cytosol [23].

The AAA (ATPase associated with various cellular activities) ATPase p97 is required for protein retrotranslocation

The cytosolic ATPase that acts on polyubiquitinated polypeptides at the ER membrane turns out to be p97 [also called VCP (valosin-containing protein), or in yeast, Cdc48], a member of the AAA ATPase family. The function of p97/Cdc48 is as a molecular chaperone in many cellular processes, including retrotranslocation, the activation of a membrane-anchored transcription factor, the formation of nuclear envelope, spindle disassembly, and the homotypic fusion of ER/Golgi membranes [24,25]. The ATPase contains two similar Walker-type ATPase domains (D1 and D2) and an additional N-terminal domain (N-domain) (Figure 2). Through its N-domain, p97 can bind to a variety of different cofactors, which explains the functional diversity of this ATPase. The cofactor that assists p97 in retrotranslocation is a dimer consisting of Ufd1 (ubiquitin fusion degradation protein-1) and Npl4 (nuclear protein localization gene 4). In yeast, mutations in each individual component of the Cdc48 complex prevent the export of various misfolded proteins from

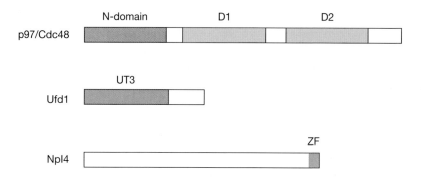

Figure 2. Ubiquitin recognition by the p97/Cdc48 complex
p97/Cdc48 consists of an N-terminal domain (N-domain) and two similar ATPase domains (D1 and D2). The p97 N-domain can bind to a cofactor complex containing Ufd1 and Npl4. The N-domain also interacts with ubiquitin chains. The N-terminal region of Ufd1 (UT3 domain) also recognizes ubiquitin. The UT3 domain and the p97 N-domain can synergistically bind ubiquitin chains linked via Lys[48]. The ZF domain in Npl4 also recognizes ubiquitin chains, but it has no preference for chain linkage.

the ER [26]. As a consequence, the unfolded-protein response (UPR), a collection of signalling transduction pathways that help rectify the folding problem in the ER, is elicited [27,28]. In yeast mutants of Ufd1 and Npl4, retrotranslocation substrates are polyubiquitinated, but the modified substrates remain associated with the ER membrane, indicating that the ATPase complex functions downstream of polyubiquitination [28,29]. In mammalian cells, p97 associates with retrotranslocating substrates in an ATP-dependent manner [27]. Overexpression of a p97 mutant defective in ATP hydrolysis stabilizes many misfolded ER proteins and triggers UPR ([27,30] and Y. Ye, unpublished work). The mutant p97 appears to be able to 'grab' at a retrotranslocating substrate, but is unable to 'pull' it out of the ER membrane. These experiments indicate that ATP hydrolysis by p97 is required to move polypeptides into the cytosol during retrotranslocation.

How p97 hydrolyses ATP when acting on substrates is unclear. Several studies showed that mutations in the D2 domain affect the ATPase activity more drastically than those in D1 [31,32], but both D1 and D2 are functionally important *in vivo* [32]. One possibility is that the two ATPase domains might alternate in ATP binding and hydrolysis [32], similar to the mechanism proposed for the p97/Cdc48-like ATPase Hsp104 (heat-shock protein 104) [33].

The p97/Cdc48 ATPase complex selectively acts on polyubiquitinated substrates
Why does p97/Cdc48 selectively act on polyubiquitinated substrates? The question was at least partially answered when several groups found that both the ATPase and its cofactors Ufd1 and Npl4 can interact with ubiquitin (Figure 2). Both p97 and Cdc48 have the capacity to bind polyubiquitin chains

[32,34,35], albeit with low affinity. In addition, the UT3 domain of Ufd1 and the Zn-finger (ZF) motif of Npl4 can both recognize ubiquitin [32,36]. The ZF motif of Npl4 does not seem to play a role in retrotranslocation. In contrast, ubiquitin recognition by p97 and Ufd1 is essential because, firstly, p97 and Ufd1 act synergistically to bind ubiquitin chains linked through Lys[48], the chain linkage preferred by the proteasome acting downstream of the ATPase complex [32]; secondly, these proteins do not recognize ubiquitin chains synthesized with a ubiquitin fusion to glutathione S-transferase (GST–ubiquitin), which may explain why poly(GST–ubiquitin)-modified substrates cannot be extracted from the ER membrane [23]; and thirdly, a cofactor complex lacking the ubiquitin binding domain of Ufd1 inhibits the US11-dependent retrotranslocation [32].

Nonetheless, ubiquitin binding is not required for the initial substrate recognition by p97. When polyubiquitination is abolished, the ATPase can still associate with retrotranslocating polypeptides in the ER membrane, but the associated substrates cannot be released into the cytosol [32]. In addition, the ATPase complex interacts with substrates modified by poly(GST–ubiquitin), presumably through a non-modified segment, because the attached poly-(GST–ubiquitin) chains on their own do not bind to either p97 or Ufd1 [23]. Based on these observations, a dual recognition model was proposed [32], in which p97/Cdc48 itself first binds a non-modified, presumably unfolded, substrate emerging from the translocation site. Once ubiquitin chains are attached to the substrate, the conjugates can be recognized by both the ATPase and Ufd1. Since interfering with ubiquitin recognition leads to the same defect as that caused by a mutant p97 lacking ATPase activity, ubiquitin binding by the p97 complex may activate the ATPase, leading to the extraction of substrates from the ER membrane. The dislocated substrates are subsequently delivered to the proteasome, which is probably mediated by a different set of ubiquitin-binding proteins that can also interact with the proteasome (see Chapter 4 for further discussion).

The requirement of ubiquitin for the function of p97 is not a unique feature for retrotranslocation. In fact, many other p97 cofactors also contain ubiquitin-binding motifs that are capable of recognizing ubiquitin. For example, p47, which regulates the function of p97 in the homotypic fusion of Golgi membranes, contains an essential UBA (ubiquitin-associated) domain that binds mono-ubiquitin [36]. During the activation of the membrane-anchored transcription factor Spt23, Cdc48 and its cofactors Ufd1 and Npl4 recognize the endoproteolytically cleaved Spt23, which is at least partially mediated by the ubiquitin conjugates attached to Spt23. The ATPase complex then mobilizes the transcription factor from the ER membrane, allowing its nuclear translocation and activation [35].

Translocation of substrates through the central pore in p97/Cdc48

How does p97/Cdc48 extract polypeptides from the membrane? Crystallography studies reveal that p97 forms a hexameric ring with a central channel [37,38]. This structure resembles the AAA ATPase ring connected to the ClpP (caseinolytic protease P) protease in *Escherichia coli* or the one docked on the 20 S core particle of the eukaryotic 26 S proteasome. In both cases, polypeptides are threaded through the central channel of the ATPase rings to reach the enzymatic sites embedded within the proteolytic particle [39]. Although p97/Cdc48 does not appear to be directly linked to the 20 S proteasome, it might 'pull' substrates out of the ER membrane by moving them through its axial channel. One complication with this model is that p97 acts on substrates containing bulky ubiquitin chains that seem to exceed the size limit of its pore. Thus, it may need to co-operate with deubiquitination enzymes to allow the removal of ubiquitin conjugates before substrates enter the channel. No such enzymes have been identified for retrotranslocation, although in p97-mediated Golgi reassembly, a deubiquitination enzyme, VCIP135, is involved [40]. In addition, because ubiquitin chains are also required downstream of p97 for substrate delivery to the proteasome, deubiquitination at p97 would mean that substrates exiting the p97 channel need to be remodified by polyubiquitination. Nonetheless, an elegant study recently demonstrated that ClpB, a p97/Cdc48-like ring ATPase in bacteria, indeed threads its substrates through its central pore [41]. The structural similarity between p97/Cdc48 and ClpB indicates that the central pore of p97 may also be important for its function.

Association of p97/Cdc48 with the ER membrane

A large fraction of the p97 ATPase complex is closely associated with the ER membrane. However, neither p97, nor its cofactors Ufd1 and Npl4, contain any transmembrane segments. Thus, a membrane receptor is required to dock the ATPase complex to the ER membrane. Recent studies have identified an ER–membrane-protein complex in mammals that provides at least one binding site for p97 and its cofactors [42]. One component of the complex, Derlin-1, belongs to a conserved multi-spanning membrane protein family. The other component of the complex, VIMP/SelS (VCP-interacting membrane protein/selenoprotein S), is a single-spanning membrane protein present only in vertebrates. The complex binds p97 via two binding sites, one in the C-terminal tail of Derlin-1, and the other in the cytosolic domain of VIMP (Y. Ye, unpublished work).

Derlin-1 appears to be a central component of the retrotranslocation pathway for many substrates [42]. The homologue of Derlin-1 in yeast, Der1, is required for the degradation of some misfolded ER proteins [15,43]. Inactivation of Derlin-1 in *Caenorhabditis elegans* induces UPR, presumably because misfolded ER proteins are not efficiently degraded in the absence of Derlin-1 [42]. In mammals, Derlin-1 associates with retrotranslocation substrates as they move across the membrane. It also binds a subset of ubiquitin ligases dedicated to the retrotranslocation pathway (Y. Ye, unpublished work). The interaction between Derlin-1 and E3 ligases is at least partially mediated by p97. This allows the simultaneous recruitment of the ATPase and the ubiquitination machinery to Derlin-1.

The role of Derlin-1 in retrotranslocation is best understood for the US11-dependent retrotranslocation of MHC class I heavy chains [42,44]. Derlin-1 can bind the viral protein US11 as well as p97. The interaction between US11 and Derlin-1 is essential for targeting heavy chains to the retrotranslocation pathway [44], whereas the interaction between Derlin-1 and p97 presumably docks the ATPase and the associated E3 enzymes to the site of translocation, allowing these enzymes to act synergistically on substrates as they emerge from the ER. Thus substrate recognition in the ER lumen is directly linked to its ubiquitination and p97-mediated dislocation in the cytosol via Derlin-1, suggesting that it may play a direct role in transferring substrates across the ER membrane, perhaps as a component of the protein-conducting channel.

A role for VIMP in retrotranslocation is suggested by its up-regulation upon ER stress [45], and by its association with retrotranslocation substrates and many components of the pathway, such as Derlin-1, p97 and E3 ligase [42]. Other Derlin-like proteins may also be involved in retrotranslocation, because the human Derlin-2 also binds p97 as well as a retrotranslocation-specific E3 ligase, Hrd1 (B. Lilley and H. Ploegh, personal communication).

A membrane channel for retrotranslocation

Retrotranslocation substrates are believed to traverse the ER membrane through a protein-conducting channel. Earlier studies suggested that the Sec61 complex, which mediates the translocation of polypeptides into the ER, might also function in retrotranslocation [2]. Although some genetic and biochemical evidence supports this view, studying some earlier works reveals that the interaction between the Sec61 complex and retrotranslocation substrates cannot be reproduced when the co-immunoprecipitation is done under more stringent conditions. In addition, no interaction between the Sec61 channel and the known components of the retrotranslocation pathway can be detected (Y. Ye, unpublished work). Thus, the Sec61 complex is unlikely to serve as a general channel for retrotranslocation.

As suggested above, several lines of evidence suggest that Derlin-1 defines the site of retrotranslocation, and may be part of the retrotranslocation channel. Consistent with this view, the Derlin family members can form homo- or hetero-oligomers in the ER membrane, resulting in a complex that contains a sufficient number of transmembrane segments for a protein channel. Nevertheless, definitive evidence is still lacking. In addition, assuming Derlin-1 can form a channel, there must be other channels for retrotranslocation because both Derlin-1 and its yeast homologue Der1 only account for the degradation of a subset of ER proteins.

Conclusion

Studies on the US11-dependent retrotranslocation of MHC class I heavy chains have outlined a pathway, from the recognition of the substrate in the ER to its degradation by the proteasome in the cytosol (Figure 3). First, US11 recognizes heavy chains and targets them to Derlin-1. Next, heavy chains are inserted into a protein-conducting channel, which may be formed by oligomerization of the Derlin proteins. Once a segment of the heavy chain has emerged into the cytosol, it is captured by p97. At the same time, a retrotranslocation complex containing p97, its cofactors and a ubiquitination enzyme is assembled. The substrate undergoes polyubiquitination and the attached polyubiquitin chains are recognized by both p97 and the cofactor Ufd1. Finally, the substrate is 'pulled' out of the ER membrane and delivered to the proteasome in the cytosol.

The retrotranslocation of some misfolded ER proteins probably occurs by the same mechanism, except that these substrates are recognized by ER chaperones, and that their targeting to Derlin-1 may require additional shuttle proteins that can interact with both Derlin-1 and chaperone-associated substrates. Some substrates seem to use a Derlin-1-independent mechanism to cross the

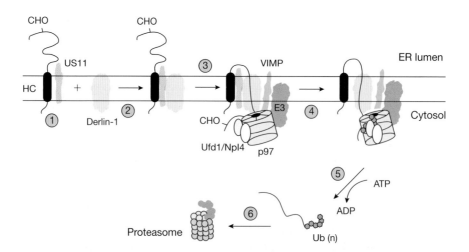

Figure 3. The US11-dependent retrotranslocation of MHC class I heavy chain
In step 1, the viral protein US11 recognizes MHC class I heavy chain (HC), a glycoprotein with a single carbohydrate chain (CHO). In step 2, HC is targeted to a multi-spanning membrane protein called Derlin-1. In step 3, HC is partially moved out of the ER through a protein-conducting channel postulated to contain Derlin-1. The emerging polypeptide is captured by the cytosolic ATPase p97, which may lead to the assembly of a complex containing the p97 cofactor complex (Ufd1–Npl4), the single-spanning membrane protein VIMP, and an unknown ubiquitin ligase. In step 4, HC undergoes polyubiquitination, while a cytosolic N-glycanase removes the attached carbohydrate chain. In step 5, the polyubiquitin chains are recognized by both p97 and the cofactor Ufd1, which may trigger the ATP hydrolysis by p97, leading to the release of HC from the ER membrane. In step 6, polyubiquitinated HC is delivered to the proteasome for degradation. Ub, ubiquitin.

membrane. In this case, the initial substrate targeting to the membrane may involve a different set of factors. Despite such diversity in the early steps of retrotranslocation, almost all retrotranslocation substrates undergo polyubiquitination, and their subsequent movement into the cytosol is dependent on this modification as well as on the ubiquitin-specific p97 ATPase complex.

Summary

- *Misfolded ER proteins are eliminated by a pathway termed retro-translocation, dislocation, or ERAD. In this process, polypeptides are moved from the ER into the cytosol, where they are degraded by the proteasome. This pathway can be hijacked by certain viruses to destroy folded cellular proteins such as MHC class I heavy chain and CD4. Polypeptides are transferred across the membrane, presumably through a protein-conducting channel.*
- *Most retrotranslocation substrates are modified by polyubiquitination on the cytosolic face of the ER membrane, before they are released into the cytosol. Polyubiquitination is required not only for the targeting of a substrate to the proteasome, but also for moving the substrate from the membrane into the cytosol.*
- *Polyubiquitinated polypeptides are released from the membrane by an ATPase complex, consisting of p97 and its cofactors Ufd1 and Npl4. The ATPase itself initially recognizes a non-modified segment of the substrate emerging from the ER. Once the substrate undergoes poly-ubiquitination, the attached ubiquitin chains are recognized by both p97 and its cofactor Ufd1, leading to the 'pulling' of the substrate into the cytosol.*
- *In mammals, p97 is recruited to the ER membrane by association with a membrane-protein complex, consisting of Derlin-1, a conserved multi-spanning membrane protein, and a single-spanning membrane protein called VIMP.*
- *p97 also interacts directly with several E3 enzymes specific for retro-translocation. This interaction appears to facilitate the association between the E3 ligases and Derlin-1. The simultaneous recruitment of p97 and the E3 ligases to Derlin-1 indicates that it represents the site from which substrates exit the ER.*

I thank Tom Rapoport and Andrew Osborne for critical reading of the manuscript, and apologize for not being able to cite all the papers relevant to the development of this field due to space constraints.

References

1. Ozcan, U., Cao, Q., Yilmaz, E., Lee, A.H., Iwakoshi, N.N., Ozdelen, E., Tuncman, G., Gorgun, C., Glimcher, L.H. & Hotamisligil, G.S. (2004) Endoplasmic reticulum stress links obesity, insulin action, and type 2 diabetes. *Science* **306**, 457–461

2. Tsai, B., Ye, Y. & Rapoport, T.A. (2002) Retro-translocation of proteins from the endoplasmic reticulum into the cytosol. *Nat. Rev. Mol. Cell Biol.* **3**, 246–255

3. Kostova, Z. & Wolf, D.H. (2003) For whom the bell tolls: protein quality control of the endoplasmic reticulum and the ubiquitin–proteasome connection. *EMBO J.* **22**, 2309–2317

4. Brodsky, J.L. & McCracken, A.A. (1999) ER protein quality control and proteasome-mediated protein degradation. *Semin. Cell Dev. Biol.* **10**, 507–513

5. Tortorella, D., Gewurz, B.E., Furman, M.H., Schust, D.J. & Ploegh, H.L. (2000) Viral subversion of the immune system. *Annu. Rev. Immunol.* **18**, 861–926

6. Sommer, T. & Jentsch, S. (1993) A protein translocation defect linked to ubiquitin conjugation at the endoplasmic reticulum. *Nature (London)* **365**, 176–179

7. Hiller, M.M., Finger, A., Schweiger, M. & Wolf, D.H. (1996) ER degradation of a misfolded luminal protein by the cytosolic ubiquitin–proteasome pathway. *Science* **273**, 1725–1728

8. Friedlander, R., Jarosch, E., Urban, J., Volkwein, C. & Sommer, T. (2000) A regulatory link between ER-associated protein degradation and the unfolded-protein response. *Nat. Cell Biol.* **2**, 379–384

9. Biederer, T., Volkwein, C. & Sommer, T. (1997) Role of Cue1p in ubiquitination and degradation at the ER surface. *Science* **278**, 1806–1809

10. Biederer, T., Volkwein, C. & Sommer, T. (1996) Degradation of subunits of the Sec61p complex, an integral component of the ER membrane, by the ubiquitin–proteasome pathway. *EMBO J.* **15**, 2069–2076

11. Bays, N.W., Gardner, R.G., Seelig, L.P., Joazeiro, C.A. & Hampton, R.Y. (2001) Hrd1p/Der3p is a membrane-anchored ubiquitin ligase required for ER-associated degradation. *Nat. Cell Biol.* **3**, 24–29

12. Tiwari, S. & Weissman, A.M. (2001) Endoplasmic reticulum (ER)-associated degradation of T cell receptor subunits. Involvement of ER-associated ubiquitin-conjugating enzymes (E2s). *J. Biol. Chem.* **276**, 16193–16200

13. Lenk, U., Yu, H., Walter, J., Gelman, M.S., Hartmann, E., Kopito, R.R. & Sommer, T. (2002) A role for mammalian Ubc6 homologues in ER-associated protein degradation. *J. Cell Sci.* **115**, 3007–3014

14. Swanson, R., Locher, M. & Hochstrasser, M. (2001) A conserved ubiquitin ligase of the nuclear envelope/endoplasmic reticulum that functions in both ER-associated and Matα2 repressor degradation. *Genes Dev.* **15**, 2660–2674

15. Vashist, S. & Ng, D.T. (2004) Misfolded proteins are sorted by a sequential checkpoint mechanism of ER quality control. *J. Cell Biol.* **165**, 41–52

16. Haynes, C.M., Caldwell, S. & Cooper, A.A. (2002) An HRD/DER-independent ER quality control mechanism involves Rsp5p-dependent ubiquitination and ER-Golgi transport. *J. Cell. Biol.* **158**, 91–101

17. Kikkert, M., Doolman, R., Dai, M., Avner, R., Hassink, G., van Voorden, S., Thanedar, S., Roitelman, J., Chau, V. & Wiertz, E. (2004) Human HRD1 is an E3 ubiquitin ligase involved in degradation of proteins from the endoplasmic reticulum. *J. Biol. Chem.* **279**, 3525–3534

18. Fang, S., Ferrone, M., Yang, C., Jensen, J.P., Tiwari, S. & Weissman, A.M. (2001) The tumor autocrine motility factor receptor, gp78, is a ubiquitin protein ligase implicated in degradation from the endoplasmic reticulum. *Proc. Natl. Acad. Sci. U.S.A.* **98**, 14422–14427

19. Meacham, G.C., Patterson, C., Zhang, W., Younger, J.M. & Cyr, D.M. (2001) The Hsc70 co-chaperone CHIP targets immature CFTR for proteasomal degradation. *Nat. Cell Biol.* **3**, 100–105

20. Imai, Y., Soda, M., Inoue, H., Hattori, N., Mizuno, Y. & Takahashi, R. (2001) An unfolded putative transmembrane polypeptide, which can lead to endoplasmic reticulum stress, is a substrate of Parkin. *Cell* **105**, 891–902

21. Yoshida, Y., Chiba, T., Tokunaga, F., Kawasaki, H., Iwai, K., Suzuki, T., Ito, Y., Matsuoka, K., Yoshida, M., Tanaka, K. & Tai, T. (2002) E3 ubiquitin ligase that recognizes sugar chains. *Nature (London)* **418**, 438–442

22. Yoshida, Y., Tokunaga, F., Chiba, T., Iwai, K., Tanaka, K. & Tai, T. (2003) Fbs2 is a new member of the E3 ubiquitin ligase family that recognizes sugar chains. *J. Biol. Chem.* **278**, 43877–43884

23. Flierman, D., Ye, Y., Dai, M., Chau, V. & Rapoport, T.A. (2003) Polyubiquitin serves as a recognition signal, rather than a ratcheting molecule, during retrotranslocation of proteins across the endoplasmic reticulum membrane. *J. Biol. Chem.* **278**, 34774–34782

24. Woodman, P.G. (2003) p97, a protein coping with multiple identities. *J. Cell Sci.* **116**, 4283–4290

25. Wang, Q., Song, C. & Li, C.C. (2004) Molecular perspectives on p97-VCP: progress in understanding its structure and diverse biological functions. *J. Struct. Biol.* **146**, 44–57

26. Bays, N.W. & Hampton, R.Y. (2002) Cdc48-Ufd1-Npl4: stuck in the middle with Ub. *Curr. Biol.* **12**, R366–R371

27. Ye, Y., Meyer, H.H. & Rapoport, T.A. (2001) The AAA ATPase Cdc48/p97 and its partners transport proteins from the ER into the cytosol. *Nature (London)* **414**, 652–656

28. Jarosch, E., Taxis, C., Volkwein, C., Bordallo, J., Finley, D., Wolf, D.H. & Sommer, T. (2002) Protein dislocation from the ER requires polyubiquitination and the AAA-ATPase Cdc48. *Nat. Cell Biol.* **4**, 134–139

29. Bays, N.W., Wilhovsky, S.K., Goradia, A., Hodgkiss-Harlow, K. & Hampton, R.Y. (2001) HRD4/NPL4 is required for the proteasomal processing of ubiquitinated ER proteins. *Mol. Biol. Cell* **12**, 4114–4128

30. Zhong, X., Shen, Y., Ballar, P., Apostolou, A., Agami, R. & Fang, S. (2004) AAA ATPase p97/valosin-containing protein interacts with gp78, a ubiquitin ligase for endoplasmic reticulum-associated degradation. *J. Biol. Chem.* **279**, 45676–45684

31. Song, C., Wang, Q. & Li, C.C. (2003) ATPase activity of p97-valosin-containing protein (VCP). D2 mediates the major enzyme activity, and D1 contributes to the heat-induced activity. *J. Biol. Chem.* **278**, 3648–3655

32. Ye, Y., Meyer, H.H. & Rapoport, T.A. (2003) Function of the p97–Ufd1–Npl4 complex in retrotranslocation from the ER to the cytosol: dual recognition of nonubiquitinated polypeptide segments and polyubiquitin chains. *J. Cell Biol.* **162**, 71–84

33. Hattendorf, D.A. & Lindquist, S.L. (2002) Cooperative kinetics of both Hsp104 ATPase domains and interdomain communication revealed by AAA sensor-1 mutants. *EMBO J.* **21**, 12–21

34. Dai, R.M. & Li, C.C. (2001) Valosin-containing protein is a multi-ubiquitin chain-targeting factor required in ubiquitin–proteasome degradation. *Nat. Cell Biol.* **3**, 740–744

35. Rape, M., Hoppe, T., Gorr, I., Kalocay, M., Richly, H. & Jentsch, S. (2001) Mobilization of processed, membrane-tethered SPT23 transcription factor by CDC48(UFD1/NPL4), a ubiquitin-selective chaperone. *Cell* **107**, 667–677

36. Meyer, H.H., Wang, Y. & Warren, G. (2002) Direct binding of ubiquitin conjugates by the mammalian p97 adaptor complexes, p47 and Ufd1–Npl4. *EMBO J.* **21**, 5645–5652

37. Zhang, X., Shaw, A., Bates, P.A., Newman, R.H., Gowen, B., Orlova, E., Gorman, M.A., Kondo, H., Dokurno, P., Lally, J., Leonard, G., Meyer, H., van Heel, M. & Freemont, P.S. (2000) Structure of the AAA ATPase p97. *Mol. Cell* **6**, 1473–1484

38. DeLaBarre, B. & Brunger, A.T. (2003) Complete structure of p97/valosin-containing protein reveals communication between nucleotide domains. *Nat. Struct. Biol.* **10**, 856–863

39. Pickart, C.M. & Cohen, R.E. (2004) Proteasomes and their kin: proteases in the machine age. *Nat. Rev. Mol. Cell Biol.* **5**, 177–187

40. Wang, Y., Satoh, A., Warren, G. & Meyer, H.H. (2004) VCIP135 acts as a deubiquitinating enzyme during p97-p47-mediated reassembly of mitotic Golgi fragments. *J. Cell Biol.* **164**, 973–978

41. Weibezahn, J., Tessarz, P., Schlieker, C., Zahn, R., Maglica, Z., Lee, S., Zentgraf, H., Weber-Ban, E.U., Dougan, D.A., Tsai, F.T. et al. (2004) Thermotolerance requires refolding of aggregated proteins by substrate translocation through the central pore of ClpB. *Cell* **119**, 653–665

42. Ye, Y., Shibata, Y., Yun, C., Ron, D. & Rapoport, T.A. (2004) A membrane protein complex medi-
     ates retro-translocation from the ER lumen into the cytosol. Nature (London) 429, 841–847
43. Knop, M., Finger, A., Braun, T., Hellmuth, K. & Wolf, D.H. (1996) Der1, a novel protein specifical-
     ly required for endoplasmic reticulum degradation in yeast. EMBO J. 15, 753–763
44. Lilley, B.N. & Ploegh, H.L. (2004) A membrane protein required for dislocation of misfolded pro-
     teins from the ER. Nature (London) 429, 834–840
45. Gao, Y., Feng, H.C., Walder, K., Bolton, K., Sunderland, T., Bishara, N., Quick, M., Kantham, L. &
     Collier, G.R. (2004) Regulation of the selenoprotein SelS by glucose deprivation and endoplasmic
     reticulum stress — SelS is a novel glucose-regulated protein. FEBS Lett. 563, 185–190

8

Fluorescent reporters for the ubiquitin–proteasome system

Florian A. Salomons, Lisette G.G.C. Verhoef and Nico P. Dantuma[1]

Department of Cell and Molecular Biology, Karolinska Institutet, Stockholm S-17177, Sweden

Abstract

Regulated turnover of proteins in the cytosol and nucleus of eukaryotic cells is primarily performed by the ubiquitin–proteasome system (UPS). The UPS is involved in many essential cellular processes. Alterations in this proteolytic system are associated with a variety of human pathologies, such as neurodegenerative diseases, cancer, immunological disorders and inflammation. The precise role of the UPS in the pathophysiology of these diseases, however, remains poorly understood. Detection of UPS aberrations has been a major challenge because of the complexity of the system. Most studies focus on various aspects of the UPS, such as substrate recognition, ubiquitination, deubiquitination or proteasome activity, and do not provide a complete picture of the UPS as an integral system. To monitor the efficacy of the UPS, a number of reporter substrates have been developed based on fluorescent proteins, such as the green fluorescent protein and its spectral variants. These fluorescent UPS reporters contain specific degradation signals that target them with high efficiency and accuracy for proteasomal degradation. Several studies have shown that these reporters can probe the functionality of the UPS in cellular and animal models and provide us with important information on the status of the UPS under various conditions.

[1]*To whom correspondence should be addressed (email nico.dantuma@cmb.ki.se).*

Moreover, these reporters can aid the identification and development of novel anti-cancer and anti-inflammatory drugs based on UPS inhibition.

Introduction

Controlled proteolysis is crucial for regulating a broad range of basic cellular processes, such as cell cycle progression, signal transduction, apoptosis, antigen presentation and protein quality control [1]. In the cytosol and nucleus of eukaryotic cells, these processes are predominantly performed by the ubiquitin–proteasome system (UPS). The UPS generally consists of two consecutive steps: conjugation of a chain of ubiquitin molecules to a substrate protein, and breakdown of the polyubiquitin-tagged protein into small polypeptides by the 26 S proteasome. In the first step, four classes of enzymes are involved, which catalyse the formation of the polyubiquitin chain: the ubiquitin-activating enzyme (E1), ubiquitin conjugating enzymes (E2s), ubiquitin ligases (E3s; see Chapter 2), and occasionally ubiquitin-chain assembly enzymes (E4s; see Chapter 1) [2]. Proteins destined for ubiquitination and degradation are singled out by a large variety of E3 enzymes, which recognize specific degradation signals within these proteins and provide them with ubiquitin chains. Degradation signals come in many forms and can be, for example, specific N-terminal amino acids, small sequence elements (such as the destruction box in cyclins), or structural motifs (such as hydrophobic stretches in misfolded proteins). In many cases, degradation signals are conditional and can be activated or inactivated by post-translational modifications. In the second step, polyubiquitinated proteins are recognized and degraded by the proteasome, a large barrel-shaped complex that harbours several proteolytically active subunits within its inner chamber [3] (see Chapter 3).

Aberrations in the UPS have been associated with a number of clinical pathologies [4], such as neurodegenerative diseases (see Chapter 11), cancer (see chapter 13), muscle wasting (see Chapter 12) and viral infection (see Chapter 10). Depending on the type of alterations, this can either lead to accelerated or delayed degradation of ubiquitinated proteins. In cancer, accelerated degradation of tumour-suppressor proteins by the UPS is a recurrent theme, which allows malignant cells to progress into uncontrolled proliferation [5]. On the other hand, the specific accumulation and deposition of misfolded proteins in neurodegenerative diseases, such as Alzheimer's, Parkinson's and Huntington's diseases, suggests inefficient clearance of these potentially toxic proteins by the UPS [6]. Because assessing the functional status of the UPS in cells and animals has shown to be a technically complicated endeavour, the precise role of the UPS in many of these pathologies remains unclear [7]. During the last few years, several groups developed fluorescent protein (FP) reporters of the UPS that allow monitoring of the UPS in cells and animals [8]. In this review, we will describe the different fluorescent UPS substrates and summarize their applications in studies on the role of the UPS in diseases, and in identification of drugs that affect the UPS.

Fluorescent UPS substrates

Fluorescent UPS reporters are based on fusions between a degradation signal or full-sized constitutive UPS substrate, and either green fluorescent protein (GFP), one of its spectral variants, or other FPs (see Table 1). The FPs that are available at present, which have been isolated from various jellyfishes and sea anemones, are generally very stable proteins, exemplified by GFP of *Aequorea victoria* with a half-life of more than 24 h [9]. Introduction of a degradation signal to FPs often results in a markedly reduced half-life of the FP due to rapid proteasomal degradation. Cells or animals expressing these reporters typically contain low levels of the FP and display low fluorescence as a consequence of the rapid turnover. Obstruction of the UPS, for example by administration of small compound inhibitors of the proteolytic activities of the proteasome, induces a dramatic increase in fluorescence intensities in affected cells and tissues that can be readily monitored by fluorimetry, flow cytometry, or fluorescence microscopy.

Since general disturbances of the UPS are likely to cause an overall accumulation of substrates, a straightforward approach would be to follow the levels of any endogenous UPS substrate. Detection of the substrate-of-interest can be aided by the ectopic overexpression of a substrate–FP fusion at levels that can be conveniently monitored by various means of fluorescence detection. A number of research groups have developed FP-tagged variants of these short-lived proteins to analyse their function and dynamics in real time with cell imaging [10–14]. Although these substrate-specific reporters can inevitably provide us with important information about the functional status of the UPS, there are several drawbacks with the usage of substrate–FP fusions as general reporters for ubiquitin-dependent proteolysis. Firstly, increased cellular levels of endogenous UPS substrates do not necessarily reflect dysfunction of the UPS, but may be due to normal regulatory events resulting in functional stabilization of the substrate–FP fusions. For example, stabilization of p53 under specific conditions is not necessarily a consequence of an impaired UPS, but can be caused by genotoxic stress [14]. Secondly, in order for these substrate–FP fusions truly to reflect the behaviour of the endogenous untagged substrates, the FP moiety should not interfere with the functional activity of the substrate. Because these fusions are biologically active, their overexpression might have unwanted side effects. Thus, for example, overexpression of cyclin–FP fusions may affect cell-cycle progression [10,11], and p53–FP fusions may induce cell-cycle arrest or apoptosis [14]. These two drawbacks with substrate–FP fusions make them less suitable as *bona fide* reporters to monitor UPS activity. A number of FP reporter substrates have been developed in which these problems have been avoided (described below).

Table 1. FP reporters for the UPS

Degradation signal	Reporter substrate	Organism	Half-life	Recognition pathway
N-end rule	Ub–Arg–FP [16]	Yeast and	10 min	E2: Ubc2 (y)
	Ub–Leu–FP [16]	mammalian cells		E3: Ubr1 (y), E3α (m), Ubr2 (m)
UFD	Ub-Gly76Val–FP [16,21,22]	Yeast, mammalian	10 min	E2: Ubc4, Ubc5 (y)
	Ub–Pro–FP [16]	cells and mice		E3: Ufd4 (y)
				E4: Ufd2 (y)
ERAD	CD3δ-FP[1]	Yeast and	90 min	E2: Ubc6, Ubc7 (y), mammalian Ubc6, Ubc7 (m)
		mammalian cells		E3: Hrd1 (y), human Hrd1 (m), gp78 (m)
	FP-MHC1 + US2 or US11 [25]	Mammalian cells	30 min	E2, E3: unknown
Polypeptide motifs	FP-CL1 [30]	Yeast and	20–30 min	E2: Ubc6, Ubc7 (y), unknown (m)
		mammalian cells		E3: unknown
	Deg1-FP [32]	Yeast	25 min cytosol	E2: Ubc6, Ubc7 (y)
			7.5 min nucleus	E3: Doa10 (y)
PEST	dFP and variants [33]	Mammalian cells	1–2 h	Antizyme (ubiquitin-independent)

List of the currently available FP reporter substrates of the UPS. These reporters are based on FPs provided with a specific degradation signal or fused to full-sized substrate of the UPS. Most of the substrates have been made with GFP and several are also available with FPs with different spectra. The ubiquitin conjugases (E2), ligases (E3) and chain assembly factors (E4) required for degradation of these reporters in yeast (y) and mammalian cells (m) are listed. [1]V. Menéndez-Benito and N.P. Dantuma, unpublished work.

These reporter substrates are targeted for UPS-dependent degradation by constitutively active degradation signals. To avoid gross changes in the cell physiology, fusions have been constructed in such a way that they are expected to lack any biological activity (Table 1).

N-end rule reporters

Varshavsky and co-workers identified the first degradation signal by studying the fate of proteins with various N-terminal residues in yeast [15]. When artificial ubiquitin (Ub) fusion proteins, such as Ub–X–β-galactosidase (X stands for any amino acid residue), are expressed in cells, the ubiquitin moieties are rapidly clipped off by deubiquitinating enzymes (DUBs). It was found that the stability of the resulting X-β-galactosidase depended on the nature of the N-terminal amino acid residue exposed after ubiquitin cleavage. Certain N-terminal amino acid residues, for example arginine, are recognized in yeast by the E3 Ubr1. In co-operation with the E2 Ubc2, this marks the protein that contains the destabilizing N-terminal amino acid with a ubiquitin chain, conjugated to the proximal lysine residue, resulting in proteasomal degradation. By changing the X amino acid in Ub–X-protein, the half-lives of proteins can vary from several minutes (for example, when X is an arginine) to several hours (for example, when X is a leucine), to a stable protein that is not degraded by the proteasome (for example, when X is a methionine). Interestingly, the N-end rule was shown to be valid not only in yeast but also in metazoans, including mouse and humans, where the substrates are recognized and targeted by the ubiquitin ligases E3α and Ubr2. Although the physiological relevance of the N-end rule has been obscure for many years, further studies have provided clear evidence for a role of this targeting system in the regulation of cardiovascular development in mice, peptide import in yeast, and chromosome segregation.

Based on the N-end rule, a set of GFP-based reporters was developed for functional analysis of the UPS in mammalian cells (Figure 1) [16]. Insertion of arginine or leucine residues as destabilizing amino acids in Ub–X-GFP resulted in proteasomal degradation of GFP, while methionine at the same position gave rise to a long-lived GFP. Ub–Arg-GFP has a half-life of approx. 10 min ([17]; V. Menéndez-Benito and N.P. Dantuma, unpublished work). Administration of proteasome inhibitors induces a striking accumulation of Ub–Arg-GFP. This reporter has also been used in yeast and mammalian models to study the activity of stabilization signals, which are motifs or domains that can counteract the activity of degradation signals and protect proteins from proteasomal degradation [18].

Ubiquitin fusion degradation (UFD) reporters

Another constitutively active degradation signal is the UFD signal. Although these ubiquitin–protein fusions differ only at one amino acid from the N-end rule substrates, they are targeted by another ubiquitin conjugase and ligase pair

N-end rule degradation signal

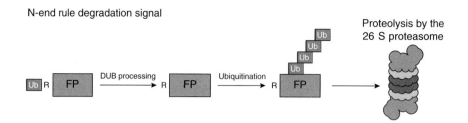

Proteolysis by the
26 S proteasome

Figure 1. Schematic representation of N-end rule reporters
Ubiquitin (Ub) is cleaved from the Ub–R–FP precursor by DUBs, exposing the destabilizing N-terminal residue, which is in this example an arginine (R). The destabilizing N-terminal residue recruits a ubiquitination enzyme that ubiquitinates the FP close to its N-terminus, resulting in degradation of the FP reporter.

and depend differentially on additional factors, such as ubiquitin-chain assembly factors and ubiquitin receptors [19]. In UFD substrates, the N-terminal ubiquitin forms the acceptor for the polyubiquitin chains that target the fusion proteins for degradation. To accomplish this, the C-terminal glycine residue of the ubiquitin moiety has been substituted for a valine, preventing cleavage by DUBs (Figure 2). Alternatively, the amino acid immediately downstream of ubiquitin can be substituted with proline, giving rise to Ub–Pro-FP. Due to the specificity and mode of action of DUBs, cleavage of the ubiquitin moiety is strongly delayed in the resulting Ub-Gly76Val–FP and Ub–Pro-FP reporters. As a consequence, these chimaeric proteins are ubiquitinated at the lysines at position 29 and 48 in their ubiquitin moiety [17]. The level of Ub-Gly76Val–GFP in cells under normal physiological conditions was barely detectable, but increased up to 150-fold after complete proteasome inhibition [16]. Accumulation of this reporter in stable cell lines correlated with the ability of inhibitors to induce cell-cycle arrest and apoptosis, two common effects of UPS dysfunction, suggesting that reporter levels give true information about the functional status of the UPS [16,20].

UFD degradation signal

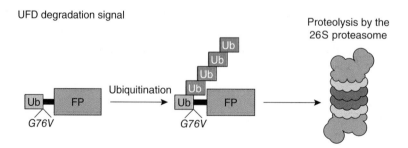

Proteolysis by the
26S proteasome

Figure 2. Schematic representation of UFD reporters
Cleavage of the N-terminal ubiquitin (Ub) is inhibited due to the Gly76Val substitution in the ubiquitin moiety or the proline residue directly downstream of ubiquitin. Polyubiquitin chains are conjugated to the N-terminal ubiquitin at the lysines at positions 29 and 48, resulting in proteasomal degradation of the fusion protein.

At present, only two models have been developed for monitoring the UPS in animals and both take advantage of UFD reporter substrates [7,21]. One of the models is based on xenotransplantion of human cervix carcinoma cells expressing a UFD-targeted luciferase into nude mice [21]. An advantage of this model is that the bioluminescent signal of luciferase allows reporter levels to be monitored in living animals, a method presently not possible for fluorescent reporters. The bioluminescence was hardly detectable in untreated xenotransplantions, but upon treatment of the mice with proteasome inhibitors, an enhancement in bioluminescence was already observed after 4 h. Although this model will be very helpful for studying the effect of inhibitors on cancer cells *in vivo*, the restricted expression of the reporter in the transplanted cancer cells makes it impossible to follow the UPS in tissues of donor mice during proteasome inhibitor treatment or during disease progression. The recently developed Ub-Gly76Val–GFP mouse model can be used for these purposes, since it is a transgenic mouse model in which expression of the GFP reporter is driven by a powerful promoter in all tissues [22]. Histological analysis of tissues from reporter mice after intraperitoneal injection with proteasome inhibitors revealed clear accumulation of Ub-Gly76Val–GFP in the liver at low inhibitor levels, and at higher inhibitor levels, reporter accumulation was found in multiple tissues.

Endoplasmic reticulum (ER)-associated degradation (ERAD) reporters

The 26 S proteasome is involved not only in degradation of aberrant cytosolic and nuclear proteins, but also in clearance of improper proteins that reside within the ER. Incorrect folding, or aberrant modifications, of proteins in the ER result in dislocation of these proteins from the ER to the cytosol, where they are recognized by E3 enzymes, ubiquitinated and degraded by the proteasome [23]. This process is known as ERAD. ERAD is part of the protein quality control machinery to which all proteins that pass the ER, such as ER-resident proteins, secretory proteins and cell surface receptors, are subjected.

MHC class I molecules are of importance in the recognition and elimination of virus-infected cells. In their attempts to avoid the cellular defence mechanism, some viruses have developed sophisticated mechanisms to block MHC class I antigen presentation. The human cytomegalovirus (CMV) expresses two proteins, US2 and US11, that interact with MHC class I molecules in the ER and target them for proteasomal degradation [24]. The removal of properly folded MHC class I heavy chain from the ER by these viral proteins resembles that of true ERAD substrates. A cellular model for MHC class I degradation was developed based on co-expression of viral US11 with FP-MHC class I (Figure 3). This model has been used for characterization of novel proteasome inhibitors and high-throughput screens [25,26].

CD3δ is a well-established ERAD substrate that has been used in a number of studies dealing with the identification of proteins involved in degradation of ER proteins [27]. CD3δ is a subunit of the T-cell receptor and, in the absence of

ERAD substrates

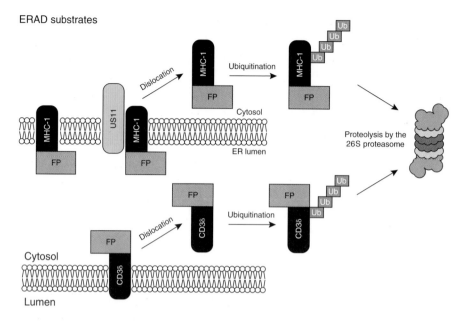

Figure 3. Schematic representation of ERAD reporters
The viral proteins US2 and US11 dislocate the FP-MHC class I fusion from the ER to the cytosol, where it is targeted for ubiquitination and degradation. FP-tagged T-cell receptor subunit CD3δ is, in the absence of its binding partners, dislocated from the ER to the cytosol and subsequently ubiquitinated and degraded by the proteasome.

its binding partners, which is the case in all cells other than T-lymphocytes, this subunit is rapidly dislocated and subjected to proteasomal degradation. FP-tagged CD3δ can be used for monitoring the efficacy of ERAD in mammalian cells (V. Menéndez-Benito and N.P. Dantuma, unpublished work). The weak ER staining observed in cells expressing CD3δ-FP is strongly enhanced on treatment with various proteasome inhibitors in a time- and dose-dependent manner.

Polypeptide motif reporters
Two screens in the budding yeast *Saccharomyces cerevisiae* resulted in the identification of a number of artificial degradation motifs that induced degradation requiring the E2s Ubc6/7. The libraries used in these screens were based on C-terminal fusions of the *lacZ* or *URA3* genes, with random oligopeptide expansions encoding stretches of 16–50 amino acids [28]. The screen was designed to search for sequence elements or structural motifs that could accelerate degradation of the LacZ and URA3 products in a wild-type strain, but were inactive in yeast lacking the Ubc6 and Ubc7 ubiquitin-conjugating (*ubc*) mutants. Interestingly, it has been shown that Ubc6 and Ubc7 also play an important role in degradation of ERAD substrates [23]. The CL1 sequence found in this screen encodes a strongly hydrophobic peptide motif. Characterization of the CL1 degradation suggested that recognition of this hydrophobic patch may be similar to recognition of the hydrophobic

membrane-spanning domains of proteins that have been dislocated from the ER [29]. Despite the fact that the CL1 degradation signal resembles ERAD substrates in some aspects, it is exclusively localized in the cytosol and nucleus and does not require the proteins important for ER dislocation of ERAD substrates [29]. Kopito and co-workers developed an FP-based reporter by introducing the CL1 degradation signal into GFP [30]. The GFP–CL1 fusion, dubbed GFP^u, was rapidly degraded by the proteasome in mammalian cells. By introduction of nuclear localization signals or nuclear export signals, this reporter could be adapted to a compartment-specific reporter [31]. No further characterization of this reporter has been performed in mammalian cells and its dependence on ubiquitin, as well as its requirements for specific ubiquitination enzymes, remains to be resolved. However, it is tempting to speculate that in mammalian cells also, this reporter may share some of the targeting system with ERAD substrates.

The Deg1 signal of the yeast transcriptional repressor Matα2 is responsible for proteasomal degradation of this repressor [32]. The Deg1 signal encompasses the first 67 amino acids of Matα2. A hydrophobic patch located within an amphipathic helix is the prominent feature for this degradation signal. Interestingly, Deg1-mediated degradation of Matα2 was most prominent in the nucleus and was much slower in the cytosol. In yeast, a Deg1-GFP reporter provided with a nuclear localization signal was efficiently transported to the nucleus followed by proteasomal degradation (Figure 4). However, when the Deg1-GFP reporter lacked a nuclear localization signal and diffused freely in the cell, the half-life was extended 3-fold, indicating a compartment-specific turnover by the UPS of this reporter.

PEST reporters

In general, the destructive action of the 26 S proteasome is directed towards ubiquitinated proteins. There are, however, a few exceptions of proteins that do not require ubiquitination for proteasomal degradation. The most well-characterized protein displaying ubiquitin-independent degradation is ornithine decarboxylase (ODC). Turnover of ODC is triggered not by ubiquitination, but instead by association with its inhibitor antizyme, which facilitates binding of ODC to the proteasome and degradation. ODC is recognized by antizyme through the presence of a PEST sequence (i.e. a sequence rich in Pro, Glu, Ser and Thr amino acids). The ODC PEST sequence has been used to generate the first FP proteasome substrates. These reporters were not originally intended for monitoring UPS activity, but for accurate analysis of promoter activity. A general problem with the usage of GFP as a reporter for monitoring promoter activity is its long half-life. Due to this, GFP will accumulate over time, giving rise to high fluorescence intensities even in the presence of low promoter activities. Hence spatial and transient fluctuations in promoter activity will be difficult to follow with GFP. To solve this problem, Li and et al. [33] aimed to develop a GFP variant with a reduced half-life. A short-lived GFP fusion was generated by

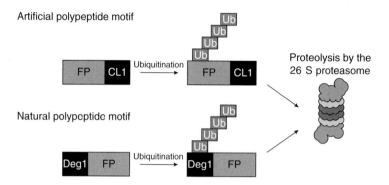

Figure 4. Schematic representation of reporters containing polypeptide degradation motifs
C-terminal insertion in an FP of the artificial CLI degradation motif results in degradation. The natural Deg1 motif of the Matα2 can induce nuclear degradation of FP.

positioning a small fragment of murine ODC at the N-terminus of GFP (Figure 5) [33]. By mutating the PEST sequence, a set of short-lived GFPs were generated, with half-lives ranging from 1–4 h in mammalian cells. It was shown that the PEST-GFP, also known as dGFP (destabilized GFP) was indeed an excellent transcriptional reporter and could reveal changes in nuclear factor κB (NF-κB) promoter activity with much greater sensitivity than stable GFP [33]. Although these reporters are not intended for monitoring the UPS, there is nothing to argue against their applicability in such an experimental set-up. Recently, PEST-GFP has been used for studying the effect of a disease-associated protein on the UPS [34]. On the other hand, some of the above-mentioned FP reporters originally developed for monitoring the UPS may be excellent transcriptional reporters. Especially when dealing with small changes in reporter levels, it is of great importance with each of these reporters to analyse whether the effects are caused by changes in degradation or synthesis [35]. Notably, the

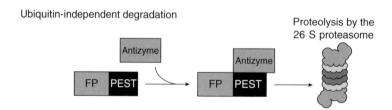

Figure 5. Schematic representation of PEST reporters
PEST sequences are degradation signals that can target FP for ubiquitin-independent degradation by the proteasome, through binding to antizyme.

PEST-GFP reporters are the only reporters that are degraded in a ubiquitin-independent manner, and may provide us with additional information, other than can be obtained with the panel of ubiquitin-dependent reporters.

Fluorescent reporters to monitor the UPS in diseases

Alterations in protein degradation by the UPS are believed to be involved in several human pathologies [4]. A number of neurodegenerative diseases, including Alzheimer's disease, Parkinson's disease and polyglutamine disorders, are caused by a change in conformation of the disease-related protein, leading to a non-native structure that has the tendency to form aggregates and inclusions. Reporters have been shown to be of particular use in studying the efficiency of the UPS in neurodegenerative and other conformational diseases [7]. Despite the fact that there are many indications suggesting a role of the UPS in neurodegenerative diseases [6], direct evidence is still lacking. This is largely because functional evaluation of the UPS has proven to be a major challenge, owing to the complexity of the system. Many studies involve biochemical assays, measuring only certain aspects of the UPS, and do not evaluate it as an integrated system. The usage of fluorescent UPS reporters can overcome these problems, since it gives a simple functional readout for the ability of the cells to cope with the continuous supply of substrates of the UPS. Moreover, the availability of several complementary reporters provides the opportunity to monitor a wide range of different ubiquitination pathways, making it possible to access the context of the UPS dysfunction.

Based on the finding that nuclear inclusions in neurodegenerative diseases contain ubiquitin and other components of the UPS, it has been postulated that the proteolytic pathway might be disturbed [6]. Indeed, a correlation between functional impairment of the UPS and inclusion formation was shown in a cellular model based on expression of the GFP-CL1 reporter substrate [30]. GFP-CL1 cell lines expressing the aggregation-prone proteins CFTRΔ508 mutant or mutant huntingtin, the protein responsible for Huntington's disease, accumulated the reporter exclusively in cells containing inclusions. Accumulation of the GFP-CL1 reporter was also found in a number of similar investigations studying mutant rhodopsin, a protein linked to the inherited form of retinitis pigmentosa [36], mutant α-synuclein, which is associated with Parkinson's disease [37], and mutant androgen receptor responsible for spinobulbar muscular atrophy [38]. Degradation of another reporter, PEST-GFP, was also inhibited by mutant ataxin-1, which is responsible for spinocerebellar ataxia type 1 (SCA1), suggesting that aggregation-prone proteins have a general inhibitory effect on the UPS [34]. Interestingly, the effect of mutant androgen receptor was strongly enhanced by the presence of transglutaminase, and was abrogated in the presence of a transglutaminase inhibitor, suggesting that not only aggregated proteins, but also primarily cross-linked proteins, may be responsible for UPS dysfunction [38]. The mechanism responsible for impairment of the UPS function, however, remains elusive. A recent study suggests that it is not caused by direct inhibition of the proteolytic activity of the proteasome, or proteasome sequestration in inclusions [31]. GFP-CL1 reporters were specifically targeted to either the nucleus or the cytosol and the effect of cytosolic and nuclear inclusions on reporter degradation was investigated [31]. GFP fluorescence was found in both cellular compartments independent of the presence of inclusions, indicating that inclusions are not the direct cause of UPS impairment. Thus the mechanisms causing UPS impairment in these cellular models, as well as the nature of the inhibitory proteins, remain to be resolved.

The aberrant ubiquitin UBB^{+1} is encoded by an abnormal transcript of the ubiquitin B gene that has a dinucleotide deletion owing to a process known as molecular misreading [39]. Although the transcript can be found in both normal and affected cells, the protein product exclusively accumulates in affected cells in a number of conformational diseases, such as Alzheimer's disease [40]. *In vitro* studies showed that UBB^{+1} can be polyubiquitinated and that the presence of ubiquitinated UBB^{+1} inhibits *in vitro* degradation of proteasome substrates [41]. It was, found in reporter cell lines expressing Ub-Gly76Val–GFP or Ub-Arg-GFP that UBB^{+1} causes a general UPS dysfunction that correlates with cell-cycle arrest [17]. Interestingly, UBB^{+1} itself is a UFD substrate of the UPS that is cleared in many cells by proteasomal degradation, while in some cells it accumulates and causes UPS dysfunction. The molecular mechanism of the inhibitory activity of UBB^{+1} is unknown.

Recently, the role of the UPS in the pathophysiology of a neurodegenerative disease was addressed for the first time *in vivo* with the transgenic UPS reporter mouse model [35]. A knock-in mouse model of mutant ataxin-7, which is responsible for SCA7, was crossed with Ub-Gly76Val–GFP reporter mice and the levels of the GFP reporter were followed during the progression of the disease in the retina, which is the primary affected tissue in this pathology. No changes in reporter levels were found in the early phase of the disease, prior to inclusion formation, suggesting that a full blockade of the UPS is not directly responsible for the accumulation of mutant ataxin-7. Late in the pathology, an increase in the levels of the reporter was found in the photoreceptor cells of the retina. However, detailed analysis revealed that this was due not to delayed turnover of the reporter, but to increased transcription of the reporter transgene. This again emphasizes the fact that short-lived reporters are very sensitive not only to changes in degradation, but also to fluctuations in synthesis. Interestingly, it has indeed been reported that SCA7 pathology is accompanied by transcriptional dysregulation [42]. Moreover, an inverse correlation was found between accumulation of the reporter and ataxin-7 inclusions [35]. These data suggest a protective role of inclusions against neuropathology and exclude a full blockade of the UPS as a necessary step in polyglutamine neuropathology. The precise role of the UPS in different diseases needs further investigation, as subtle changes in the UPS cannot be excluded based on these experiments.

The UPS as a therapeutic target in diseases

In vitro and *in vivo* studies suggest that inhibition of the proteasome may have a therapeutic effect in several diseases, including cancer and inflammation (see Chapter 14). Small compound inhibitors of the proteasome have been used for many years as experimental tools in laboratories [43]. It is well-established that cancer cells are sensitive to these inhibitory compounds and often induce cell-cycle arrest and apoptosis. Some proteasome inhibitors have originally been identified as compounds with anticancer activity, which was later assigned to their proteasome inhibitory activity [44]. This has inspired researchers to probe into the anticancer potential of proteasome inhibitors, which has resulted in the introduction of the proteasome inhibitor Velcade, also known as bortezomib or PS-341, into the clinics for the treatment of multiple myeloma [45].

Given the fact that the UPS is of crucial importance for most cells, the specific effect on cancer cells is surprising. It is tempting to speculate that inhibitors that are more specific, or target other events in ubiquitin-dependent proteolysis, can be used with greater precision and fewer side effects for the treatment of cancer and other diseases. To develop such new inhibitors, cellular models expressing the fluorescent UPS reporters could be extremely suitable in high-throughput screens of large chemical-compound libraries. Recently, FP-MHC-I/US11 reporter cells have been used to screen 16 320 compounds for inhibition of ERAD [25]. This has led to the identification of two compounds, named eeyarestatin I and II, which blocked dislocation of substrates from the ER membrane without affecting proteasomal degradation of cytosolic substrates. Transgenic-animal reporter models for the UPS can be used to evaluate further the bioavailability and therapeutic effects of compounds *in vivo* [21,22].

Conclusions

In this review, we have outlined the different FP reporters that are currently used for functional analysis of the UPS in cell lines and animals. With the help of these reporters, questions that were impossible to address only a short while ago can now be studied with great accuracy. The availability of mouse models, for the UPS in particular, opens up several new avenues. These model systems allow us, for the first time, to study the *in vivo* efficacy of the UPS during disease progression or administration of specific compounds, such as proteasome inhibitors. The collection of characterized FP substrates can be used for the generation of other UPS reporter mice, which will hopefully give us a more complete picture of the behaviour of different classes of UPS substrates *in vivo*. In order to manipulate and modify this crucial and delicate system in such a way that it is likely to impart a therapeutic effect, we have to understand fully the role of the UPS in these pathologies. This is a target that may now be in closer reach with the development of FP reporters for the UPS.

Summary

- *FP-based proteins with degradation signals can be used to monitor the efficacy of the UPS in cellular and mouse models.*
- *The collection of fluorescent reporters allows us to study the behaviour of different UPS substrates in parallel.*
- *FP reporters of the UPS have been used to study the status of the UPS in cellular and animal models for human diseases.*
- *Cellular and animal reporter models can be used for drug development, involving high-throughput screens for specific inhibitors of the UPS, and for studying the bioavailability of inhibitors.*

We thank Dr Christa Maynard for her critical reading of the manuscript. The development of FP-reporter substrates in our laboratory was supported by grants awarded by the Swedish Research Council, Swedish Cancer Society, the Wallenberg Foundation, the Nordic Center of Excellence Neurodegeneration and the Karolinska Institute.

References

1. Hershko, A. & Ciechanover, A. (1998) The ubiquitin system. *Annu. Rev. Biochem.* **67**, 425–479
2. Pickart, C.M. (2001) Mechanisms underlying ubiquitination. *Annu. Rev. Biochem.* **70**, 503–533
3. Voges, D., Zwickl, P. & Baumeister, W. (1999) The 26 S proteasome: a molecular machine designed for controlled proteolysis. *Annu. Rev. Biochem.* **68**, 1015–1068
4. Schwartz, A.L. & Ciechanover, A. (1999) The ubiquitin–proteasome pathway and pathogenesis of human diseases. *Annu. Rev. Med.* **50**, 57–74
5. Pagano, M. & Benmaamar, R. (2003) When protein destruction runs amok, malignancy is on the loose. *Cancer Cell* **4**, 251–256
6. Ciechanover, A. & Brundin, P. (2003) The ubiquitin proteasome system in neuordegenerative diseases: sometimes the chicken, sometimes the egg. *Neuron* **40**, 427–446
7. Lindsten, K. & Dantuma, N.P. (2003) Monitoring the ubiquitin/proteasome system in conformational diseases. *Ageing Res. Rev.* **2**, 433–449
8. Neefjes, J. & Dantuma, N.P. (2004) Fluorescent probes for proteolysis: Tools for drug discovery. *Nat. Rev. Drug Discov.* **3**, 58–69
9. Zhang, J., Campbell, R.E., Ting, A.Y. & Tsien, R.Y. (2002) Creating new fluorescent probes for cell biology. *Nat. Rev. Mol. Cell Biol.* **3**, 906–918
10. Clute, P. & Pines, J. (1999) Temporal and spatial control of cyclin B1 destruction in metaphase. *Nat. Cell Biol.* **1**, 82–87
11. den Elzen, N. & Pines, J. (2001) Cyclin A is destroyed in prometaphase and can delay chromosome alignment and anaphase. *J. Cell Biol.* **153**, 121–136
12. Jackman, M., Kubota, Y., den Elzen, N., Hagting, A. & Pines, J. (2002) Cyclin A- and cyclin E-Cdk complexes shuttle between the nucleus and the cytoplasm. *Mol. Biol. Cell* **13**, 1030–1045
13. Li, X., Fang, Y., Zhao, X., Jiang, X., Duong, T. & Kain, S.R. (1999) Characterization of NFκB activation by detection of green fluorescent protein-tagged IκB degradation in living cells. *J. Biol. Chem.* **274**, 21244–21250

14. Norris, P.S. & Haas, M. (1997) A fluorescent p53GFP fusion protein facilitates its detection in mammalian cells while retaining the properties of wild-type p53. *Oncogene* **15**, 2241–2247

15. Varshavsky, A. (1996) The N-end rule: functions, mysteries, uses. *Proc. Natl. Acad. Sci. U.S.A.* **93**, 12142–12149

16. Dantuma, N.P., Lindsten, K., Glas, R., Jellne, M. & Masucci, M.G. (2000) Short-lived green fluorescent proteins for quantifying ubiquitin/proteasome-dependent proteolysis in living cells. *Nat. Biotechnol.* **18**, 538–543

17. Lindsten, K., de Vrij, F.M., Verhoef, L.G., Fischer, D.F., van Leeuwen, F.W., Hol, E.M., Masucci, M.G. & Dantuma, N.P. (2002) Mutant ubiquitin found in neurodegenerative disorders is a ubiquitin fusion degradation substrate that blocks proteasomal degradation. *J. Cell Biol.* **157**, 417–427

18. Heessen, S., Masucci, M.G. & Dantuma, N.P. (2005) The UBA2 domain functions as an intrinsic stabilization signal that protects Rad23 from proteasomal degradation. *Mol. Cell* **18**, 225–235

19. Johnson, E.S., Ma, P.C., Ota, I.M. & Varshavsky, A. (1995) A proteolytic pathway that recognizes ubiquitin as a degradation signal. *J. Biol. Chem.* **270**, 17442–17456

20. Myung, J., Kim, K.B., Lindsten, K., Dantuma, N.P. & Crews, C.M. (2001) Lack of proteasome active site allostery as revealed by subunit-specific inhibitors. *Mol. Cell* **7**, 411–420

21. Luker, G.D., Pica, C.M., Song, J., Luker, K.E. & Piwnica-Worms, D. (2003) Imaging 26 S proteasome activity and inhibition in living mice. *Nat. Med.* **9**, 969–973

22. Lindsten, K., Menendez-Benito, V., Masucci, M.G. & Dantuma, N.P. (2003) A transgenic mouse model of the ubiquitin/proteasome system. *Nat. Biotechnol.* **21**, 897–902

23. Plemper, R.K. & Wolf, D.H. (1999) Retrograde protein translocation: ERADication of secretory proteins in health and disease. *Trends Biochem. Sci.* **24**, 266–270

24. Ploegh, H.L. (1998) Viral strategies of immune evasion. *Science* **280**, 248–253

25. Fiebiger, E., Hirsch, C., Vyas, J.M., Gordon, E., Ploegh, H.L. & Tortorella, D. (2004) Dissection of the dislocation pathway for type I membrane proteins with a new small molecule inhibitor, eeyarestatin. *Mol. Biol. Cell* **15**, 1635–1646

26. Kessler, B.M., Tortorella, D., Altun, M., Kisselev, A.F., Fiebiger, E., Hekking, B.G., Ploegh, H.L. & Overkleeft, H.S. (2001) Extended peptide-based inhibitors efficiently target the proteasome and reveal overlapping specificities of the catalytic β-subunits. *Chem. Biol.* **8**, 913–929

27. Yang, M., Omura, S., Bonifacino, J.S. & Weissman, A.M. (1998) Novel aspects of degradation of T cell receptor subunits from the endoplasmic reticulum (ER) in T cells: importance of oligosaccharide processing, ubiquitination, and proteasome-dependent removal from ER membranes. *J. Exp. Med.* **187**, 835–846

28. Gilon, T., Chomsky, O. & Kulka, R.G. (1998) Degradation signals for ubiquitin system proteolysis in Saccharomyces cerevisiae. *EMBO J.* **17**, 2759–2766

29. Gilon, T., Chomsky, O. & Kulka, R.G. (2000) Degradation signals recognized by the Ubc6p-Ubc7p ubiquitin-conjugating enzyme pair. *Mol. Cell. Biol.* **20**, 7214–7219

30. Bence, N.F., Sampat, R.M. & Kopito, R.R. (2001) Impairment of the ubiquitin–proteasome system by protein aggregation. *Science* **292**, 1552–1555

31. Bennett, E.J., Bence, N.F., Jayakumar, R.& Kopito, R.R. (2005) Global impairment of the ubiquitin–proteasome system by nuclear or cytoplasmic protein aggregates precedes inclusion body formation. *Mol. Cell* **17**, 351–365

32. Lenk, U. & Sommer, T. (2000) Ubiquitin-mediated proteolysis of a short-lived regulatory protein depends on its cellular localization. *J. Biol. Chem.* **275**, 39403–39410

33. Li, X., Zhao, X., Fang, Y., Jiang, X., Duong, T., Fan, C., Huang, C.C. & Kain, S.R. (1998) Generation of destabilized green fluorescent protein as a transcription reporter. *J. Biol. Chem.* **273**, 34970–34975

34. Park, Y., Hong, S., Kim, S.J. & Kang, S. (2005) Proteasome function is inhibited by polyglutamine-expanded ataxin-1, the SCA1 gene product. *Mol. Cells* **19**, 23–30

35. Bowman, A.B., Yoo, S.Y., Dantuma, N.P. & Zoghbi, H.Y. (2005) Neuronal dysfunction in a
     polyglutamine disease model occurs in the absence of ubiquitin–proteasome system impairment
     and inversely correlates with the degree of nuclear inclusion formation. *Hum. Mol. Genet.* **14**,
     679–691

36. Illing, M.E., Rajan, R.S., Bence, N.F. & Kopito, R.R. (2002) A rhodopsin mutant linked to autosomal
     dominant retinitis pigmentosa is prone to aggregate and interacts with the ubiquitin proteasome
     system. *J. Biol. Chem.* **277**, 34150–34160

37. Petrucelli, L., O'Farrell, C., Lockhart, P.J., Baptista, M., Kehoe, K., Vink, L., Choi, P., Wolozin, B.,
     Farrer, M., Hardy, J. & Cookson, M.R. (2002) Parkin protects against the toxicity associated with
     mutant α-synuclein: proteasome dysfunction selectively affects catecholaminergic neurons. *Neuron*
     36, 1007–1019

38. Mandrusiak, L.M., Beitel, L.K., Wang, X., Scanlon, T.C., Chevalier-Larsen, E., Merry, D.E. & Trifiro,
     M.A. (2003) Transglutaminase potentiates ligand-dependent proteasome dysfunction induced by
     polyglutamine-expanded androgen receptor. *Hum. Mol. Genet.* **12**, 1497–1506

39. van Leeuwen, F.W., de Kleijn, D.P., van den Hurk, H.H., Neubauer, A., Sonnemans, M.A., Sluijs,
     J.A., Koycu, S., Ramdjielal, R.D., Salehi, A., Martens, G.J. et al. (1998) Frameshift mutants of β
     amyloid precursor protein and ubiquitin-B in Alzheimer's and Down patients. *Science* **279**,
     242–247

40. Fischer, D.F., de Vos, R.A., van Dijk, R., de Vrij, F.M., Proper, E.A., Sonnemans, M.A., Verhage,
     M.C., Sluijs, J.A., Hobo, B., Zouambia, M. et al. (2003) Disease-specific accumulation of mutant
     ubiquitin as a marker for proteasomal dysfunction in the brain. *FASEB J.* **17**, 2014–2024

41. Lam, Y.A., Pickart, C.M., Alban, A., Landon, M., Jamieson, C., Ramage, R., Mayer, R.J. & Layfield, R.
     (2000) Inhibition of the ubiquitin–proteasome system in Alzheimer's disease. *Proc. Natl. Acad. Sci.*
     U.S.A. **97**, 9902–9906

42. La Spada, A.R., Fu, Y.H., Sopher, B.L., Libby, R.T., Wang, X., Li, L.Y., Einum, D.D., Huang, J.,
     Possin, D.E., Smith, A.C. et al. (2001) Polyglutamine-expanded ataxin-7 antagonizes CRX function
     and induces cone-rod dystrophy in a mouse model of SCA7. *Neuron* **31**, 913–927

43. Lee, D.H. & Goldberg, A.L. (1998) Proteasome inhibitors: valuable new tools for cell biologists.
     Trends Cell Biol. **8**, 397–403

44. Meng, L., Kwok, B.H., Sin, N. & Crews, C.M. (1999) Eponemycin exerts its antitumor effect
     through the inhibition of proteasome function. *Cancer Res.* **59**, 2798–2801

45. Adams, J. & Kauffman, M. (2004) Development of the proteasome inhibitor Velcade
     (Bortezomib). *Cancer Invest.* **22**, 304–311

9

Transgenic manipulation of the ubiquitin–proteasome system

Douglas A. Gray[1]

Ottawa Health Research Institute, 501 Smyth Road, Ottawa, Ontario K1H 8L6, Canada

Abstract

The transgenic approach has been used in model systems from yeast to mammals to address basic research questions, and to achieve agricultural, pharmaceutical or industrial objectives. In basic research, transgenic organisms have generated novel observations that could not have been obtained otherwise. This chapter concentrates on the use of transgenics in deciphering the operation of the UPS (ubiquitin–proteasome system) in the yeast, plant, nematode, fly, and mouse model systems, and will touch on ways in which transgenic manipulation of the UPS has been exploited for agricultural, pharmaceutical, and industrial applications.

Introduction

A transgenic organism is one in which the genome has been altered by the addition of sequences not originally present in the germline DNA of that species. There are two main reasons why one would want to manipulate the UPS (ubiquitin–proteasome system) using transgenic methodology. The first is to gain some insight into the functioning of the UPS itself by perturbing its operation and observing the phenotypic consequences. Much of our understanding of the UPS has been deduced from experiments involving

[1]email dgray@ohri.ca

genetic manipulation of UPS components, either adding novel, genetically engineered UPS genes to the genome's existing repertoire or using genetic recombination to alter the endogenous UPS genes. The second rationale for transgenic manipulation of the UPS is to take advantage of its components in the pursuit of some agricultural, industrial, pharmaceutical, or basic research objective not directly associated with UPS function. One could reasonably argue that such approaches have been used to best effect in yeast (where genetic manipulations are straightforward and rapid), but transgenic research has been done with more complex eukaryotes and has been very informative. The summary of the research that follows cannot be considered comprehensive, but is intended to demonstrate what is possible using transgenic approaches, by touching upon some highlights of this powerful research methodology.

Experiments in yeast

As other chapters in this volume make evident, many of the mechanistic details of the UPS were first uncovered in the budding yeast *Saccharomyces cerevisiae*. It is relatively straightforward to introduce and express transgenes in yeast, and with an efficient system of homologous recombination, the organism is amenable to replacement of endogenous genes with their genetically engineered and often mutant counterparts. Through such experiments it has been possible to elucidate the roles of ubiquitin chains of various topologies (ubiquitin has seven lysine residues, at least six of which are exposed on the surface of the globular domain and could theoretically participate in isopeptide-bond formation with the C-terminal glycine of another ubiquitin molecule). The growth of yeast cells is slowed by overexpression of a number of mutant isoforms, but cells are non-viable if their sole source of ubiquitin is a K48R (substitution of the lysine at position 48 with arginine) or G76A (glycine to alanine) mutant isoform, owing to complete inhibition of proteolysis [1]. Cells expressing only K63R mutant ubiquitin are viable, but sensitive to DNA damage, demonstrating that chains assembled through Lys^{63} linkages are involved in DNA repair [2]. Indeed the power of yeast genetics and the site-directed mutation approach have been combined in an exhaustive examination of every surface-exposed residue in yeast ubiquitin [3].

The transgenic approach has also been very fruitful in yeast, in elucidating the existence and functional aspects of the N-end rule. Many proteins are expressed as proproteins that are processed by endoproteolytic cleavage into mature forms; in fact ubiquitin itself is invariably translated as a proprotein composed either of tandemly repeated ubiquitin subunits or of ubiquitin fused to ribosomal subunit peptides [4]. Ubiquitin may serve a chaperone function in such fusions, assisting in the proper folding of the appended polypeptide. This property has been exploited in increasing the yield of poorly translated, transgene-encoded products in the industrial workhorse *Escherichia coli* [5].

Like any cellular translation product, a proprotein will have methionine at its N-terminus, but the N-terminal residue of the processed protein will be dictated by its primary sequence and the position of the protease cleavage site. It is therefore possible that a processed polypeptide could have any of the twenty amino acids at its N-terminus, and, as it happens, the identity of this residue plays a key role in dictating its stability. This phenomenon has been established in organisms from *E. coli* to humans, and has been designated the N-end rule by Varshavsky [6]. Transgenes encoding fusions of the structure ubiquitin–Xaa-β-galactosidase (where X is one of the 20 possible amino acid residues) were created. Like the natural ubiquitin–ribosomal-peptide fusions, such test fusions are efficiently cleaved by DUBs (deubiquitinating enzymes) to produce β-galactosidase with various N-terminal residues. It was determined that certain N-terminal residues (for example Gly, Val or Ala) would impart stability to the test protein whereas others (Arg, Leu, Phe) would result in a very short half-life. Using transgenic methodologies, the N-end rule has been demonstrated (and in some cases exploited) in complex metazoans.

Experiments in plants

The technology for introducing foreign genes into plant genomes is well advanced; indeed this technology is the basis for a large and often controversial industry (genetically modified foods). The ubiquitin promoter has been utilized to obtain constitutive expression of transgenes in plants, as has the strategy of expressing proteins as ubiquitin fusions (see above) to be processed by DUBs [7]. Expression of epitope-tagged ubiquitin has served as an effective means of isolating ubiquitinated substrates from plant cells for identification and further analysis [8]. Plants have also provided us with an important insight into a recurrent structural arrangement in the UPS. The most commonly used model system in plants is *Arabidopsis thaliana*, which like most higher plants uses different developmental programmes in light compared with dark. Mutants that inappropriately use the light programme when growing in the dark are designated COP (constitutive photomorphogenesis). The gene mutated in one such mutant (*COP9*) was found to encode a novel protein of 197 amino acids that could restore the functional light response when expressed from a transgene [9]. COP9 protein functions in a multimeric complex designated the CSN (COP9 signalosome), a component of a light-sensitive signalling cascade in plants. The CSN is conserved in other species including mammals, where it functions in other pathways including cell-cycle checkpoints. The CSN has striking structural similarity to the lid of the proteasome, with a proteasome counterpart for each CSN subunit. The similarity of CSN and the 19 S lid may reflect divergent (or convergent) evolution, but there are intriguing connections in function that require further investigation (reviewed in [10]).

Experiments in nematodes

It would be fair to say that the nematode model system has not been exploited to the same extent as the yeast or plant systems in fleshing out our understanding of ubiquitin–proteasome biology, but transgenic manipulation of the UPS in worms has provided some penetrating insights within specialized fields, most notably neuroscience. *Caenorhabditis elegans* is a favourite of neuroscientists because it has a nervous system that is of sufficient complexity to endow the nematode worm with simple patterns of behaviour, but is not so complex so as to thwart to the construction of wiring diagrams (greatly facilitated by the transparency of the organism and a complete understanding of its cell lineages). *C. elegans* is a useful model system for the study of synapses, the junctions through which neuronal transmission of impulses occurs. There is an emerging body of evidence from a variety of model systems to the effect that the plasticity of synapses (modulation of their activity, which is thought to play a role in establishing memory, for example) involves alterations in protein abundance through proteasome-mediated degradation. Burbea et al. [11] demonstrated that in transgenic worms engineered to overexpress epitope-tagged ubiquitin in a specific subset of neurons, synapses were modified by ubiquitination and degradation of glutamate receptors (involved in fast excitatory neurotransmission). More recently, the same group has shown that the regulation of glutamate receptors in this population of neurons is mediated by the APC (anaphase-promoting complex) [12]. This finding comes as a surprise; the APC (also known as the cyclosome) is a multi-subunit E3 (ubiquitin ligase) complex whose well-established function is in the regulation of cell-cycle transitions. Neurons are post-mitotic cells that apparently make use of the APC machinery for this unrelated and wholly unexpected function. The appropriation of the APC for a synaptic role (the cell-cycle function of the APC predates the evolution of nervous systems) probably occurred early in metazoan evolution; the synaptic function of the APC has also been documented in *Drosophila melanogaster* [13].

Experiments in flies

As in the nematode worm, transgenesis has been of more use in studying particular roles of the UPS in the fly than in studying the UPS itself, and (as in the worm) one area that has benefited greatly from transgenic manipulation of the UPS in this model system is neuroscience. The nervous system of flies is rather more complex than that of worms, and has a crowning feature of supreme use to neuroscientists: the compound eye. Fly eyes are made up of repeated elements of the nervous system and are macroscopic. One can use them as a 'read out' of neuronal health, and they have been heavily exploited in studies of neurodegeneration. There are many neurodegenerative diseases for which the fly eye has been useful, but the polyglutamine disorders (diseases in which an abnormally long stretch of glutamine residues occurs in the causative protein) are illustrative. If one expresses in the eyes of transgenic flies the expanded polyglutamine protein (the mutant huntingtin protein of Huntington's disease, for example, or one of the ataxin proteins associated with the spinocerebellar ataxias) the eyes will have a roughened appearance indicating neuronal degeneration. It is possible to conduct a genetic screen to identify modifiers of the severity of the eye degeneration, and such a screen will identify components of the UPS [14]. A second approach is to identify components of the UPS that physically associate with the polyglutamine protein, then to assess the contribution of these components in flies that are transgenic for both the polyglutamine protein and the UPS component. Through such an approach it has been demonstrated that an E4 (polyubiquitin chain conjugation factor) protein that associates with ataxin-3 and promotes its degradation has therapeutic potential in limiting the neurodegeneration induced by this toxic entity [15]. Remarkably, normal ataxin-3 is itself a ubiquitin-specific protease whose activity is involved in the suppression of neurodegeneration *in vivo*, as demonstrated in transgenic flies [16].

Experiments in mice

Given the slow reproductive rate and the greater genomic complexity of the mammalian system it is not surprising that experiments involving manipulation of the mammalian UPS have not been as numerous as in other model systems. The manipulation of the mammalian germline is a daunting task (relative to the yeast germline, for example), but there are questions involving the mammalian UPS that simply cannot be answered in any other way. Clearly one cannot address the role of the UPS in signalling pathways [for example the NF-κB (nuclear factor κB) pathway], DNA repair systems [for example involving BRCA1 (breast-cancer susceptibility gene 1)] or disease states in simple model systems lacking some or all of the relevant components. The mammalian model system of choice for genetic manipulation is the mouse, and methodologies for germline manipulation of the mouse are continuously being refined. As in other systems, it is possible to introduce expression cassettes containing a gene of interest into the mouse germline in order to accomplish constitutive, inducible or tissue-specific expression. Using gene targeting one can also manipulate genes in the mouse germline to generate mice in which all cells receive a mutated copy of the gene of interest, or mice in which a mutation-generating recombination event will occur in specific cells or at specific times (conditional mutations). All of these strategies have been used or are currently in use to exploit known aspects of the UPS that can improve expression of transgenes, or to reveal novel aspects of the functioning of the UPS in the mouse model system.

In the production of transgenic mice it is sometimes desirable to have the gene of interest expressed widely and at high levels (rather than in a tissue-specific manner). For ubiquitous expression it is hardly surprising that a ubiquitin promoter might serve the purpose, and the human ubiquitin C promoter has been shown to function admirably. The ubiquitin C promoter drives expression of transgenes in most if not all mouse tissues [17], with expression detectable as early as the morula stage of embryogenesis [18]. The utility of the ubiquitin C promoter is exemplified by a body of work modelling reproductive disorders arising from abnormally high levels of serum oestradiol. Sustained elevation of oestradiol has been orchestrated by placing expression of the human aromatase p450 cDNA under the control of the ubiquitin C promoter. In male transgenic mice overexpressing aromatase, the development of the male reproductive tissues is inhibited, and functional mammary glands develop [19].

In mammalian cells (as in prokaryotes and yeast) one can take advantage of the efficient translation and folding of ubiquitin to enhance the production of proteins that may otherwise have lower abundance. In eukaryotic cells and in transgenic mice, a ubiquitin–EGFP (enhanced green fluorescent protein) fusion product is efficiently processed by DUBs, resulting in abundant expression of the fluorescent protein marker [18,20]. The strategy of expressing proteins as ubiquitin fusions also allows for the production of proteins that, once processed by DUBs, will have an amino acid other than methionine at the N-terminus (described in more detail in the yeast section above). This strategy can be used to circumvent the requirement for processing of proproteins to generate active, mature polypeptides. As an example, the active form of the pro-apoptotic protein Smac/DIABLO has an absolute requirement for an alanine residue at the N-terminus, and processing of the proprotein is not efficient in cells transfected with plasmids encoding the full length protein. Cells expressing a fusion of ubiquitin with the active Smac/DIABLO polypeptide efficiently cleave the ubiquitin moiety, bypassing the requirement for mitochondrial processing of the proprotein, and generating biologically active Smac/DIABLO [21].

Arguably the simplest manipulations of the UPS in the mouse involve addition of transgenes encoding ubiquitin itself to the mouse germline. The objectives of such manipulations might be to increase the ubiquitin pools by supplying additional wild-type ubiquitin, or to perturb the functioning of the system by incorporating mutations in ubiquitin that would interfere with chain assembly in a dominant negative fashion. One might also incorporate an epitope tag to facilitate the detection of ubiquitin and ubiquitin conjugates, as well as some form of reporter system to monitor the expression of the transgene in living animals. These were the strategies employed in the author's laboratory in the generation of transgenic mice expressing wild-type or mutant ubiquitin (the source of the ubiquitin DNA was human, but this is of no functional significance given the perfect identity of mouse and human ubiquitin amino acid sequences). A hexahistidine epitope tag was incorporated at the N-terminus of ubiquitin to allow detection of transgene-derived ubiquitin by Western blotting and enrichment of ubiquitin conjugates by nickel affinity chromatography. EGFP was appended to the C-terminus of the ubiquitin to serve as a reporter of gene expression, with the expectation that cellular DUBs would efficiently cleave the fluorescent protein from ubiquitin and free its C-terminus for conjugation. The human ubiquitin C promoter was used to drive expression in most, if not all, tissues. The strategy is shown schematically in Figure 1. As expected, fluorescence could easily be detected in the resulting mice [18]; in living mice the retinas demonstrated intense fluorescence when illuminated with blue light. Mice expressing wild-type human ubiquitin or the mutant isoforms K48R or K63R were viable and fertile, with no obvious phenotype. Although the analysis of these transgenic lines is ongoing, it is apparent that the K48R mice are resistant to neurotoxic insults [22] and show features of delayed aging [23]. The molecular basis of the hardiness of K48R mice is not yet understood — one might expect such mice to be sickly as a consequence of impaired proteolysis. At least some of the positive *in vivo* effects of K48R mutant ubiquitin may be

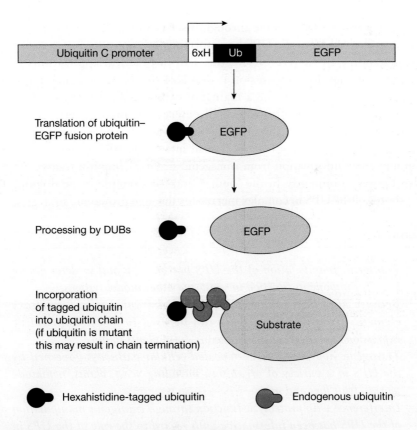

Figure 1. Strategy for incorporation of epitope-tagged ubiquitin into protein conjugates
Transgene-derived ubiquitin (black) is initially expressed as a fusion protein with EGFP. Following processing, the tagged ubiquitin competes with endogenous ubiquitin pools (blue) for incorporation into conjugates. At high levels of expression, mutant ubiquitin interferes with normal chain assembly. The EGFP protein serves as a reporter for expression levels, but does not participate in the formation of conjugates. Ub, ubiquitin; 6xH, hexahistidine.

attributable to stabilization of transcriptional mediators whose degradation is associated with disease or aging [24].

The UPS is impaired or overwhelmed in many disease conditions and declines in efficiency with age [25]. Recently it has been demonstrated that the subunits of the proteasome are co-ordinately regulated, and production of proteasomes can be stimulated by forced expression of just one subunit [26]. It may therefore be possible to restore flagging proteasome activity through a relatively simple genetic intervention. One can monitor the efficiency of the UPS *in vivo* using a transgenic mouse in which a destabilized version of a fluorescent protein is expressed constitutively. In this transgenic reporter mouse, proteasome inhibition results in accumulation of the otherwise unstable protein and its fluorescence becomes detectable [27]. Such reagents should prove very valuable in future evaluation of UPS-based therapeutics.

Conclusion

Manipulation of the germline through insertion of genes and/or regulatory elements derived from the UPS has enormous use not only in expanding our understanding of the UPS itself, but also in practical applications where constitutive, high-level expression is desirable. In the future, such transgenic animals will continue to be a mainstay of biomedical research, but it is expected that new applications will emerge through genetic crosses of transgenic animals with the growing repertoire of 'knock-out' animals, or through 'knockdown' approaches [(small interfering siRNA) etc. RNA] that can mine new information from transgenic strains. Ubiquitin transgenics will also figure prominently in the 'omics' era, for example in cataloguing the substrates of the UPS in complex metazoans through proteomic strategies.

Summary

- *Transgenic manipulation of the UPS has been pivotal in determining how its components function in yeast and other model systems.*
- *Because ubiquitin is expressed in all eukaryotic cells, regulatory elements from ubiquitin genes can be used to direct constitutive expression of transgenes in metazoans, from plants to mice.*
- *Transgenic approaches have revealed cellular pathways governed by the UPS in a variety of organisms, including yeast, plants, nematode worms, fruit flies and mice.*
- *Interference with proteolytic function through transgenic manipulation of the UPS has been informative with regard to the role of the UPS in diseases, most notably the neurodegenerative diseases.*

References

1. Finley, D., Sadis, S., Monia, B.P., Boucher, P., Ecker, D.J., Crooke, S.T. & Chau, V. (1994) Inhibition of proteolysis and cell cycle progression in a multiubiquitination-deficient yeast mutant. *Mol. Cell. Biol.* **14**, 5501–5509

2. Spence, J., Sadis, S., Haas, A.L. & Finley, D. (1995) A ubiquitin mutant with specific defects in DNA repair and multiubiquitination. *Mol. Cell. Biol.* **15**, 1265–1273

3. Sloper-Mould, K.E., Jemc, J.C., Pickart, C.M. & Hicke, L. (2001) Distinct functional surface regions on ubiquitin. *J. Biol. Chem.* **276**, 30483–30489

4. Finley, D., Bartel, B. & Varshavsky, A. (1989) The tails of ubiquitin precursors are ribosomal proteins whose fusion to ubiquitin facilitates ribosome biogenesis. *Nature (London)* **338**, 394–401

5. Butt, T.R., Jonnalagadda, S., Monia, B.P., Sternberg, E.J., Marsh, J.A., Stadel, J.M., Ecker, D.J. & Crooke, S.T. (1989) Ubiquitin fusion augments the yield of cloned gene products in *Escherichia coli*. *Proc. Natl. Acad. Sci. U.S.A.* **86**, 2540–2544

6. Bachmair, A., Finley, D. & Varshavsky, A. (1986) *In vivo* half-life of a protein is a function of its amino-terminal residue. *Science* **234**, 179–186

7. Hondred, D., Walker, J.M., Mathews, D.E. & Vierstra, R.D. (1999) Use of ubiquitin fusions to augment protein expression in transgenic plants. *Plant Physiol.* **119**, 713–724

8. Ling, R., Colon, E., Dahmus, M.E. & Callis, J. (2000) Histidine-tagged ubiquitin substitutes for wild-type ubiquitin in *Saccharomyces cerevisiae* and facilitates isolation and identification of *in vivo* substrates of the ubiquitin pathway. *Anal. Biochem.* **282**, 54–64

9. Wei, N., Chamovitz, D.A. & Deng, X.W. (1994) Arabidopsis COP9 is a component of a novel signaling complex mediating light control of development. *Cell* **78**, 117–124

10. Li, L. & Deng, X.W. (2003) The COP9 signalosome: an alternative lid for the 26 S proteasome? *Trends Cell Biol.* **13**, 507–509

11. Burbea, M., Dreier, L., Dittman, J.S., Grunwald, M.E. & Kaplan, J.M. (2002) Ubiquitin and AP180 regulate the abundance of GLR-1 glutamate receptors at postsynaptic elements in *C. elegans*. *Neuron* **35**, 107–120

12. Juo, P. & Kaplan, J.M. (2004) The anaphase-promoting complex regulates the abundance of GLR-1 glutamate receptors in the ventral nerve cord of *C. elegans*. *Curr. Biol.* **14**, 2057–2062

13. van Roessel, P., Elliott, D.A., Robinson, I.M., Prokop, A. & Brand, A.H. (2004) Independent regulation of synaptic size and activity by the anaphase-promoting complex. *Cell* **119**, 707–718

14. Fernandez-Funez, P., Nino-Rosales, M.L., de Gouyon, B., She, W.C., Luchak, J.M., Martinez, P., Turiegano, E., Benito, J., Capovilla, M., Skinner, P.J. et al. (2000) Identification of genes that modify ataxin-1-induced neurodegeneration. *Nature (London)* **408**, 101–106

15. Matsumoto, M., Yada, M., Hatakeyama, S., Ishimoto, H., Tanimura, T., Tsuji, S., Kakizuka, A., Kitagawa, M. & Nakayama, K.I. (2004) Molecular clearance of ataxin-3 is regulated by a mammalian E4. *EMBO J.* **23**, 659–669

16. Warrick, J.M., Morabito, L.M., Bilen, J., Gordesky-Gold, B., Faust, L.Z., Paulson, H.L. & Bonini, N.M. (2005) Ataxin-3 suppresses polyglutamine neurodegeneration in *Drosophila* by a ubiquitin-associated mechanism. *Mol. Cell* **18**, 37–48

17. Schorpp, M., Jager, R., Schellander, K., Schenkel, J., Wagner, E.F., Weiher, H. & Angel, P. (1996) The human ubiquitin C promoter directs high ubiquitous expression of transgenes in mice. *Nucleic Acids Res.* **24**, 1787–1788

18. Tsirigotis, M., Thurig, S., Dube, M., Vanderhyden, B.C., Zhang, M. & Gray, D.A. (2001) Analysis of ubiquitination in vivo using a transgenic mouse model. *BioTechniques* **31**, 120–126, 128, 130

19. Li, X., Makela, S., Streng, T., Santti, R. & Poutanen, M. (2003) Phenotype characteristics of transgenic male mice expressing human aromatase under ubiquitin C promoter. *J. Steroid Biochem. Mol. Biol.* **86**, 469–476

20. Tsirigotis, M., Zhang, M., Chiu, R.K., Wouters, B.G. & Gray, D.A. (2001) Sensitivity of mammalian cells expressing mutant ubiquitin to protein-damaging agents. *J. Biol. Chem.* **276**, 46073–46078

21. Hunter, A.M., Kottachchi, D., Lewis, J., Duckett, C.S., Korneluk, R.G. & Liston, P. (2003) A novel ubiquitin fusion system bypasses the mitochondria and generates biologically active Smac/DIABLO. *J. Biol. Chem.* **278**, 7494–7499

22. Zhang, M., Thurig, S., Tsirigotis, M., Wong, P.K., Reuhl, K.R. & Gray, D.A. (2003) Effects of mutant ubiquitin on ts1 retrovirus-mediated neuropathology. *J. Virol.* **77**, 7193–7201

23. Rasoulpour, R.J., Schoenfeld, H.A., Gray, D.A. & Boekelheide, K. (2003) Expression of a K48R mutant ubiquitin protects mouse testis from cryptorchid injury and aging. *Am. J. Pathol.* **163**, 2595–2603

24. Tsirigotis, M., Tang, M.Y., Beyers, M., Zhang, M., Woulfe, J. & Gray, D.A. (2005) Delayed spinocerebellar ataxia in transgenic mice expressing mutant ubiquitin. *Neuropathol. Appl. Neurobiol.*, in the press

25. Gray, D.A., Tsirigotis, M. & Woulfe, J. (2003) Ubiquitin, proteasomes, and the aging brain. *Sci. Aging Knowl. Environ.* **2003**, RE6

26. Chondrogianni, N., Tzavelas, C., Pemberton, A.J., Nezis, I.P., Rivett, A.J. & Gonos, E.S. (2005) Overexpression of proteasome β_5 assembled subunit increases the amount of proteasome and confers ameliorated response to oxidative stress and higher survival rates. *J. Biol. Chem.* **280**, 11840–11850

27. Lindsten, K., Menendez-Benito, V., Masucci, M.G. & Dantuma, N.P. (2003) A transgenic mouse model of the ubiquitin/proteasome system. *Nat. Biotechnol.* **21**, 897–902

10

Targeting of host-cell ubiquitin pathways by viruses

Julia Shackelford[1] and Joseph S. Pagano

Lineberger Comprehensive Cancer Center, The University of North Carolina at Chapel Hill, Chapel Hill, NC 27599-7295, U.S.A.

Abstract

The ability of viruses to co-opt cell signalling pathways has, over millions of years of co-evolution, come to pervade nearly every facet of cellular functions. Recognition of the extent to which the ubiquitin–proteasome system can be directed or subverted by viruses is relatively recent. Viral products interact with, and adjust, the ubiquitin–proteasome machinery precisely and at many levels, and they do so at distinct stages of viral life-cycles. The implications for both cells and viruses are fundamental, and understanding viral strategies in this context opens up fascinating new areas for research that span from basic cell biology to therapeutic interventions against both viruses and malignancies.

Introduction

Many aspects of the life cycle of viruses rely on specific interactions between viral products and regulatory systems of the target cells. Over millions of years of co-evolution with their hosts, viruses have developed highly effective strategies that disrupt integrated functions of the cell and transmute cellular functions into viral functions that serve propagation of the virus. As the UPS (ubiquitin–proteasome system) is the nexus for many fundamental cellular processes, it is not surprising that viruses reprogramme this machinery according to viral needs.

[1]To whom correspondence should be addressed (email shackelfordj@yahoo.com).

Ubiquitin-dependent proteasomal degradation is one of the essential modes whereby the lifetime of cell-signalling participants is controlled, and viruses lose no opportunity to interfere with the UPS on every possible level. As will become apparent in this chapter, viral strategies are based on specific modulations rather than on extreme changes in ubiquitin–proteasome activity. This is because normally functioning proteasomes are too important for the survival of infected cells, and a serious imbalance in protein processing by the UPS would be detrimental to virus propagation. Moreover, the UPS offers an enzymatic way for a viral protein of low abundance to deal with a cellular target present in stoichiometrically greater amounts.

Knowledge of how viruses can affect host ubiquitin-dependent machinery grows with our understanding of the purpose of this system in general. We have to keep in mind that the term UPS embraces today much more than the simple concept that 'the protein is ubiquitinated, therefore it will be destroyed'. Participation of ubiquitination in cell signalling is not limited to protein destruction by the proteasome. Ubiquitin and ubiquitin-like modifications are an integral part of the regulatory machinery of many cell processes, and through modulation of the UPS, viruses can successfully interrupt different aspects of 'normal' cell function.

In this chapter we discuss some known aspects of the relationships between animal viruses and the UPS. We place the emphases on three areas of viral manipulation of host-cell machinery with respect to ubiquitination: interruption of signal transduction pathways, inhibition of cellular immune responses to viral infection, and virion assembly and release from the host cell.

Dysregulation of cell-signalling pathways by tumour viruses: ubiquitination and deubiquitination

In 1911, Peyton Rous described a sarcoma that could be transmitted in chickens by inoculating them with a cell-free filtrate, later identified as containing RSV (Rous sarcoma virus). The era of oncogenic viruses had begun. Over the last 40–50 years, much knowledge of the molecular biology of cell transformation by oncogenic DNA and RNA viruses has accumulated. For example, the discovery of reverse transcriptase, which synthesizes DNA using the information in the viral RNA, and the identification of important transcriptional factors, such as AP-1 (activator protein 1) or tumour-suppressor proteins, such as p53, came from studying animal viruses [1].

A number of human viruses from different families are implicated in carcinogenesis [1,2]. Several HPVs (human papillomaviruses) are detectable in virtually all cervical cancers worldwide and in some other cancers (including some head and neck cancers). The contribution of HBV (hepatitis B virus) and HCV (hepatitis C virus) to HCC (hepatocellular carcinoma) has long been recognized. Other viruses that present a substantial cancer risk in certain populations include EBV (Epstein–Barr virus; associated with various lymphoid malignancies and nasopharyngeal cancer), HTLV-1 (human T-cell lymphotropic virus type-1; associated with adult T-cell leukaemia/lymphoma), KSHV [Kaposi's sarcoma-associated herpesvirus (human herpesvirus-8)], polyoma viruses [e.g. JCV (JC virus); associated with brain tumours], and SV40 (simian virus 40; associated with mesothelioma) (Table 1).

In spite of differences among human oncogenic viruses, the general strategy is the same: to protract cell-cycle progression and protect cells from apoptosis, resulting in the perpetuation of the virus genome. Therefore the common cellular targets for tumour virus oncoproteins are the most important transcriptional factors involved in oncogenesis, such as c-Myc, NF-κB (nuclear factor κB), AP-1 and p53 [1]. Because there are innumerable cellular pathways that can regulate the transcriptional machinery of the cell, there are many opportunities for tumour viruses to dysregulate them, to the benefit of the virus. As a part of the basic functional machinery of the cell, the UPS is inevitably involved in viral oncogenesis.

HPVs

Perhaps one of the most striking examples of the ability of oncogenic viruses to redirect the UPS to the advantage of the virus is provided by HPVs that are associated with malignant lesions of the anogenital tract [1]. More than 99% of cervical carcinomas harbour at least one copy of a high-risk HPV genome. The viral *E6* and *E7* genes are the only viral genes that are generally retained and expressed, and are essential for malignant progression and maintenance of the transformed phenotype. Both viral proteins interact with important negative cell-regulatory proteins, namely E6 with the tumour suppressor protein p53 and E7 with the pRbs (retinoblastoma proteins). Both E6 and E7 utilize the UPS to target these proteins for degradation and, thus, inactivation [3] (Figure 1).

Table 1. Human oncogenic viruses

Virus family	Virus	Human tumours
Papovaviridae	HPV	Cervical cancer
		Anogenital cancer
	JCV	Brain tumours
	SV40	Mesothelioma
Hepadnaviridae	HBV	Hepatocellular carcinoma
	HCV	Hepatocellular carcinoma
Herpesviridae	EBV	Nasopharyngeal carcinoma
		Burkitt's lymphoma
		Hodgkin's lymphoma
		B-cell lymphoproliferative diseases
	KSHV	Kaposi's sarcoma
		Primary effusion lymphoma
Retroviridae	HTLV-1	Adult T-cell leukaemia

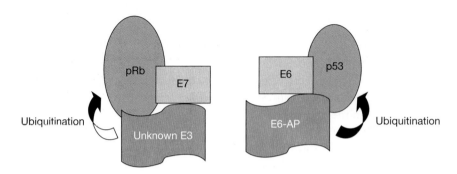

Figure 1. HPV oncoproteins utilize the UPS to inactivate cellular tumour suppressor proteins
Expression of the HPV E7 oncoprotein induces the proteasome-mediated degradation of pRb family members. The HPV E6 oncoprotein utilizes distinct E3 complexes that are normally not involved in p53 degradation to target p53 for ubiquitination and subsequent degradation via the proteasome.

One of the major biochemical functions of the oncogenic E7 protein is induction of cellular DNA replication in differentiated epithelial cells. In differentiated cells, pRb and the related protein p130 bind E2F transcription factors to repress the expression of the replication enzyme genes [4,5]. E7 disrupts the interaction between pRb and E2F, resulting in the release of the E2F factors in their transcriptionally active forms. E7 induces degradation of pRb through the ubiquitin–26 S proteasome, but the mechanism is still unknown. The ubiquitin-dependent proteolysis of pRb involves both N- and C-terminal regions of E7 that are also critical for the transforming function of E7, suggesting that the proteolysis of pRb is linked to the transforming function of E7 [3]. One of the possibilities is that, similar to the E6–p53 interaction (see below), E7 recruits a cellular E3 (ubiquitin ligase) to target pRb for ubiquitination and subsequent degradation. Another suggestion is that E7 may function as an adaptor between pRb and the proteasome, thereby targeting pRb directly to the proteasome without prior ubiquitination. No evidence has yet been provided to support any of these hypotheses. More recent studies showed that the E7 oncoprotein is itself regulated by the ubiquitin–proteasome pathway. The components of this regulatory ubiquitin-dependent cascade have been identified. In the presence of UbcH7 [E2 (ubiquitin-conjugating enzyme) H7], the SCF (Skp1–Cdc53/Cullin 1–F-box protein) E3 complex was shown to be responsible for E7 ubiquitination *in vitro* [6].

As a conclusion we have to admit that in spite of progress in the last few years, many questions remain unanswered about the relationship between E7 proteins and the UPS.

Much more has been achieved in understanding how another HPV oncogenic product, E6, dysregulates the cellular UPS. First, E6 recruits the E3 E6-AP (E6-associated protein). The dimeric E6–E6-AP complex then binds to p53, resulting in the E6-AP-mediated ubiquitination of p53 in the presence of certain E2s (UbcH5, UbcH7, or UbcH8) that interact functionally with E6-AP. Finally, polyubiquitinated p53 is recognized and degraded by the proteasome in HPV-infected cells. Although each of these steps can be reconstituted *in vitro* with highly purified proteins, it is still not clear how polyubiquitinated p53 is transferred from the E6–E6-AP complex to the proteasome *in vivo*.

E6-AP was originally isolated and identified as a cellular protein that binds to high-risk E6 proteins and is required by HPV E6 protein to bind efficiently to p53 [1]. E6-AP contains the C-terminal E3 HECT (homologous to E6-AP C-terminus) domain that interacts with a number of E2 enzymes, including UbcH5, UbcH6, UbcH7 and UbcH8. Unlike other known E3s, which presumably function as bridging proteins between substrate proteins and E2s, HECT domain E3s have been proposed to catalyse directly the final attachment of ubiquitin to their substrate proteins [7]. From the perspective of cell biology this is an interesting situation because the virus product preferentially alters endogenous substrate specificity: normally, p53 is a target for Mdm2 (murine double minute clone 2 oncoprotein) E3 [8,9], which belongs to a different, RING (really interesting new gene)-finger-containing class of E3s. What is the physiological relevance of this finding? It is well established that Mdm2-induced degradation of p53 is inhibited upon treatment of cells with appropriate stress stimuli, including genotoxic stress. Therefore one of the possibilities is that E6 targets p53 for degradation under conditions when the normal pathway for p53 degradation is not functional. This hypothesis is supported by results obtained in experimental cell-culture systems, where E6 was ectopically expressed from heterologous promoters. In contrast to parental cells (that do not express E6), p53 levels did not increase in E6-expressing cells in response to genotoxic stress [3,10]. Moreover, expression of E6 in various cell types results in an increased rate of mutagenesis and genetic instability. Since p53 plays an important role in preserving genome integrity, this connection suggests that expression of E6 interferes with p53 activity not only under conditions of stress, but also under apparently normal growth conditions.

Several E6-independent substrates of E6-AP have been reported, including HHR23A and HHR23B (the human homologues of *Saccharomyces cerevisiae* RAD23), Blk (a member of the Src-family of non-receptor tyrosine kinases), Bak (a human pro-apoptotic protein), and Mcm7 (which is involved in DNA replication). With respect to cervical carcinogenesis, an attractive but purely speculative possibility is that E6 not only tricks E6-AP into ubiquitinating p53, but that it also influences the turnover rate of E6-AP substrates in general. This hypothesis is supported by the observation that binding of E6 targets E6-AP for self-ubiquitination and degradation [11]. Thus even if E6 does not directly influence the substrate specificity of E6-AP, an E6-induced decrease of intracellular E6-AP levels should have profound effects on the stability of E6-AP substrates. However, if this is indeed the case, future investigation is needed to prove it.

As well as p53, numerous cellular proteins have been reported to interact with the HPV E6 proteins and to be targeted for proteasomal degradation in an E6-AP-dependent (e.g. Bak, c-Myc, Mcm7, hScrib) or E6-AP-independent [e.g. hDlg (human discs large), MAGI-1 (membrane-associated guanylate kinase with inverted domain structure 1), MUPP-1 (multiple PDZ domain-containing protein 1)] manner [3]. This apparent difference may seem surprising but opens up the exciting possibility that E6 has the capacity to interact specifically with at least two different E3s. To resolve this issue, it will be important to reconstitute E6-induced ubiquitination of E6-AP-independent targets of E6 in vitro and to identify all the components involved [3]. Similarly, it will be interesting to see whether, in cells derived from E6-AP null mice, the respective murine homologues of hDlg and hScrib are targeted for degradation by E6 or not.

Adenoviruses

In the viral world, the ability to target p53 for degradation is not restricted to papillomavirus products. It has been demonstrated that a complex consisting of the E1B 55 kDa and the E4ORF6 proteins of adenoviruses (that have oncogenic properties in cell-culture systems and in animal models) binds to and induces the degradation of p53 via the UPS. In this case, the adenoviral oncoproteins are part of an E3 complex whose structure is reminiscent of the class of CBC (Cullin-2 elongin B/C complex) E3s. CBC E3s were first described in the context of the pVHL (von Hippel–Lindau tumour suppressor protein 1). In analogy to the pVHL CBC, the E1B/E4ORF6-containing complex consists of the elongins B and C, the RING-finger protein Rbx1 (RING box protein 1)/Roc that interacts with its respective E2 enzyme, and Cullin-5, which serves as a platform to bring these different proteins into a multi-subunit complex (Figure 2). Whether, like E6, the E1B/E4ORF6-containing complex can circumvent the normal stability regulation of p53 remains to be determined [1,12,13].

HBV

HBX (the X product of HBV) can activate the transcription of a variety of viral and cellular genes [14,15] and induce liver cancer in certain transgenic-mouse models. Since HBX does not bind to DNA directly, its activity is thought to be mediated via protein–protein interactions. HBX has been shown to enhance transcription through AP-1 and AP-2 and to activate various signal transduction pathways. Several studies have also identified possible cellular targets of HBX, including members of the CREB (cAMP-response-element-binding protein)/ATF (activating transcription factor) family, the TATA-box-binding protein, RNA polymerase subunit RPB5, the UV-damage DNA-binding protein, and the replicative senescence $p55^{sen}$ protein. HBX also interacts with p53 and inhibits its function. HBX binds to the proteasome complex in vitro and in vivo, and this interaction leads to inhibition of the chymotryptic peptidase and protease activities of the proteasome [16–18].

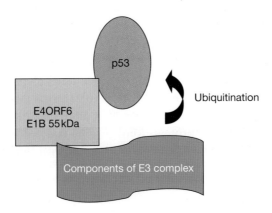

Figure 2. Adenoviral oncoproteins utilize the UPS to inactivate the p53 tumour suppressor
A complex of oncogenic adenovirus (E4ORF6/E1B 55 kDa) utilizes distinct E3 proteins or E3 complexes that are normally not involved in p53 degradation to target p53 for ubiquitination and subsequent degradation via the proteasome.

Some authors propose an intriguing hypothesis that HBX functions to counteract the increased proteolytic function of the cells.

Herpes simplex virus

Although HSV (herpes simplex virus) is not on the list of viruses showing oncogenic potential, this does not mean that problems caused by HSV infection are limited to annoying cold sores. HSV infections have a worldwide distribution and have been described in the medical literature for centuries [1].

Among other HSV gene products, ICP0 (infected cell protein 0) holds a special place in the ubiquitin–proteasome pathway. ICP0 is a unique example of a viral E3 protein with two independent E3 sites. The N-terminus of ICP0 contains a RING-finger domain that is found in the largest known class of E3s. The RING domain of ICP0 can induce the accumulation of polyubiquitin chains in the presence of the E2s UbcH5a and UbcH6 *in vitro*, and is required for ubiquitin-dependent degradation of ICP0 substrates *in vivo*. The targets of the RING domain of ICP0 include PML (promyelocytic leukaemia) antigen and Sp100, constituents of nuclear structures known as ND10 (nuclear domain 10). In addition to PML antigen and ND10 components, ICP0 has been reported to cause the degradation of the catalytic subunit of the DNA-dependent protein kinase and centromeric proteins C and A [19,20].

The C-terminal region of ICP0 contains a different E3 domain that does not have a RING finger and binds the E2 enzyme UbcH3. UbcH3 is the major E2 in the E1 (ubiquitin-activating enzyme)/E2/E3 complex that promotes ubiquitination and degradation of cyclin D1. Together with the evidence that ICP0 can stabilize cyclin D1 without binding to it, these results lead to the attractive hypothesis that the C-terminal domain of ICP0 acts as a pseudo-E3, competitively inhibiting proteasomal degradation of cyclin D1 [19].

In general, despite intensive research and enormous interest, it is still not clear how the functions encoded in ICP0 account for its phenotype in either infected or transfected cells. So far all evidence leads to the conclusion that ICP0 is a multifunctional protein and that its role in viral infection reflects the sum of its multiple and diverse functions. It is more than likely that the number and diversity of cellular proteins known to be targeted for destruction by ICP0 will increase, and therefore more information regarding its functions will be forthcoming.

Gamma herpesviruses

Knowledge of viral modulation of the host cell signalling through the UPS has been augmented by new information. The product of KSHV [the IE (immediate-early) nuclear transcription factor RTA (replication transcription activator), a DNA-binding nuclear transcription factor that can act as the trigger for the entire KSHV lytic cycle] encodes E3 activity [21]. IRF7 (interferon regulatory factor 7), a key mediator of type I interferon induction, is targeted by RTA for ubiquitin-dependent proteasomal degradation. RTA promotes polyubiquitination of IRF7 in an *in vitro* cell-free assay, demonstrating that RTA itself has E3 activity. Interestingly, RTA has an unconventional intrinsic E3 activity; therefore the authors suggest that the RTA non-canonical domain associated with its E3 activity may represent as-yet-unidentified variants of Cys- plus His-rich E3s.

Increasingly, EBV is proving to be remarkably versatile in its use of the UPS. In contrast to KSHV, the EBV oncoprotein LMP-1 (latent membrane protein 1) appears to regulate IRF7 by ubiquitination at ubiquitin Lys^{63}, which leads to activation, not degradation, of the protein (L. Huye and J. Pagano, unpublished work). Quite possibly, EBV might also induce proteasomal disposal of IRF7 in later interactions.

For several years, Wnt signalling has been the object of intense attention in diverse biological areas. A central effector of the Wnt pathway is β-catenin, a multifunctional protein that was first identified as a component of the cadherin cell-adhesion complex. Normally the level of 'free' β-catenin in the cytoplasm is tightly regulated by rapid degradation through the UPS. To control levels of β-catenin, EBV can manipulate two distinct degradation pathways: the classical GSK3β (glycogen synthase kinase 3β)-dependent destruction machinery and the Siah-1 E3, which does not require phosphorylation of β-catenin. Both phenomena can operate in the same cells, possibly governed by different EBV gene products. Interestingly LMP-1, which can activate HIF (hypoxia-inducible factor) 1a, the oxygen-sensing transcription factor, appears to do so in part by affecting the level of Siah-1 (S. Kondo, K.L. Jang, J. Shackelford and J. Pagano, unpublished work).

In conclusion, it is pretty clear that the targeting of cellular proteins for proteasomal degradation through ubiquitination by way of viral or cellular

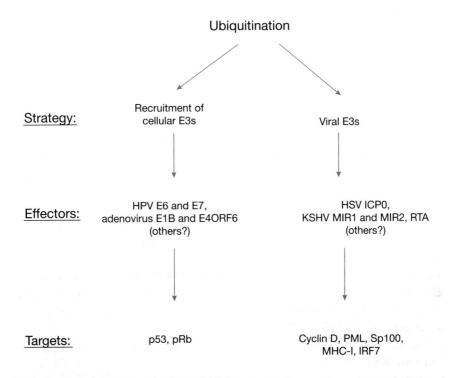

Figure 3. Oncogenic viruses and ubiquitination
Viruses may regulate the E3 step of the ubiquitin–proteasome machinery either by recruiting a cellular enzyme or by expressing ligases encoded by a specific viral gene. The range of cellular targets affected is broad.

E3s is an important aspect of infection and cell transformation by tumour viruses (Figure 3).

Deubiquitination

Although the ability of tumour viruses to manipulate the process of ubiquitination is now appreciated, whether viral manipulation of the opposite branch of these linked systems — deubiquitination — also holds true remains largely unstudied. If oncogenic viruses target signalling pathways in a ubiquitin-dependent manner, and DUBs (deubiquitinating enzymes) are also important regulators of these pathways, it would be logical to suggest that tumour viruses should affect cellular deubiquitinating processes as well. Consistent with this hypothesis, ICP0 binds HAUSP (herpes virus-associated ubiquitin-specific protease), a DUB that is important for p53 stabilization, thus adding another route for a viral product to inactivate p53. Interestingly, EBNA1 (EBV nuclear antigen 1) also interacts with HAUSP, and this interaction influences EBNA1 transcriptional activity [22].

Recently, two cytokine-inducible DUBs (DUB-1 and DUB-2) have been described. These haematopoietic-specific genes with unclear function are rapidly induced after cytokine stimulation. IL-2 (interleukin-2)-inducible DUB-2 is constitutively expressed in HTLV-1-transformed cells. This DUB prolongs cytokine-induced activation of STATs (signal transduction and activators of transcription) and suppresses apoptosis following cytokine withdrawal. Since IL-2 is constitutively expressed in HTLV-1-infected cells, this may be an example of where an oncogenic virus regulates DUB expression indirectly, through the activation of another gene [23].

That a human oncogenic virus might direct synthesis of its own DUB is an intriguing scenario that has recently been examined. Adenovirus infection increases deubiquitinating activity in infected cells via Avp (adenovirus proteinase), which can function as a DUB *in vitro* and *in vivo* [24]. Compared with classical DUBs, Avp seems to act as an enzyme of low specificity, which suggests that this viral DUB might deubiquitinate different viral and cellular ubiquitinated substrates, although none have yet been identified.

In EBV latently infected B-lymphocytes, β-catenin is stabilized, cytoplasmic β-catenin is associated with active DUBs, and the Wnt pathway is activated [25]. This observation supports the concept that, as a human tumour virus, EBV might affect signalling pathways through dysregulation of cellular deubiquitinating machinery [23].

Conclusions

It has become clear that a number of proteins regulating cellular mechanisms for homoeostasis in all eukaryotes may be controlled by both ubiquitination and deubiquitination, and that oncogenic viruses play a certain role in dysregulation of cell-signalling pathways that intervene in this system. In normal cells, the balance between the two processes is probably determined by a dynamic equilibrium and is highly regulated. Tumour viruses may affect ubiquitination directly by using their own ubiquitinating enzymes, or indirectly, by use of endogenous cellular components of the UPS. The recent studies of DUBs encoded by oncogenic viruses, as well as the evidence that a tumour virus can regulate cell-signalling pathways through deubiquitination, suggest the same possibility for the deubiquitinating system, and this has begun to open this new area of viral functionality (Figure 4).

Viral infection and the immune response: down-regulation of antigen presentation

Most multicellular organisms are capable of defending themselves from infectious intruders by mounting an immune response. The specificity of the T-lymphocyte of the immune system of higher vertebrates determines antigenic peptides bound to cell-surface MHC molecules. There are two classes of MHCs: MHC class I presents endogenous antigenic fragments to CD8[+] T-cells, and MHC class II presents exogenous antigen peptides to CD4[+] T-cells. The system provides continual surveillance against potential danger by

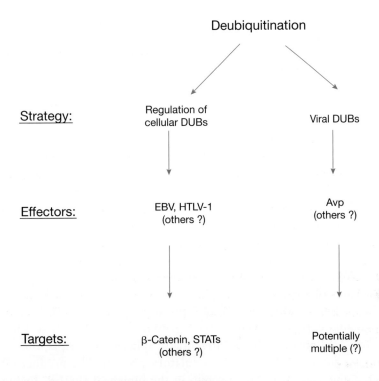

Figure 4. Oncogenic viruses and deubiquitination
Viruses may also affect deubiquitination, by redirecting cellular DUBs or by expressing a virally encoded DUB. Knowledge of these pathways that dysregulate the UPS by viruses is more recent.

monitoring whether cells are synthesizing 'foreign' proteins. In this process, MHC class I molecules bind oligopeptide fragments derived from a cell's expressed proteins and display them on the cell surface. Under normal physiological conditions, all of the class-I-presented peptides are derived from normal autologous sequences to which the immune system is non-reactive owing to self-tolerance. However, if the cell is infected by viruses or is expressing mutant gene products, then non-native peptides will be displayed and will stimulate CTLs (cytotoxic T-lymphocytes) to kill the affected cell.

By generating peptides from intracellular antigens, which are then presented to T-cells, the UPS plays a central role in this type of cellular immune response. The generation of peptide-loaded MHC class I molecules mostly requires the proteolytic generation of peptides with a preferred length of 8–10 amino acids in the cytosol and the transport of peptides via TAP (transporter associated with antigen processing) proteins into the ER (endoplasmic reticulum). There, peptides bind to MHC class I proteins, followed by transport of the peptide-loaded MHC molecules to the cell surface. One of the characteristics of the MHC class I antigen-presentation pathway is that several of its components are induced by the cytokine IFNγ (interferon-γ). These include the MHC class I heavy-chain, the TAP proteins, several of the 20 S proteasome subunits [LMP2 (low-molecular mass polypeptide 2), LMP7 and MECL-1 (multicatalytic endopeptidase complex-like-1)] and the proteasome activator PA28.

Although the immune system has evolved machinery to eradicate virally infected cells, many viruses can persist inside cells to cause latent or chronic infection of the host. One mechanism used by the virus to avoid recognition by immune surveillance is the down-regulation of MHC class I antigen presentation [26,27].

HCMV (human cytomegalovirus)

The degradation of MHC class I heavy-chains by HCMV is an example of this strategy. HCMV encodes four immunomodulatory proteins [gp (glycoprotein) US2, gpUS3, gpUS6 and gpUS11], which decrease cell-surface expression of MHC class I proteins. These are single-transmembrane-spanning, immunoglobulin-domain-family proteins that probably arose by duplication of a single ancestral gene. In the presence of any one of these viral proteins, MHC class I proteins fail to translocate to the infected cell surface; importantly, cell-surface MHC expression is not reduced by infection with a US2-US11 mutant virus. The US3 gene product, gpUS3, is an IE gene product that prevents egress of MHC class I proteins from the ER to the Golgi apparatus. US3 encodes three differentially spliced transcripts, only one of which encodes an MHC class I modulatory protein. The product of US6, gpUS6, complexes with TAP protein in the lumen of the ER, locking the conformation of TAP to prevent ATP-dependent peptide loading. The products of US2 and US11, gpUS2 and gpUS11 respectively, target newly synthesized MHC class I heavy chains for destruction via a pathway that involves ubiquitin-dependent retrograde transport, or 'dislocation', of the heavy chains from the ER to the cytosol, where the proteins are degraded by proteasomes. An Ig-like ER-luminal domain of gpUS2 is essential for this process and engages the α3 domain of the MHC class I heavy chain.

Overall, the CMV-encoded modulatory functions that have been acquired by the virus probably ensure survival and adaptation to the wide range of mammalian host species in which they are found [28–30].

KSHV

The UPS is involved in the sorting of proteins within compartments of the endocytic pathway. An increasing number of examples show that the down-regulation of antigen-presenting MHC class I molecules can also be achieved after membrane delivery by targeting into the endocytic pathway. The proteins required for this process are identified for KSHV.

KSHV K3 and K5 proteins [also known as MIR1 (modulator of immune recognition 1) and MIR2] have E3 activity that induces ubiquitin conjugation to MHC class I in transfected cells, and a critical cysteine residue in the PHD (plant homeodomain) of K5 protein is required for its self-ubiquitination *in vitro*. Similarly, the K3 protein of murine γ-herpesvirus also down-modulates the MHC class I in a PHD-dependent manner. The C-terminal domain of K3 and the cytoplasmic tail of MHC class I are essential for the association of K3 with newly synthesized MHC class I molecules in the ER membrane and their subsequent degradation. [31].

EBV

An interesting example of how a virus avoids immune-system responses comes from EBNA1, which is required for EBV to maintain latency. CTLs specific for EBNA1 can be readily isolated from EBV-infected subjects, but they fail to recognize cells expressing endogenous EBNA1. This viral protein contains Gly-Ala residues that prevent EBNA1 degradation within the proteasome and additionally sequester the cleaved viral products in a cytoplasmic compartment, rendering them inaccessible for presentation by MHC class I molecules. Although EBNA1 is not the only viral protein expressed during EBV latency, its inaccessibility to proteasomes makes a perfect camouflage to prevent recognition by the immune system [32].

Contribution of the UPS to retrovirus release

Interestingly, some enveloped RNA viruses have evolved sophisticated strategies to exploit the UPS at late stages in their replication. Critical steps in the retrovirus life cycle are virion assembly and fusion with the plasma membrane of infected cells and the final release or budding from the host cell [33]. Studies by several independent groups showed that proteasome inhibitors interfere with the budding process of several viruses. The retroviral Gag protein is essential for the budding process, and it contains conserved motifs (late budding or L domains) like PPXY (Pro-Pro-Xaa-Tyr) or PTAP (Pro-Thr-Ala-Pro) sequences. Using the PPXY motif as bait in a two-hybrid system, several groups subsequently identified WW domain-containing HECT E3s such as Nedd4 (neural precursor cell expressed developmentally down-regulated 4) or Nedd4-like proteins. A functional E3 is required for viral budding, as expression of the WW domains alone inhibits the release of mature viral particles from the host cell. In the case of Ebola virus, the late domain-containing protein VP40 (viral protein 40) is a target for ubiquitin conjugation by the Nedd4 yeast homologue Rsp5. Thus E3s (HECT-type) are involved in viral budding through their recruitment to the PPXY motifs in the late budding domains [34].

Another exciting discovery that involves the UPS involves HIV budding. Unlike other retroviruses, HIV does not contain the PPXY motif in the Gag protein, but has a PTAP motif, which has been implicated in viral budding. By using the yeast two-hybrid screen with HIV Gag as bait, two groups identified Tsg101 (tumour susceptibility gene 101) as a binding partner. The PATP motif in the HIV Gag protein mediates direct binding with the UEV (ubiquitin E2 variant) domain in the N-terminus of Tsg101. More importantly, depletion of Tsg101 by use of small interfering RNAs significantly reduced budding of

HIV from infected cells. Structural studies of the Tsg101 UEV domain in the complex with the HIV PTAP motif demonstrated that the UEV domain forms a binding groove that makes close contacts with the PTAP residues. The importance of Tsg101 in HIV budding is further supported by the finding that overexpression of the N-terminal UEV domain of Tsg101 inhibits HIV budding, suggesting that the full-length Tsg101 is required for facilitating virus release. As described above, Tsg101 belongs to the UEV family that contains E2 homologous sequences but not the active cysteine, and it functions in late endosomal trafficking for the activated epidermal growth factor receptor in mammalian cells. In yeast, the Tsg101 homologue Vps23 (vacuolar-protein sorting 23) forms a multimolecular complex with other Vps proteins, called ESCRT (endosomal sorting complex required for transport)-1, which recognizes monoubiquitinated cargo and helps sort it into MVBs (multi-vesicular bodies). Interestingly, the MVB pathway is quite similar to the viral budding process, both of which involve invagination of lipid membrane. In addition, a recent study showed that Tsg101 is recruited, together with other ESCRT-1 components, to the late budding domain [35]. One distinctive difference is that Tsg101 binds directly to the PTAP motif in HIV instead of the ubiquitinated cargo protein, as in the MVB pathway in the yeast.

Studies of the role of UPS in virus budding are of more than academic interest, as virus-release machinery may constitute a novel target for the development of anti-retroviral therapies. Currently, two E3s, in addition to one E3-like protein, have been identified as regulators of HIV budding. These ligases might represent interesting targets for therapeutic intervention [36,37].

Despite considerable recent progress in our understanding of the role of the UPS in retroviral budding, fundamental questions remain to be answered. The search for answers is likely to keep this an exciting field of study for the foreseeable future.

Viruses and ubiquitin-like modifications

Understanding of the importance of post-transcriptional protein–protein modifications is no longer limited to ubiquitin-dependent alterations. Ubiquitin-like proteins also participate in signal transduction in general and virus–host-cell relations in particular.

SUMO (small ubiquitin modifier) belongs to a growing number of ubiquitin-like proteins that covalently modify their target proteins. Although some evidence supports a role of SUMO modification in regulating protein stability, most examples still support a model by which SUMO alters the interaction properties of its targets, often affecting their subcellular localization behaviour. The PML protein localizes both in the nucleoplasm and in matrix-associated multi-protein complexes known as nuclear bodies. PML is essential for the proper formation and the integrity of the nuclear bodies. Modification of PML by SUMO was shown to be required for its localization in nuclear bodies. The finding that early gene products from several DNA viruses alter or disrupt the PML nuclear bodies [38] provided much impetus to investigate the effects of viral proteins on SUMO conjugation.

It could thus be shown that the disruption of nuclear bodies by HSV-ICPO, CMV-IE1 and EBV IE protein BZLF1 correlates with abrogation of sumoylation of PML and SP100. In contrast, the adenoviral E4ORF3 product, while also altering but not entirely disrupting the PML nuclear bodies, causes no such effect. Later work extended these findings by showing that some IE viral gene products are themselves substrates for sumoylation. These include CMV-IE1, and -IE2 proteins, BPV (bovine papillomavirus) and HPV E1 proteins and the EBV-BZFL1 protein. The significance of sumoylation in this context remains poorly understood, but for BPV-E1 it appears necessary for normal nuclear localization, whereas for CMV-IE2, sumoylation enhances IE2-mediated transactivation. These results provide additional evidence that SUMO modification plays a critical role in nuclear body dynamics, although it remains to be determined whether viral-induced PML and SP100 de-sumoylation causes nuclear body dispersal or vice versa [39].

Conclusion

From the first steps of infection to the last moment of release, viruses establish specific alliances within the cell, selectively altering its functional systems, including the UPS. The ability of tumour viruses to transform cells includes redirection of signalling pathways. Since ubiquitin-dependent degradation is the main way to control the lifetime of a plethora of cell signalling regulators, viruses successfully intervene in the 'normal' work of the UPS and, as a result, alter the activity of transduction pathways.

The UPS is also centrally positioned within the panoply of immune and inflammatory responses. Ubiquitin-dependent sorting is the source of antigenic peptides that are presented to the immune system, and many viruses have developed escape mechanisms that manipulate the UPS in order to persist in the infected host.

Viral budding is another example whereby the UPS serves the needs of viruses, namely, the process of their release from host cells. Even though there are still many questions, findings in this area may open up approaches for therapeutic antiviral applications.

In general, although there is certainly progress in understanding the relationships between viruses and the UPS, this is just the beginning. Recounting a few puzzles that have recently yielded to investigation only begins to sketch how viruses target host-cell ubiquitin and ubiquitin-like pathways.

The UPS is integral to the cell machinery that today we call post-transcriptional protein–protein covalent modifications. The essential role of such modifications in different aspects of cell signalling directed by viruses is becoming increasingly obvious and will provide rich fields for discovery.

Summary

- *Human tumour viruses dysregulate UPS-dependent protein turnover of many central transcriptional factors, such as p53, pRb and β-catenin.*
- *Viral intervention in ubiquitin-dependent pathways can include modulation of both of the processes that precede the destruction of proteins (ubiquitination and deubiquitination).*
- *Oncogenic viruses can express their own E3s, triggering ubiquitination of host protein targets, or utilize viral products to interrupt host cell E3 ubiquitinating complexes.*
- *Many viruses have developed mechanisms to escape the cellular immune response by inhibiting ubiquitin-dependent antigen presentation of MHC molecules.*
- *RNA viruses use host ubiquitin–proteasome pathways for viral release from host cells.*
- *The relationship between viruses and host ubiquitin-dependent pathways is not limited to exploitation of the UPS, but applies also to ubiquitin-like modifications.*

Owing to space restrictions, references to certain works have not been included in the list below. A complete set of references is available from the corresponding author.

References

1. Knipe, D.M. & Howley, P.M. (eds) (2001) *Fields Virology*, 4th edn, Lippincott Williams & Wilkins, Philadelphia, PA
2. Pagano, J.S., Blaser, M., Buendia, M.A., Damania, B., Khalili, K., Raab-Traub, N. & Roizman, B. (2004) Infectious agents and cancer: criteria for a causal relation. *Semin. Cancer Biol.* **14**, 453–471
3. Scheffner, M. & Whitaker, N.J. (2003) Human papillomavirus-induced carcinogenesis and the ubiquitin–proteasome system. *Semin. Cancer Biol.* **13**, 59–67
4. Frolov, M.V. & Dyson, N.J. (2004) Molecular mechanisms of E2F-dependent activation and pRB-mediated repression. *J. Cell Sci.* **117**, 2173–2181
5. Dimova, D.K. & Dyson, N.J. (2005) The E2F transcriptional network: old acquaintances with new faces. *Oncogene* **24**, 2810–2826
6. Oh, K.J., Kalinina, A., Wang, J., Nakayama, K., Nakayama, K.I. & Bagchi, S. (2004) The papillomavirus E7 oncoprotein is ubiquitinated by UbcH7 and Cullin 1- and Skp2-containing E3 ligase. *J. Virol.* **78**, 5338–5346
7. Liu, Y.C. (2004) Ubiquitin ligases and the immune response. *Annu. Rev. Immunol.* **22**, 81–127
8. Vargas, D.A., Takahashi, S. & Ronai, Z. (2003) Mdm2: A regulator of cell growth and death. *Adv. Cancer Res.* **89**, 1–34
9. Oren, M. (2003) Decision making by p53: life, death and cancer. *Cell Death Differ.* **10**, 431–442
10. Hengstermann, A., Linares, L.K., Ciechanover, A., Whitaker, N.J. & Scheffner, M. (2001) Complete switch from Mdm2 to human papillomavirus E6-mediated degradation of p53 in cervical cancer cells. *Proc. Natl. Acad. Sci. U.S.A.* **98**, 1218–1223
11. Kao, W.H., Beaudenon, S.L., Talis, A.L., Huibregtse, J.M. & Howley, P.M. (2000) Human papillomavirus type 16 E6 induces self-ubiquitination of the E6AP ubiquitin-protein ligase. *J. Virol.* **74**, 6408–6417

12. Ben-Israel, H. & Kleinberger, T. (2002) Adenovirus and cell cycle control. *Front. Biosci.* **7**, d1369–d1395

13. Russell, I.A., Royds, J.A. & Braithwaite, A.W. (2004) Exploitation of cell cycle and cell death controls by adenoviruses: the road to a productive infection. *Prog. Mol. Subcell. Biol.* **36**, 207–243

14. Koike, K. (2002) Hepatocarcinogenesis in hepatitis viral infection: lessons from transgenic mouse studies. *J. Gastroenterol.* **37** (Suppl 13), 55–64

15. Anzola, M. (2004) Hepatocellular carcinoma: role of hepatitis B and hepatitis C viruses proteins in hepatocarcinogenesis. *J. Viral. Hepat.* **11**, 383–393

16. Stohwasser, R., Holzhutter, H.G., Lehmann, U., Henklein, P. & Kloetzel, P.M. (2003) Hepatitis B virus HBx peptide 116–138 and proteasome activator PA28 compete for binding to the proteasome alpha4/MC6 subunit. *Biol. Chem.* **384**, 39–49

17. Wang, T., Wang, Y., Wu, M.C., Guan, X.Y. & Yin, Z.F. (2004) Activating mechanism of transcriptor NF-κB regulated by hepatitis B virus X protein in hepatocellular carcinoma. *World J. Gastroenterol.* **10**, 356–360

18. Zhang, Z., Protzer, U., Hu, Z., Jacob, J. & Liang, T.J. (2004) Inhibition of cellular proteasome activities enhances hepadnavirus replication in an HBX-dependent manner. *J. Virol.* **78**, 4566–4572

19. Hagglund, R. & Roizman, B. (2004) Role of ICP0 in the strategy of conquest of the host cell by herpes simplex virus 1. *J. Virol.* **78**, 2169–2178

20. Everett, R.D. (2000) ICP0, a regulator of herpes simplex virus during lytic and latent infection. *Bioessays* **22**, 761–770

21. Yu, Y., Wang, S.E. & Hayward, G.S. (2005) The KSHV immediate-early transcription factor RTA encodes ubiquitin E3 ligase activity that targets IRF7 for proteosome-mediated degradation. *Immunity* **22**, 59–70

22. Holowaty, M.N., Sheng, Y., Nguyen, T., Arrowsmith, C. & Frappier, L. (2003) Protein interaction domains of the ubiquitin-specific protease, USP7/HAUSP. *J. Biol. Chem.* **278**, 47753–47761

23. Shackelford, J. & Pagano, J.S. (2004) Tumor viruses and cell signalling pathways: deubiquitination versus ubiquitination. *Mol. Cell. Biol.* **24**, 5089–5093

24. Balakirev, M.Y., Jaquinod, M., Haas, A.L. & Chroboczek, J. (2002) Deubiquitinating function of adenovirus proteinase. *J. Virol.* **76**, 6323–6331

25. Shackelford, J., Maier, C. & Pagano, J.S. (2003) Epstein-Barr virus activates β-catenin in type III latently infected B lymphocyte lines: association with deubiquitinating enzymes. *Proc. Natl. Acad. Sci. U.S.A.* **100**, 15572–15576

26. Rivett, A.J. & Hearn, A.R. (2004) Proteasome function in antigen presentation: immunoproteasome complexes, peptide production, and interactions with viral proteins. *Curr. Protein Pept. Sci.* **5**, 153–161

27. Reinstein, E. (2004) Immunologic aspects of protein degradation by the ubiquitin–proteasome system. *Isr. Med. Assoc. J.* **6**, 420–424

28. Collins, R.W. (2004) Human MHC class I chain related (MIC) genes: their biological function and relevance to disease and transplantation. *Eur. J. Immunogenet.* **31**, 105–114

29. Harari, A., Zimmerli, S.C. & Pantaleo, G. (2004) Cytomegalovirus (CMV)-specific cellular immune responses. *Hum. Immunol.* **65**, 500–506

30. Mocarski, Jr, E.S. (2004) Immune escape and exploitation strategies of cytomegaloviruses: impact on and imitation of the major histocompatibility system. *Cell. Microbiol.* **6**, 707–717

31. Benichou, S. & Benmerah, A. (2003) The HIV nef and the Kaposi-sarcoma-associated virus K3/K5 proteins: "parasites"of the endocytosis pathway. *Med. Sci. (Paris)* **19**, 100–106

32. Masucci, M.G. (2004) Epstein-Barr virus oncogenesis and the ubiquitin–proteasome system. *Oncogene* **23**, 2107–2115

33. Morita, E. & Sundquist, W.I. (2004) Retrovirus budding. *Annu. Rev. Cell Dev. Biol.* **20**, 395–425

34. Martin-Serrano, J., Eastman, S.W., Chung, W. & Bieniasz, P.D. (2005) HECT ubiquitin ligases link viral and cellular PPXY motifs to the vacuolar protein-sorting pathway. *J. Cell Biol.* **168**, 89–101

35. Martin-Serrano, J., Perez-Caballero, D. & Bieniasz, P.D. (2004) Context-dependent effects of L domains and ubiquitination on viral budding. *J. Virol.* **78**, 5554–5563

36. Klinger, P.P. & Schubert, U. (2005) The ubiquitin–proteasome system in HIV replication: potential targets for antiretroviral therapy. *Exp. Rev. Anti-infect. Ther.* **3**, 61–79

37. Li, F. & Wild, C. (2005) HIV-1 assembly and budding as targets for drug discovery. *Curr. Opin. Investig. Drugs* **6**, 148–154

38. Dohmen, R.J. (2004) SUMO protein modification. *Biochim. Biophys. Acta* **1695**, 113–131

39. Wilson, V.G. & Rangasamy, D. (2001) Intracellular targeting of proteins by sumoylation. *Exp. Cell Res.* **271**, 57–65

The ubiquitin–proteasome system and neurodegenerative disorders

Robert Layfield*[1], James Lowe†
and Lynn Bedford*

School of Biomedical Sciences, University of Nottingham Medical School, Queen's Medical Centre, Nottingham NG7 2UH, U.K. and †School of Molecular Medical Sciences, University of Nottingham Medical School, Queen's Medical Centre, Nottingham NG7 2UH, U.K.

Abstract

As in all other mammalian tissues, the UPS (ubiquitin–proteasome system) is fundamental to normal brain function. A consistent feature of the major human neurodegenerative disorders is the accumulation of disease-related proteins, in non-native conformations, as protein aggregates within neurons or glial cells. Often the proteins in these aggregates are post-translationally conjugated with ubiquitin, suggesting a possible link between pathological protein-aggregation events in the nervous system and dysfunction of the UPS. Genetic evidence clearly demonstrates that disruption of ubiquitin-mediated processes can lead to neurodegeneration; however, the relationship between the UPS and idiopathic neurodegenerative disorders is less clear. In the latter cases, although a number of different mechanisms could potentially contribute to dysfunction of the UPS and promote the neurodegenerative process, whether UPS dysfunction is causally related to disease pathogenesis, or alternatively arises as a result of the pathological state, and indeed whether

[1]To whom correspondence should be addressed
  (email robert.layfield@nottingham.ac.uk).

ubiquitinated inclusions are harmful or beneficial to cells, remains to be clarified.

Introduction

Human neurodegenerative disorders represent a clinically and pathologically diverse group of conditions, in which the selective loss of neurons in specific areas of the brain underlies the individual disease symptoms. Most are complex disorders in which genetic and environmental factors interact. A common feature seen in the majority of neurodegenerative disorders is the presence of abnormal protein aggregates within neurons (and sometimes glial cells), which are covalently and post-translationally conjugated to the protein ubiquitin. This commonality has focused attention on the role of the UPS (ubiquitin–proteasome system) in both pathological events within the nervous system as well as normal brain function.

The UPS controls memory and learning

Given the range of cellular pathways and physiological processes in which ubiquitin is involved, many of which are described throughout this volume, it is not surprising that normal function of the nervous system largely depends upon ubiquitin conjugation/deconjugation and the UPS.

Synaptic remodelling in response to activity and external stimuli is central to memory formation in the brain. Neuronal plasticity involves changes in the molecular and structural organization of the synapse, as well as neurotransmission. This remodelling of the synapse requires co-ordinated protein synthesis and proteolysis, and the UPS is increasingly acknowledged to play a critical role in regulating the abundance of key proteins at neuronal synapses and hence in normal brain function. The PSD (postsynaptic density) is pivotal to the learning-related synaptic activity within the brain. Recent work in primary rat hippocampal neurons shows that the UPS is integral in the functional and molecular reorganization of the PSD in response to synaptic activity [1]. Multiple classes of postsynaptic proteins were found to be involved in PSD remodelling, but only a subset of postsynaptic scaffold proteins, including Shank, GKAP (guanylate kinase-associated protein) and AKAP (A-kinase anchoring protein) 79/150, are ubiquitinated and targeted to the proteasome for degradation by synaptic activity. The enhanced turnover of other proteins in active PSDs may also be influenced by the ubiquitin-dependent degradation of the scaffolding molecules. Activity-associated proteasome-dependent post-synaptic modifications are accompanied by altered synaptic signalling to CREB (cAMP-response-element-binding protein) and ERK (extracellular-signal-regulated kinase)/MAPK (mitogen-activated protein kinase) pathways, each of which have specific roles in synapse dynamics involved in information storage and processing.

In addition to modulating protein turnover in the PSD, proteasome-regulated proteolysis also has a role in the presynaptic density. The levels of presynaptic DUNC-13 (*Drosophila* homologue of UNC-13), a protein that regulates synaptic vesicle priming to control synaptic transmission strength, is specifically regulated by the UPS in the *Drosophila* NMJ (neuromuscular junction) synapse, and the rate of degradation of presynaptic DUNC-13 modulates the strength of synapse neurotransmission by affecting presynaptic efficacy [2].

The concept that proteasome-mediated degradation is central to multiple levels of synaptic modulation is supported by work on sensory-motor synapses of *Aplysia* (a type of sea slug). The learning-related switch from short-term to long-term facilitation in *Aplysia* involves UPS substrates functioning in both the presynaptic and post-synaptic densities of sensory-motor synapses [3]. A ubiquitin C-terminal hydrolase [a DUB (deubiquitinating enzyme)] was previously found to be required for long-term facilitation, suggesting a role for the UPS in *Aplysia* neuronal plasticity [4].

Axonal regeneration is another major area of interest in the mature central nervous system. The formation of a new growth cone following axonal damage is necessary for extension of the axon and hence successful regeneration. It is understandable that remodelling to form this specialized structure at the tip of an axon is accompanied by the synthesis of new proteins and the regulated degradation of existing ones. Although local protein synthesis plays a significant role in this process, intra-axonal protein degradation, including proteasome-regulated degradation, was recently highlighted as part of the mechanism involved in new growth-cone formation following axonal injury [5].

Taken together, it is becoming increasingly clear that the UPS is critical to learning and memory formation within the brain, regulating synaptic neurotransmission and downstream signalling by modulating local synaptic protein concentration. This function in plasticity may explain in part the subset of human neurodegenerative diseases that are caused by mutations affecting ubiquitin pathway genes, described later in this chapter.

Ubiquitin and neurodegeneration

Lessons from immunohistochemistry
Long before ubiquitin was implicated in the normal physiological processes described above, a tantalizing link between the UPS and pathological events in the nervous system had already been uncovered.

A consistent feature of the major human neurodegenerative disorders such as Alzheimer's disease, which causes the majority of cases of dementia in the Western world, is the presence of abnormal protein aggregates in the diseased brain. In Alzheimer's disease, these deposits include filamentous inclusions within neurons called neurofibrillary tangles, and extracellular-protein deposits termed amyloid plaques or senile plaques. Since these aggregates are thought to be involved in, or at the very least to be an indicator of, the pathological process, identification of the specific proteins deposited provides a logical route towards advancing the understanding of disease. For example, the finding that the Aβ (amyloid β) peptide is the major constituent of amyloid plaques led to the discovery that rare familial cases of early-onset Alzheimer's disease are caused by highly penetrant mutations in the gene encoding the amyloid precursor protein [6]. Likewise, the identification of hyper-phosphorylated filamentous forms of the microtubule-associated tau protein as a principal constituent of paired helical filaments, which make up neurofibrillary tangles, eventually led to the discovery that certain frontotemporal dementias (but not Alzheimer's disease) are caused by mutations in the *tau* gene [7].

In the late 1980s, over 70 years after Alois Alzheimer made his first pathological description of the disorder, ubiquitin was identified as a new player in the neurodegenerative process. Using immunohistochemical techniques with antibodies raised against the ubiquitin protein, workers in several research groups almost simultaneously reported intense staining of neurofibrillary tangles as well as neurites (axons or dendrites) associated with amyloid plaques, in brain sections taken from patients with Alzheimer's disease [8,9] (Figure 1). Other structures were also seen with ubiquitin antibodies, including persiomatic granules [10], dystrophic neurites, and dot-like bodies in white matter [11]. Soon after, it was realized that ubiquitin staining was not only a feature of the lesions in cases of Alzheimer's disease, but could also be detected in inclusions in other disorders involving tau pathology (so-called tauopathies, such as Pick's disease), as well as in disorders involving α-synuclein pathology

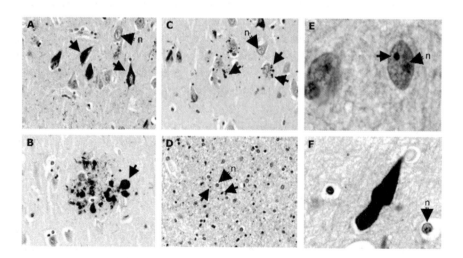

Figure 1. Ubiquitin-immunoreactive structures in Alzheimer's disease (A–D) and Huntington's disease (E and F) brain sections
For comparison, some nuclei are indicated (n). (**A**) Neurofibrillary tangles. (**B**) Neuritic plaque (a prominent 'bulbous' dystrophic neurite is arrowed). (**C**) Perisomatic granules. (**D**) Dot-like ubiquitin immunoreactivity. (**E**) Huntington's disease neuronal intranuclear inclusion. (**F**) Huntington's disease dystrophic neurite.

Table 1 Ubiquitin-positive inclusions which characterise human degenerative disorders

Disorder	Pathology stained
Alzheimer's disease	Neurofibrillary tangles, neuritic plaques, perisomatic granules, neuropil threads, dot-like bodies
Dementia with Lewy bodies	Cortical Lewy bodies, Lewy neurites
Parkinson's disease	Brainstem Lewy bodies, Lewy neurites
Pick's disease	Pick bodies
ALS	MND inclusions
Frontotemporal dementia	Neuronal inclusions
Multiple system atrophy	Glial cytoplasmic inclusions
Huntington's disease	Intranuclear inclusions, dystrophic neurites
Spinocerebellar ataxias	Intranuclear inclusions of polyglutamine-containing aggregates
*Alcoholic liver disease	Mallory bodies (liver)
*Cytoplasmic muscle myopathy	Cytoplasmic bodies (muscle)

*The disorders indicated affect tissues outside of the nervous system.

(synucleinopathies, including Parkinson's disease), in polyglutamine diseases (e.g. Huntington's disease), and in ALS [amyotrophic lateral sclerosis, also known as MND (motor neuron disease)] [12–14] (Table 1). Interestingly, in the case of polyglutamine diseases, ubiquitin inclusions are sometimes found to be present in the nucleus, in contrast to the other disorders where the aggregates are principally cytoplasmic.

Ubiquitin immunohistochemistry soon facilitated worldwide diagnostic awareness of a 'new' neurological condition, dementia with Lewy bodies. Inclusion bodies, previously very hard to see by conventional staining, could now be easily detected by light microscopy in the cerebral cortex of affected patients. It became apparent that this was the second commonest neurodegenerative cause of dementia after Alzheimer's disease, and the technique was adopted as the recommended method for detection of inclusions in a clinical setting [15,16]. The availability of ubiquitin-immunohistochemistry revolutionized the pathological diagnosis of MND by allowing identification of a novel inclusion in affected neurons [13,17]. A 'new' form of dementia was soon discovered, representing the commonest cause of frontotemporal dementia, in which inclusion bodies resemble those seen in the non-motor cortex in MND [18]. In addition to neurons, in some conditions (e.g. progressive supranuclear palsy) glial cells were found to involve ubiquitin inclusions, and ubiquitin-immunoreactivity of protein aggregates was also found to extend beyond the nervous system, with Mallory bodies in alcoholic liver disease as well as cytoplasmic bodies in muscle being stained by anti-ubiquitin [12]. In fact, it seemed that in almost every disorder in which protein aggregation was occurring, ubiquitin immunoreactivity could be detected.

© 2005 The Biochemical Society

In Alzheimer's disease and Parkinson's disease (and presumably the other protein conformation disorders) it is now clear that ubiquitin not only co-localizes with the filamentous protein aggregates that are composed of tau and α-synuclein (a presynaptic protein which may be involved in regulating synaptic transmission) respectively, but is covalently conjugated to modified (phosphorylated and truncated) forms of these proteins [19,20]. Ubiquitinated tau protein purified from brains of patients with Alzheimer's disease includes forms with polyubiquitin chains which are Lys^{48}-linked, suggesting attempted proteasomal degradation. In other cases, for example MND, the nature of the ubiquitinated proteins within the inclusions remains elusive, but once identified will no doubt be most informative in understanding the disease process.

Although suggestions had been made that the UPS was participating in a common biological response designed to eliminate abnormal proteins (the ubiquitin-intermediate filament response), the definition of the aggresomal response by Kopito and colleagues [20a] reinforced the important association between the UPS and protein aggregation in disease [21]. Regardless of whether the events that can be seen and characterized *post mortem* represent a normal cellular response to the accumulation of aggregated proteins, and/or a failed attempt by the UPS to degrade some form(s) of the aggregated protein, these combined observations gave some of the first indications of a possible link between protein aggregation events and UPS dysfunction. Whether protein aggregation leads to UPS dysfunction, or vice versa, and in fact whether ubiquitin inclusions are harmful or beneficial to cells, remain areas of intense debate.

Lessons from genetics

Genetic evidence clearly links disruption of ubiquitin-mediated processes and some neurodegenerative disorders. Studies of genetic forms of Parkinson's disease and parkinsonism have been particularly fruitful in highlighting the importance of the UPS for neuronal health.

The most common cause of heritable parkinsonism is mutations affecting the *parkin* gene. The parkin protein is an E2 (ubiquitin-conjugating enzyme)-dependent RING (really interesting new gene)-finger E3 (ubiquitin ligase) enzyme, and seven presumed substrates for parkin's ligase activity have been identified to date. α-Synuclein is a key component of Lewy bodies in cases of Parkinson's disease, and a glycosylated form of α-synuclein is ubiquitinated by parkin [22], with accumulation of non-glycosylated α-synuclein being evident in parkin-deficient brains. In addition, synphilin-1, an α-synuclein-interacting protein, is ubiquitinated by parkin [23] as are p38 and CDCrel-1 [24,25]. p38 functions within the aminoacyl-tRNA synthetase multiprotein complex involved in mammalian protein synthesis, and is present in dopaminergic neurons of the adult midbrain (a brain region affected in Parkinson's disease) and also in Lewy bodies. CDCrel-1 is a member of the septin synaptic-vesicle-associated protein family.

Interaction and ubiquitination of synaptotagmin implicates parkin in the control of neurotransmitter trafficking at the presynaptic terminal [26]. Moreover, synaptotagmin XI immunoreactivity is evident in Lewy bodies in cases of idiopathic Parkinson's disease. The misfolded Pael receptor [Pael-R (parkin-associated endothelin-receptor-like receptor)], a putative G-protein-coupled seven transmembrane protein, is ubiquitinated by parkin, which is necessary to protect the cell against Pael-R-induced endoplasmic reticulum stress [27]. Parkin may also function as part of an SCF (Skp1–Cdc53/Cul1–F-box protein)-like E3 macromolecule, interacting with hSel-10 and Cullin-1, together with the E2 UbcH7 [28]. Via hSel-10, a cyclin-E-interacting protein, the parkin E3 complex is implicated in the control of neuronal survival, ubiquitinating and thereby regulating the levels of pro-apoptotic cyclin E. To support this role, mid-brain parkin-deficient neurons, for example, have increased cyclin E levels.

It is hypothesized that the ubiquitination of parkin substrates targets the proteins for proteasomal degradation. Disease-linked mutations impair the E3 function of parkin, and hence the underlying cause of neurodegeneration may be alterations in protein turnover by the UPS, leading to the accumulation of substrates of parkin and compromised cell survival. These proteins are often evident in, and are components of, Lewy bodies in the idiopathic Parkinson's diseased brain, suggesting similarities in disease mechanisms. However, despite considerable emphasis being placed on the identification of potential substrates for parkin, a recent *in vivo* analysis demonstrated that the steady-state levels of at least three of these substrates, CDCrel-1, α-synuclein and synphilin-1, are unaltered in parkin-deficient mouse brains [29]. However, their synaptic activity may be modulated by parkin-mediated ubiquitination. The parkin$^{-/-}$ phenotype implicates additional factors in the mechanism of neurodegeneration.

Recent work has identified an interesting relationship between parkin and synphilin-1 that may be related to the formation of Lewy bodies [30]. Parkin appears to have the ability to ubiquitinate synphilin-1 with both Lys^{48}- and Lys^{63}-linked polyubiquitin chains, with the relative levels of either type of modification being dependent on the parkin to synphilin-1 expression ratio. Surprisingly, Lys^{63}-linked ubiquitination of synphilin-1 by parkin seems to occur at 'normal' relative expression levels of these proteins. Furthermore, the proteasomal-independent ubiquitin Lys^{63} linkages appear to be predominant in Lewy-like inclusions formed by parkin, synphilin-1 and α-synuclein co-expression. Together, this work suggests that Lewy body formation may require functional parkin, and supporting this, some cases of familial parkinsonism carrying *parkin* mutations do not present with Lewy bodies [31].

In addition to *parkin* mutations, a missense mutation (Ile^{93}→Met) in the gene encoding UCH-L1 (ubiquitin C-terminal hydrolase L1, also known as PGP9.5), an abundant neuronal enzyme, was identified in a German family with a strong history of Parkinson's disease [32]. Although the physiological function of this protein is not completely understood, it appears that decreased protease function associated with the Ile^{93}→Met mutation leads to defects in protein turnover *in vivo*. Investigations of the gracile axonal dystrophy (*gad*) mouse, which is characterized by an in-frame deletion in the *UCH-L1* gene, including exons 7 and 8 that harbour a catalytic residue, strengthened the importance of UCH-L1 in neurodegeneration [33]. Work has also shown that UCH-L1 has dimerization-dependent E3 activity *in vitro* [34]. This ligase function catalyses Lys^{63}-linked polyubiquitination of α-synuclein, similar to that described for parkin, and a decreased E3 activity was linked to a decreased susceptibility to Parkinson's disease, which may explain the protective effects of a Ser^{18}Tyr polymorphism (a naturally occurring variant of the parkin sequence).

Overall, perturbations in the UPS, whether they involve ubiquitination, deubiquitination, or both, are clearly linked to neurodegeneration. Although attention has focused on Parkinson's disease and related disorders owing to the comparative wealth of information gleaned from heritable forms of these conditions, it seems quite likely that in the future rarer human neurodegenerative disorders will also be found to be caused by mutations in ubiquitin-pathway enzymes.

Molecular misreading: a novel type of mutation affecting the UPS?

Although genetic mutations affecting ubiquitin-pathway enzymes have not, at least to date, been found in cases of Alzheimer's disease, detailed molecular studies of this disorder have led to the identification of a novel mechanism which might account for the ubiquitin pathology that is a feature of Alzheimer's disease, as well as some other neurodegenerative disorders.

In 1998, a mutant frameshifted form of ubiquitin, termed UBB+1, was found to be a component of some of the pathological hallmarks of the Alzheimer's disease brain, including the neurofibrillary tangles [35]. Rather than resulting from germline mutations, the UBB+1 protein appears to arise by a mechanism known as 'molecular misreading', where correct genetic information gives rise to aberrant gene products owing to mistakes during protein synthesis. UBB+1 immunoreactivity is also a feature of elderly (but not young) control brains, indicating that molecular misreading may represent an age-dependent event marking the early stages of neurodegeneration. As with ubiquitin-immunostaining, immunoreactivity to UBB+1 has also been found in a range of other human degenerative conditions, including Huntington's disease, and in particular disorders characterized by tau pathology such as frontotemporal dementias and Pick's disease [36], although interestingly not in synucleinopathies (despite the fact that the misreading event still occurs in these conditions).

So how might UBB+1 expression contribute to neurodegeneration? The UBB+1 protein has an identical sequence to wild-type ubiquitin for the first 75 amino acid residues, with the C-terminal glycine residue (Gly^{76}) of the wild-type sequence replaced by 20 residues of 'nonsense' sequence in the mutant gene product. This defective C-terminus of UBB+1 means that the

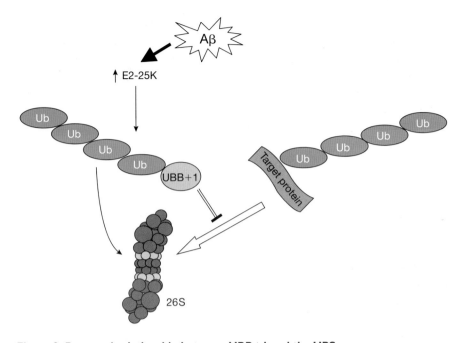

Figure 2. Proposed relationship between UBB+1 and the UPS
Ubiquitination of target proteins with a minimum of four ubiquitins (Ub) [49] is a signal for their 26 S proteasomal degradation (right). UBB+1 lacks the C-terminal Gly^{76} residue necessary for conjugation to target proteins, but can itself be ubiquitinated by wild-type ubiquitin. Aβ may contribute to the generation of polyubiquitinated UBB+1 by upregulating expression of the E2-25K E2. Polyubiquitinated UBB+1 can act as a potent competitive inhibitor of ubiquitin-dependent protein degradation, or may itself be a substrate of the 26 S proteasome.

mutant protein cannot, like wild-type ubiquitin, be conjugated to target proteins. However, since the rest of the ubiquitin sequence is intact, UBB+1 can itself be ubiquitinated (now known to be via both Lys^{29}- and Lys^{48}-linked chains) by wild-type ubiquitin [37] (Figure 2). The resulting polyubiquitinated UBB+1 can act as potent competitive inhibitor of the 26 S proteasome, while resisting disassembly by DUBs. In the simplest model, polyubiquitinated UBB+1 could accumulate upon aging, impairing the 26 S proteasome with catastrophic consequences for the UPS. Of particular interest is the finding that the E2-25K E2, which is capable of generating polyubiquitinated UBB+1, is one of the targets found to be up-regulated in neurons exposed to Aβ peptide [38]. This intriguing observation, coupled with the findings that E2-25K is in fact required for Aβ-induced neurotoxicity, as well as for neurotoxicity mediated by UBB+1, is suggestive of a possible direct molecular link between Aβ and UPS dysfunction in Alzheimer's-related disorders. A recent unique *in vitro* model of nuclear-inclusion formation in Huntington's disease further implicated UBB+1 as an aggravating factor in protein aggregation and neurodegeneration, also confirming a central role for the UPS in polyglutamine diseases [39].

A possible explanation as to why UBB+1 accumulation is only a feature of tauopathies and polyglutamine diseases (but not synucleinopathies) has also been suggested; the UBB+1 protein itself appears to be a UPS substrate, and in this regard, UBB+1 accumulation may be a sensor or 'reporter' of UPS dysfunction [36]. So UBB+1 accumulation in neurons in certain neurodegenerative disorders may in fact reflect impairment of the UPS by a mechanism which does not necessarily involve UBB+1.

Mechanisms of ubiquitin inclusion formation

The human neurodegenerative disorders that are characterized by ubiquitin-immunoreactive inclusions can essentially be viewed as protein aggregation disorders, in which the accumulation of the protein aggregates is likely to be related to the disease process. Although in rarer familial disorders, protein accumulation leading to aggregation events can in some cases be directly linked to dysfunctional protein turnover (be that of the mutant proteins themselves, or because of defective UPS components), clearly a major, but unresolved, question remains, related to the significance of ubiquitin inclusions in the more common idiopathic human neurodegenerative disorders (i.e. in the absence of obvious genetic mutations). There are several possibilities that might account for the presence of ubiquitinated protein aggregates in these cases (Figure 3), which include the following:

(1) That a generalized failure of the UPS, upon, for example, aging occurs. Although age-dependent changes in the activity of a number of components of the UPS have been reported, and various mechanisms have been proposed that might account for such changes (such as proteasome inhibition by mutant UBB+1), the observation that the inclusions generally contain a single ubiquitinated protein (for example ubiquitinated tau protein in the case of Alzheimer's disease), rather than accumulations of mixtures of ubiquitinated proteins, would argue against any primary general failure of the UPS.

(2) That ubiquitination is a stabilizing signal that has served to aggregate toxic oligomers of abnormal protein into an inert form, as an inclusion body [40]. The evidence for this potential role is supported by experiments in which reduction of inclusion-body formation in certain models of protein aggregation disease leads to increased cell death [41]. In this regard, in some instances ubiquitin inclusions may have a clearly neuroprotective function, i.e. may be beneficial to cells [42]. Further experimental data suggest that the purpose of inclusion-body formation may be to eliminate material via the autophagic pathway [43].

(3) That ubiquitin inclusions are indicative of a normal UPS degradative response to the accumulation of aggregated proteins. It may be significant that certain E3s appear to have a specificity for disease-related forms of cellular proteins, for example the CHIP (C-terminus of the heat-shock-protein-70-interacting protein) E3 targets Alzheimer's disease-like phosphorylated forms of tau pro-

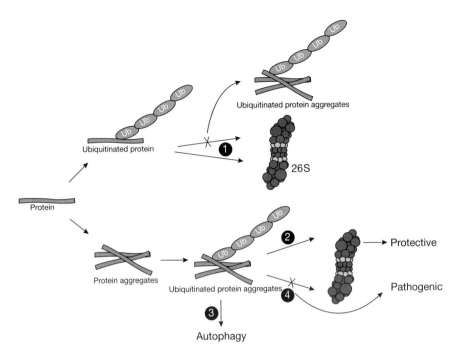

Figure 3. Mechanisms to account for the accumulation of ubiquitinated protein aggregates in neurodegenerative-disease brains
Upper branch: a generalized failure of the UPS (**1**) could lead to the accumulation and aggrega-tion of ubiquitinated proteins. Lower branch: ubiquitination may be part of a normal protective cellular response to protein aggregates that delivers ubiquitinated protein aggregates to the 26 S proteasome (**2**) or signals (activates) autophagy once the capacity of the proteasome is exceeded (**3**). Failure of this response, perhaps at the level of proteasome inhibition (**4**), could have patho-logical consequences.

tein [44]. The localization of proteasome subunits within protein aggregates *in vivo* is further supportive of such a model [45].

(4) A combination of 1 and 3 above, that is to say ubiquitin inclusions rep-resent the failure (or perhaps remnants) of a normal UPS response to the pres-ence of protein aggregates. Within this model, different mechanisms could account for impairment of proteasome function in the pathological state, for example protein-aggregation events [46] which are initiated for reasons that are currently unclear, and/or direct inhibition of proteasome function by (at least in the case of Alzheimer's disease) Aβ peptide [47] or tau fibrils [48].

Conclusion

In conclusion, normal functioning of the nervous system relies upon the UPS, and disruption of ubiquitin-mediated processes, including proteasomal degradation, can in some cases directly cause neurodegeneration. Immunohistochemical evidence also indicates an involvement of ubiquitin in the disease process of the more common cases of idiopathic neurodegenerative disorders, and a significant future challenge will be to understand more fully the relationship between dysfunction of the UPS and protein aggregation events in the nervous system.

Summary

- *The UPS is essential for normal functioning of the nervous system.*
- *The accumulation of ubiquitinated protein aggregates within neurons in tauopathies, synucleinopathies, as well as polyglutamine diseases, is a hallmark of the major human neurodegenerative disorders.*
- *These inclusions usually contain a single major ubiquitinated protein.*
- *Studies of rare familial cases of neurodegenerative disorders, in particular Parkinson's disease-related conditions, show that disruption of ubiquitin-mediated processes resulting from loss-of-function mutations affecting ubiquitin pathway enzymes can directly cause neurodegeneration.*
- *A frameshifted mutant form of ubiquitin, UBB+1, which arises through a novel mechanism termed molecular misreading, may be related to the pathogenesis of a range of human disorders.*
- *The significance of the presence of ubiquitinated inclusions in cases of idiopathic neurodegenerative disorders is still unclear; whether UPS dysfunction is causally related to disease pathogenesis in these cases, or arises as a result of the disease process, is a key question.*

The authors thank Research into Ageing, the Wellcome Trust, the Neuroscience Support Group at the QMC, and the Alzheimer's Research Trust, for support of work which led to some of the findings and concepts described throughout this essay.

References

1.   Ehlers, M.D. (2003) Activity level controls postsynaptic composition and signalling via the ubiquitin–proteasome system. *Nat. Neurosci.* **6**, 231–242
2.   Speese, S.D., Trotta, N., Rodesch, C.K., Aravamudan, B. & Broadie, K. (2003) The ubiquitin proteasome system regulates presynaptic protein turnover and synaptic efficacy. *Curr. Biol.* **13**, 899–910
3.   Zhao, Y., Hegde, A.N. & Martin, K.C. (2003) The ubiquitin proteasome system functions as an inhibitory constraint on synaptic strengthening. *Curr. Biol.* **13**, 887–898
4.   Hegde, A.N., Inokuchi, K., Pei, W., Casadio, A., Ghirardi, M., Chain, D.G., Martin, K.C., Kandel, E.R. & Schwartz, J.H. (1997) Ubiquitin C-terminal hydrolase is an immediate-early gene essential for long-term facilitation in *Aplysia*. *Cell* **89**, 115–126
5.   Verma, P., Chierzi, S., Codd, A.M., Campbell, D.S., Meyer, R.L., Holt, C.E. & Fawcett, J.W. (2005) Axonal protein synthesis and degradation are necessary for efficient growth cone regeneration. *J. Neurosci.* **25**, 331–342
6.   Goate, A., Chartier-Harlin M.C., Mullan, M., Brown, J., Crawford, F., Fidani, L., Giuffra, L., Haynes, A., Irving, N., James, L. et al. (1991) Segregation of a missense mutation in the amyloid precursor protein gene with familial Alzheimer's disease. *Nature (London)* **349**, 704–706

7. Hutton, M., Lendon, C.L, Rizzu, P., Baker, M., Froelich, S., Houlden, H., Pickering-Brown, S., Chakraverty, S., Isaacs, A., Grover, A. et al. (1998) Association of missense and 5′-splice-site mutations in tau with the inherited dementia FTDP-17. Nature (London) 393, 702–705

8. Mori, H., Kondo, J. & Ihara, Y. (1987) Ubiquitin is a component of paired helical filaments in Alzheimer's disease. Science 235, 1641–1644

9. Perry, G., Friedman, R., Shaw, G. & Chau, V. (1987) Ubiquitin is detected in neurofibrillary tangles and senile plaque neurites of Alzheimer disease brains. Proc. Natl. Acad. Sci. U.S.A. 84, 3033–3036

10. Probst, A.M.C., Herzig, M.C., Mistl, C., Ipsen, S. & Tolnay, M. (2001) Perisomatic granules (non-plaque dystrophic dendrites) of hippocampal CA1 neurons in Alzheimer's disease and Pick's disease: a lesion distinct from granulovacuolar degeneration. Acta Neuropathol. 102, 636–644

11. Dickson, D.W., Wertkin, A., Kress, Y., Ksiezak-Reding, H. & Yen, S.H. (1990) Ubiquitin immunoreactive structures in normal human brains. Distribution and developmental aspects. Lab. Invest. 63, 87–99

12. Lowe, J., Blanchard, A., Morrell, K., Lennox, G., Reynolds, L., Billett, M., Landon, M. & Mayer, R.J. (1988) Ubiquitin is a common factor in intermediate filament inclusion bodies of diverse type in man, including those of Parkinson's disease, Pick's disease, and Alzheimer's disease, as well as Rosenthal fibres in cerebellar astrocytomas, cytoplasmic bodies in muscle, and mallory bodies in alcoholic liver disease. J. Pathol. 155, 9–15

13. Lowe, J., Lennox, G., Jefferson, D., Morrell, K., McQuire, D., Gray, T., Landon, M., Doherty, F.J. & Mayer, R.J. (1988) A filamentous inclusion body within anterior horn neurones in motor neurone disease defined by immunocytochemical localisation of ubiquitin. Neurosci. Lett. 94, 203–210

14. DiFiglia, M., Sapp, E., Chase, K.O., Davies, S.W., Bates, G.P., Vonsattel, J.P. & Aronin, N. (1997) Aggregation of huntingtin in neuronal intranuclear inclusions and dystrophic neurites in brain. Science 277, 1990–1993

15. McKeith, I.G., Galasko, D., Kosaka, K., Perry, E.K., Dickson, D.W., Hansen, LA., Salmon, D.P., Lowe, J., Mirra, S.S., Byrne, E.J. et al. (1996) Consensus guidelines for the clinical and pathologic diagnosis of dementia with Lewy bodies (DLB): report of the consortium on DLB international workshop. Neurology 47, 1113–1124

16. McKeith, I.G., Perry, E.K. & Perry, R.H. (1999) Report of the second dementia with Lewy body international workshop: diagnosis and treatment. Consortium on dementia with Lewy bodies. Neurology 53, 902–905

17. Leigh, P.N., Anderton, B.H., Dodson, A., Gallo, J.M., Swash, M. & Power D.M. (1988) Ubiquitin deposits in anterior horn cells in motor neurone disease Neurosci. Lett. 93, 197–203

18. Jackson, M., Lennox, G. & Lowe, J. (1996) Motor neurone disease-inclusion dementia. Neurodegeneration 5, 339–350

19. Morishima-Kawashima, M., Hasegawa, M., Takio, K., Suzuki, M., Titani, K. & Ihara, Y. (1993) Ubiquitin is conjugated with amino-terminally processed tau in paired helical filaments. Neuron 10, 1151–1160

20. Sampathu, D.M., Giasson, B.I., Pawlyk, A.C., Trojanowski, J.Q. & Lee, V.M. (2003) Ubiquitination of α-synuclein is not required for formation of pathological inclusions in α-synucleinopathies. Am. J. Pathol. 163, 191–100

20a Johnston, J.A., Ward, C.L. & Kopito, R.R. (1998) Aggresomes: a cellular response to misfolded proteins. J. Cell Biol. 143, 1883–1898

21. Olanow, C.W., Perl, D.P., DeMartino, G.N. & McNaught, K.S. (2003) Lewy-body formation is an aggresome-related process: a hypothesis. Lancet Neurol. 3, 496–503

22. Shimura, H., Schlossmacher, M.G., Hattori, N., Frosch, M.P., Trockenbacher, A., Schneider, R., Mizuno, Y., Kosik, K.S. & Selkoe, D.J. (2001) Ubiquitination of a new form of α-synuclein by parkin from human brain: implications for Parkinson's disease. Science 293, 263–269

23. Chung, K.K., Zhang, Y., Lim, K.L., Tanaka, Y., Huang, H., Gao, J., Ross, C.A., Dawson, V.L. & Dawson, T.M. (2001) Parkin ubiquitinates the α-synuclein-interacting protein, synphilin-1: implications for Lewy-body formation in Parkinson disease. Nat. Med. 7, 1144–1150

24. Zhang, Y., Gao, J., Chung, K.K., Huang, H., Dawson, V.L. & Dawson, T.M. (2000) Parkin functions as an E2-dependent ubiquitin-protein ligase and promotes the degradation of the synaptic vesicle-associated protein, CDCrel-1. *Proc. Natl. Acad. Sci. U.S.A.* **97**, 13354–13359

25. Corti, O., Hampe, C., Koutnikova, H., Darios, F., Jacquier, S., Prigent, A., Robinson, J.C., Pradier, L., Ruberg, M., Mirande, M. et al. (2003) The p38 subunit of the aminoacyl-tRNA synthetase complex is a Parkin substrate: linking protein biosynthesis and neurodegeneration. *Hum. Mol. Genet.* **12**, 1427–1437

26. Huynh, D.P., Scoles, D.R., Nguyen, D. & Pulst, S.M. (2003) The autosomal recessive juvenile Parkinson disease gene product, parkin, interacts with and ubiquitinates synaptotagmin XI. *Hum. Mol. Genet.* **12**, 2587–2597

27. Imai, Y., Soda, M., Inoue, H., Hattori, N., Mizuno, Y. & Takahashi, R. (2001) An unfolded putative transmembrane polypeptide, which can lead to endoplasmic reticulum stress, is a substrate of Parkin. *Cell* **105**, 891–902

28. Staropoli, J.F., McDermott, C., Martinat, C., Schulman, B., Demireva, E. & Abeliovich, A. (2003) Parkin is a component of an SCF-like ubiquitin ligase complex and protects postmitotic neurons from kainate excitotoxicity. *Neuron* **37**, 735–749

29. Goldberg, M.S., Fleming, S.M., Palacino, J.J., Cepeda, C., Lam, H.A., Bhatnagar, A., Meloni, E.G., Wu, N., Ackerson, L.C., Klapstein, G.J., et al. (2003) Parkin-deficient mice exhibit nigrostriatal deficits but not loss of dopaminergic neurons. *J. Biol. Chem.* **278**, 43628–43635

30. Lim, K.L., Chew, K.C., Tan, J.M., Wang, C., Chung, K.K., Zhang, Y., Tanaka, Y., Smith, W., Engelender, S., Ross, C.A., Dawson, V.L. & Dawson, T.M. (2005) Parkin mediates nonclassical, proteasomal-independent ubiquitination of synphilin-1: implications for Lewy body formation. *J. Neurosci.* **25**, 2002–2009

31. Mata, I.F., Lockhart, P.J. & Farrer, M.J. (2004) Parkin genetics: one model for Parkinson's disease. *Hum. Mol. Genet.* **13**, R127–R133

32. Leroy, E., Boyer, R., Auburger, G., Leube, B., Ulm, G., Mezey, E., Harta, G., Brownstein, M.J., Jonnalagada, S., Chernova, T., et al. (1998) The ubiquitin pathway in Parkinson's disease. *Nature (London)* **395**, 451–452

33. Saigoh, K., Wang, Y.L., Suh, J.G., Yamanishi, T., Sakai, Y., Kiyosawa, H., Harada, T., Ichihara, N., Wakana, S., Kikuchi, T. & Wada, K. (1999) Intragenic deletion in the gene encoding ubiquitin carboxy-terminal hydrolase in gad mice. *Nat. Genet.* **23**, 47–51

34. Liu, Y., Fallon, L., Lashuel, H.A., Liu, Z. & Lansbury, Jr, P.T. (2002) The UCH-L1 gene encodes two opposing enzymatic activities that affect α-synuclein degradation and Parkinson's disease susceptibility. *Cell* **111**, 209–218

35. Van Leeuwen, F.W., de Kleijn, D.P., Van den Hurk, H.H., Neubauer, A., Sonnemans, M.A., Sluijs, J.A., Koycu, S., Ramdjielal, R.D., Salehi, A., Martens, G.J. et al. (1998) Frameshift mutants of beta amyloid precursor protein and ubiquitin-B in Alzheimer's and Down patients. *Science* **279**, 242–247

36. Fischer, D.F., De Vos, R.A., Van Dijk, R., De Vrij, F.M., Proper, E.A., Sonnemans, M.A., Verhage, M.C., Sluijs, J.A., Hobo, B., Zouambia, M. et al. (2003) Disease-specific accumulation of mutant ubiquitin as a marker for proteasomal dysfunction in the brain. *FASEB J.* **17**, 2014–2024

37. Lam, Y.A., Pickart, C.M., Alban, A., Landon, M., Jamieson, C., Ramage, R., Mayer, R.J. & Layfield R. (2000) Inhibition of the ubiquitin–proteasome system in Alzheimer's disease. *Proc. Natl. Acad. Sci. U.S.A.* **97**, 9902–9906

38. Song, S., Kim, S.Y., Hong, Y.M., Jo, D.G., Lee, J.Y., Shim, S.M., Chung, C.W., Seo, S.J., Yoo, Y.J., Koh, J.Y. et al. (2003) Essential role of E2-25K/Hip-2 in mediating amyloid-β neurotoxicity. *Mol. Cell* **12**, 553–563

39. De Pril, R., Fischer, D.F., Maat-Schieman, M.L., Hobo, B., De Vos, R.A., Brunt, E.R., Hol, E.M., Roos, R.A. & Van Leeuwen F.W. (2004) Accumulation of aberrant ubiquitin induces aggregate formation and cell death in polyglutamine diseases. *Hum. Mol. Genet.* **13**, 1803–1813

40. Gray, D.A. (2001) Damage control — a possible non-proteolytic role for ubiquitin in limiting neurodegeneration. *Neuropathol. Appl. Neurobiol.* **27**, 89–94

41. Saudou, F., Finkbeiner, S., Devys, D. & Greenberg, M.E. (1998) Huntingtin acts in the nucleus to induce apoptosis but death does not correlate with the formation of intranuclear inclusions. *Cell* **95**, 55–66

42. Arrasate, M., Mitra, S., Schweitzer, E.S., Segal, M.R. & Finkbeiner, S. (2004) Inclusion body formation reduces levels of mutant huntingtin and the risk of neuronal death. *Nature (London)* **431**, 805–810

43. Webb, J.L., Ravikumar, B., Atkins, J., Skepper, J.N. & Rubinsztein, D.C. (2003) α-synuclein is degraded by both autophagy and the proteasome. *J. Biol. Chem.* **278**, 25009–25013

44. Shimura, H., Schwartz, D., Gygi, S.P. & Kosik, K.S. (2004) CHIP–Hsc70 complex ubiquitinates phosphorylated tau and enhances cell survival. *J. Biol. Chem.* **279**, 4869–4876

45. Fergusson, J., Landon, M., Lowe, J., Dawson, S.P., Layfield, R., Hanger, D.P. & Mayer, R.J. (1996) Pathological lesions of Alzheimer's disease and dementia with Lewy bodies brains exhibit immunoreactivity to an ATPase that is a regulatory subunit of the 26 S proteasome. *Neurosci. Lett.* **219**, 167–170

46. Bennett, E.J., Bence, N.F., Jayakumar, R. & Kopito, R.R. (2005) Global impairment of the ubiquitin–proteasome system by nuclear or cytoplasmic protein aggregates precedes inclusion body formation. *Mol. Cell* **17**, 351–365

47. Gregori, L., Hainfeld, J.F., Simon, M.N. & Goldgaber, D. (1997) Binding of amyloid beta protein to the 20 S proteasome. *J. Biol. Chem.* **272**, 58–62

48. Keck, S., Nitsch, R., Grune, T. & Ullrich O. (2003) Proteasome inhibition by paired helical filament-tau in brains of patients with Alzheimer's disease. *J. Neurochem.* **85**, 115–122

49. Thrower, J.S., Hoffman, L., Rechsteiner, M. & Pickart, C.M. (2000) Recognition of the polyubiquitin proteolytic signal. *EMBO J.* **19**, 94–102

12

The ubiquitin–proteasome system and skeletal muscle wasting

Didier Attaix[1], Sophie Ventadour,
Audrey Codran, Daniel Béchet, Daniel Taillandier
and Lydie Combaret

Human Nutrition Research Centre of Clermont-Ferrand and INRA,
Nutrition and Protein Metabolism Unit, 63122 Ceyrat, France

Abstract

The ubiquitin–proteasome system (UPS) is believed to degrade the major contractile skeletal muscle proteins and plays a major role in muscle wasting. Different and multiple events in the ubiquitination, deubiquitination and proteolytic machineries are responsible for the activation of the system and subsequent muscle wasting. However, other proteolytic enzymes act upstream (possibly m-calpain, cathepsin L, and/or caspase 3) and downstream (tripeptidyl-peptidase II and aminopeptidases) of the UPS, for the complete breakdown of the myofibrillar proteins into free amino acids. Recent studies have identified a few critical proteins that seem necessary for muscle wasting {i.e. the MAFbx (muscle atrophy F-box protein, also called atrogin-1) and MuRF-1 [muscle-specific RING (really interesting new gene) finger 1] ubiquitin–protein ligases}. The characterization of their signalling pathways is leading to new pharmacological approaches that can be useful to block or partially prevent muscle wasting in human patients.

[1]To whom correspondence should be addressed (email attaix@clermont.inra.fr).

Introduction

Skeletal muscle is the major protein reservoir in the body. This tissue exhibits very high plasticity and muscle proteins can be mobilized into free amino acids under disuse conditions (i.e. immobilization, denervation etc.), in starvation and in numerous pathological states (cancer cachexia, AIDS, sepsis, renal failure, diabetes, burn injury, trauma etc.) [1,2]. In the latter instances, both depressed protein synthesis and enhanced proteolysis in skeletal muscle provide the organism with free amino acids. These amino acids are used for providing energy (by direct oxidation and neoglucogenesis), as precursors of acute-phase protein synthesis in the liver, and to maintain protein synthesis in vital organs (e.g. heart, brain, lungs) (Figure 1).

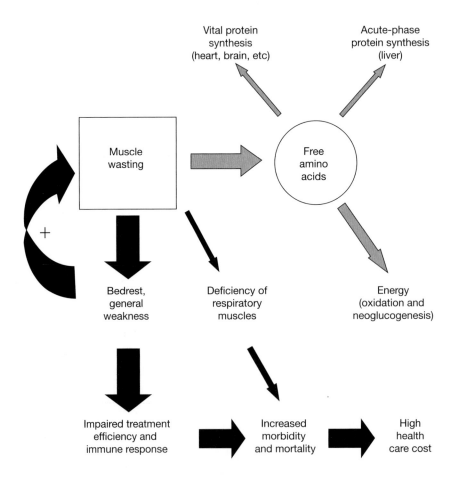

Figure 1. Positive and negative effects of muscle wasting
Positive effects (blue arrows) of muscle wasting prevail in the initial catabolic phase and negative effects (black arrows) prevail in sustained catabolic conditions.

Whether muscle atrophy results mainly from either depressed protein synthesis or enhanced proteolysis in catabolic states is still a matter of debate. However, the increased proteolysis contributes greatly to muscle wasting; various treatments that only block muscle proteolysis, without any detectable effect on protein synthesis, result in an improvement in muscle mass (see [3] for an example). Furthermore, during the last 10 years, overwhelming evidence that the UPS (ubiquitin–proteasome system) plays a key role in the control of muscle mass has been provided. We review this evidence and discuss recent findings that may lead to the development of strategies to prevent or limit muscle wasting.

The ubiquitination/deubiquitination machinery is up-regulated in muscle wasting

The UPS involves two successive steps. The target protein is polyubiquitinated (i.e. tagged by the covalent attachment of a polyubiquitin degradation signal) and then it is recognized by the 26 S proteasome, which degrades the substrate into peptides (Figure 2).

Polyubiquitination involves the sequential action of the ubiquitin-activating enzyme (E1), ubiquitin-conjugating enzymes (E2s) and ubiquitin–protein ligases (E3s) (Figure 2). Increased skeletal muscle mRNA levels for ubiquitin have been reported in several catabolic states in both rodents and humans [1,2]. This adaptation prevails in both type-I and -II skeletal muscle fibres, but is more marked in the latter, as is the increased proteolysis. Elevated ubiquitin mRNA levels reflect increased transcription in muscles from acidotic and diabetic rats [4]. *In vitro* studies with glucocorticoid-treated L6 muscle cells demonstrated that Sp1 and MEK1 [MAPK (mitogen-activated protein kinase)/ERK (extracellular-signal-regulated kinase) kinase-1) regulated ubiquitin transcription [4].

E1 has low expression in skeletal muscle and its mRNA level is not regulated in catabolic states [1]. This is not surprising because E1 is an extremely active enzyme, capable of charging excess amounts of E2 with ubiquitin, and is a common element in all pathways of ubiquitination.

There are possibly up to 40 E2s in mammalian cells. However, only a rather small number of E2s are overexpressed in several, but not all, instances of muscle wasting. This includes the 14 kDa E2 [or HR6B/UBC2 (ubiquitin-conjugating enzyme 2)], the 20 kDa E2, and UBC4/UBC5 isoforms [5].

One E2 generally interacts with one or a limited number of E3 species (and conversely), which recognize specific protein substrates. E3s form by far the largest family of ubiquitination enzymes, with a possible 1000 members in humans. However, only a limited number of E3s that are up-regulated in muscle wasting have been identified. The first was E3α/UBR1 (ubiquitin protein ligase E3 component n-recogin 1), the ubiquitous N-end rule RING (really interesting new gene)-finger ligase that functions with the 14 kDa E2. Both

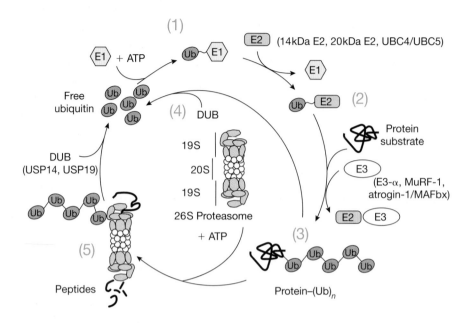

Figure 2. Schematic representation of the muscle UPS
Steps (1) to (3): polyubiquitination. The free ubiquitin (Ub) forms a thiol ester bond with the E1
(1), and then with an E2 (2); a given E2 and/or E3 covalently attaches a polyubiquitin degradation
signal to the protein substrate (3). Step (4): deubiquitination. Erroneously tagged protein substrates can be deubiquitinated by the DUBs. Step (5): breakdown of the substrate. The polyubiquitin degradation signal is recognized by at least the non-ATPase S5a and the ATPase S6' subunits of the 19 S complex and detached from the substrate. The latter is unfolded, injected into
the proteolytic chamber of the 20 S proteasome where it is cut into peptides, and the polyubiquitin degradation signal is recycled into free ubiquitin. The E2, E3 and DUB species that are activated in muscle wasting are shown in parentheses.

enzymes are involved in the ubiquitination of soluble muscle proteins.
Although increased mRNA levels for the 14 kDa E2 and E3α have been
observed in various catabolic models by Northern blotting, their respective
protein levels did not change in such instances [1,5]. Furthermore, and surprisingly, gene microarray experiments did not reveal any substantial increase in the
expression of the two enzymes [6]. Finally, knockout mice for the 14 kDa E2
and E3α do not exhibit substantial changes in muscle size in the fasted and fed
states respectively [5]. Thus the physiological significance of the N-end rule
pathway in muscle protein ubiquitination remains totally unclear. Two muscle-
specific E3s, called atrogin-1/MAFbx (muscle atrophy F-box protein) and
MuRF-1 (muscle-specific RING-finger 1) that seem to be systematically overexpressed in several catabolic conditions have been identified [7]. Atrogin-
1/MAFbx and MuRF-1 interact with the α-actinin-2–calcineurin A complex in
cardiomyocytes [8] and with titin, telethonin, myotilin, nebulin, troponin I,
troponin T1, troponin T3 and myosin light-chain-2 in skeletal muscle cells [9].
There has been much interest in the elucidation of the mechanisms that regulate

the expression of these E3s because knockout mice for either enzyme were partially resistant to muscle atrophy. The increased transcription of atrogin-1/MAFbx is under the control of FoxO (forkhead box O), the forkhead transcription factor [10], while MuRF-1 transcription is driven by the activation of NF-κB (nuclear factor κB) [11]. However, the latter paper challenged the role of atrogin-1/MAFbx in muscle wasting. Indeed, in these experiments where muscle wasting was clearly ubiquitin-dependent, the mRNA levels for atrogin-1/MAFbx were normal [11].

Skeletal muscle also contains many isoforms of DUBs (deubiquitinating enzymes), which are very active in soluble muscle extracts. UBP45 (ubiquitin-binding protein 45) and UBP69 are two DUBs involved in the regulation of cell differentiation [5]. At least two other DUBs are overexpressed in muscle wasting. Gene array studies in four different muscle wasting conditions have identified USP14 (ubiquitin-specific protease 14), which associates with the proteasome [6]. Another recent paper has also identified USP19, a DUB that does not bind to the proteasome [12]. Although it is unknown whether the protein levels of either USP14 or USP19 are modified under such circumstances, it is likely that the up-regulation of such enzymes helps to recycle free ubiquitin more efficiently when the UPS is stimulated (Figure 2). However, the pattern of expression of USP19 is not strictly parallel to the enhanced ubiquitin-dependent proteolysis, but is inversely proportional to muscle mass. Indeed, preliminary data indicate that this enzyme may have very specific substrates and could play a role in cell growth [12].

In vivo muscle ubiquitin-conjugates accumulate in some wasting conditions [1,2,5], suggesting that their breakdown by the 26 S proteasome is rate-limiting. However, in other studies there was no accumulation of ubiquitin-conjugates although the UPS was activated (see [13] for an example). Several explanations may account for such discrepancies. Intracellular levels of ubiquitin-conjugates depend on ubiquitination rates, on their rates of breakdown, and on DUB activities. Thus the apparent level of ubiquitin-conjugates may not change globally, although these distinct processes may be regulated. For example, an increased rate of ubiquitination could be totally masked by an enhanced breakdown of the conjugates. *In vitro* rates of ubiquitination of endogenous ^{125}I-labelled ubiquitin conjugates and of a model substrate of the N-end rule pathway (i.e. [^{125}I]α-lactalbumin) increase in soluble muscle extracts from rats in various catabolic conditions [14,15]. Conversely, rates of ubiquitination decreased in muscle extracts of thyroid-hormone-deficient animals (where overall protein breakdown falls) and rose after treatment with these hormones [14].

The 26 S proteasome is up-regulated in muscle wasting

Various mechanisms that regulate the proteolytic/peptidase activities of the proteasome (e.g. the synthesis, processing and post-translational modifications of proteasome subunits, the assembly of 20 S and 26 S proteasomes, the binding of proteasome activators and inhibitors etc.) are very poorly documented in skeletal muscle. Thus in the following section we concentrate on established observations in muscle wasting.

About 10 years ago, the increased proteolysis seen in atrophying incubated muscles from starved, denervated, tumour-bearing, acidotic, septic and insulinopaenic rats was found to be ATP-dependent. By contrast, the inhibition of calpains and/or cathepsins in such muscles does not eliminate the elevated rates of proteolysis [1,2,13]. ATP is required for the activation of ubiquitin by E1 and proteolysis by the 26 S proteasome. The demonstration that only proteasome inhibitors (lactacystin, MG132) also suppress the enhanced rates of overall proteolysis in wasting conditions [1–4,15] provided strong support for a major role of the proteasome in the breakdown of muscle proteins.

Proteasomes are tightly associated with myofibrils in mature skeletal muscle [16] and possess five peptidase activities as reported in other cell types (chymotrypsin-, trypsin- or caspase-like, and branched-chain amino acid- or small neutral amino acid-preferring activities [17]). Compared to other tissues, both peptidase and proteolytic activities are low in rat muscle. Studies with artificial substrates have shown that the chymotrypsin-like peptidase activity increases in some muscle wasting conditions, but is unchanged in diabetes (reviewed in [1]). Discrepancies between rates of overall muscle proteolysis and some specific proteasome activities may have several explanations. First, the 20 S proteasome population comprises at least six distinct subtypes in skeletal muscle, including constitutive proteasomes, immunoproteasomes, and their intermediate forms. Thus the properties of a 20 S proteasome population isolated from muscle represent the average properties of the whole set of proteasomes subtypes. Secondly, the hydrolysis of artificial substrates may not reflect the *in vivo* situation with endogenous substrates. However, and contrastingly, both chymotrypsin- and trypsin-like peptidase activities were reduced when skeletal muscle proteasome-dependent proteolysis was impaired by chemotherapy [1,18,18a].

Expression and protein content of 20 S proteasome subunits

The 20 S proteolytic core associates with two 19 S regulatory complexes to form a 26 S proteasome (Figure 2). Numerous groups have reported that enhanced ATP- and/or proteasome-dependent rates of muscle proteolysis correlate with elevated mRNA levels for the β catalytic and α non-catalytic subunits of the 20 S proteasome [1–4]. However, gene array experiments have shown that a small number of subunits are actually overexpressed in different muscle wasting conditions [6]. There is very limited information about the protein levels of 20 S proteasome subunits in catabolic states. Increased protein abundance of one 20 S proteasome subunit correlates with enhanced mRNA levels for other subunits in cancer cachexia (reviewed in [1]). Conversely, when proteasome-dependent proteolysis was inhibited by chemotherapy to below basal levels, mRNA levels for 20 S proteasome subunits correlated with reduced protein levels of the two subunits [18,18a]. The overexpressed RC9 (rat C9) subunit entered active translation in the atrophying unweighted soleus muscle [1], and an increase in transcribed RC3 proteasome subunit mRNA was observed in acidosis [4]. Glucocorticoids [1,2,4] and TNF-α (tumour necrosis factor α) [1,3] up-regulate mRNA levels for 20 S proteasome subunits. Glucocorticoids induce proteasome C3 subunit transcription in L6 muscle cells by opposing the suppression of its transcription by NF-κB, whereas the glucocorticoid-dependent increased transcription of ubiquitin involves Sp1 and MEK1 [4]. Thus the increased co-ordinated transcription of several genes in the UPS results from the activation of alternative signalling pathways.

Expression and protein content of subunits of the 19 S complex

Some, but not all, mRNA levels for ATPase and non-ATPase subunits of the 19 S complex are also up-regulated in muscle wasting. However, this up-regulation clearly depends on a given catabolic state [1,5,15]. Furthermore, the mRNA levels and protein contents of the individual 19 S subunits are regulated independently, and do not systematically correlate with rates of proteolysis [3,18,18a]. The selective increased expression of some 20 S or 19 S proteasome subunits strongly suggests that these subunits may be rate-limiting in assembly of the mature complex [6]. Furthermore, these findings also suggest that, in muscle, in contrast to findings in yeast, different transcription factors or co-regulators appear to affect the expression of subgroups of proteasome subunits.

The major substrates of the muscle UPS are still poorly characterized

In several experiments, polyubiquitinated proteins accumulated preferentially in the myofibrillar, but not in the soluble, fraction of muscles from rodents in a catabolic state [1,3,19]. Furthermore, only ATP-depletion [1,13] and proteasome inhibitors (but not inhibitors of the cathepsins or calpains) [1,2] suppress the elevated 3-methylhistidine release by incubated atrophying muscles. Post-translational modifications of actin and pale myosins form 3-methylhistidine and its rate of appearance in incubation media only reflects the breakdown of these myofibrillar proteins [1]. These observations lead to the widely accepted concept that the major contractile proteins are substrates of the UPS. However, only a single myofibrillar protein has been identified so far as a ubiquitinated substrate of the proteasome. A yeast two-hybrid screen was performed to search for interaction partners of MuRF-1 in cultured myocytes that might be targets of its E3 activity. This screen identified troponin I as a MuRF-1 partner protein in these cells [20]. Other myofibrillar proteins (i.e. nebulin, troponins T1 and T3, myosin-light-chain-2 etc.) that also interact with MuRF-1 have been recently identified in skeletal muscle cells [9]. By contrast, other yeast two-hybrid screen experiments identified either α-actinin-2–calcineurin A complex [8] or MyoD [21] as binding partners of atrogin-1/MAFbx E3. Thus the proteins that are ubiquitinated in the myofibrillar fraction are still unidentified, except cardiac troponin I. Furthermore, substantial additional experiments are clearly required to demonstrate that the major contractile proteins (actin and pale myosin heavy chains) are actually ubiquitinated. Alternatively, the 26 S proteasome also degrades non-ubiquitinated protein substrates. In skeletal muscle at least, troponin C is degraded by the 26 S proteasome via a ubiquitin-independent mechanism [1]. Oxidized proteins are also believed to be degraded by the 20 S proteasome in a ubiquitin-independent fashion [1].

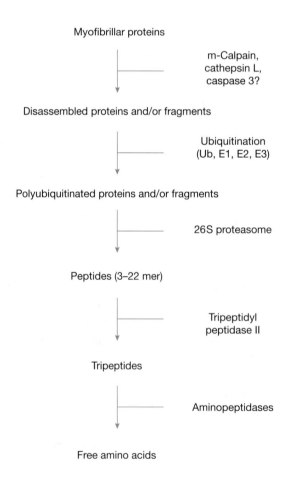

Figure 3. Schematic representation of the breakdown of myofibrillar proteins in skeletal muscle
The precise roles of calpains, cathepsin L and caspase 3 in the initial steps (upstream of the UPS) are still hypothetical, in contrast with steps downstream of the UPS. Ub, ubiquitin.

Functional relationships with other proteolytic enzymes

The 26 S proteasome degrades proteins only into peptides. Except when presented on MHC class I molecules, these peptides must undergo further hydrolysis, releasing free amino acids [1]. The extralysosomal peptidase TPP II (tripeptidyl-peptidase II) degrades peptides generated by the proteasome into tripeptides, which are further hydrolysed into free amino acids by aminopeptidases (Figure 3). TPP II expression, protein content and activity increases in septic muscles. In addition, the glucocorticoid receptor antagonist RU 38486 blunts these adaptations, indicating that glucocorticoids participate in the up-regulation of TPP II (reviewed in [1]).

Conversely, other proteases may act upstream of the proteasome (Figure 3). Specific interactions between the myofibrillar proteins appear to protect them from ubiquitin-dependent degradation, and the rate-limiting step in their degradation is probably their dissociation from the myofibril [1]. Calpains play key roles in the disassembly of sarcomeric proteins and in Z-band disintegration, resulting in the release of myofilaments. These data suggest that calpains are acting upstream of the proteasome [1]. Caspase 3 has also been implicated in the initial breakdown of actin [22]. Finally, cathepsin L is differentially up-regulated in various wasting conditions, and cathepsin L mRNA levels closely follow adaptations in the UPS [23]. These observations have been confirmed by gene-array experiments [5]. It remains to be demonstrated clearly whether there are functional connections between calpains, caspase 3, cathepsin L and the UPS. However, the expression of several proteolytic genes (including those encoding cathepsin L and several key components of the UPS) was down-regulated in mice knocked out for the muscle-specific calpain p94 (reviewed in [1]).

Signalling pathways responsible for muscle wasting

Major advances have been made in the elucidation of signalling pathways that regulate the UPS in muscle (see [24] for a recent detailed review). In brief, various cytokines (i.e. TNF-α, interleukin-6 etc.), hormones (i.e. glucocorticoids) and myostatin up-regulate the UPS [1–4,13,24]. Conversely, insulin or IGF-1 (insulin-like growth factor-1) inhibit the UPS [1,2,4,10]. The current concept is that the NF-κB transcription factor family mediates the activation of the UPS in most, if not all, muscle catabolic states via upstream signalling molecules that include cytokines and/or reactive oxygen species [11,24] (Figure 4).

Possible strategies to prevent muscle wasting

Muscle wasting is a key metabolic adaptation that presents many advantages in the short-term (see above). However, sustained muscle wasting rapidly becomes deleterious because the ability of the organism to recover from stress and/or pathologies is rapidly impaired; it results in prolonged hospitalization.

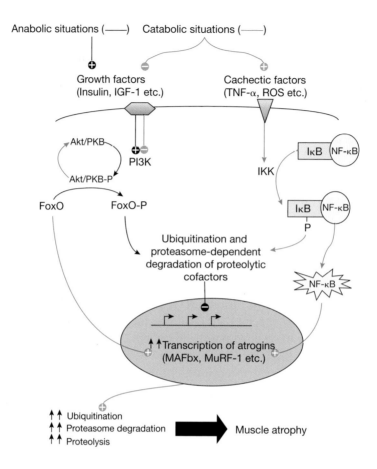

Figure 4. Schematic representation of the signalling pathways that trigger or repress the UPS in catabolic and anabolic conditions respectively
In catabolic conditions (blue lines) cachectic factors, such as TNF-α and/or reactive oxygen species (ROS), trigger IKK [IκB (inhibitory κB) kinase complex], which phosphorylates IκB and activates the IκB/NF-κB signalling pathway. PI3K (phosphoinositide 3-kinase) is also repressed (either because insulin and/or IGF-I circulating levels are low or because insulin and/or IGF-I resistance prevails). Thus, both Akt/PKB (protein kinase B) and the FoxO transcription factor are poorly phosphorylated (P). All these events lead to increased transcription of atrogins (i.e. atrophy genes), which ultimately results in a stimulation of the UPS and in muscle atrophy. By contrast, in anabolic situations (black lines) insulin and/or IGF-I activate PI3K. In that case, both Akt and FoxO are highly phosphorylated, and the latter event is ultimately responsible for repressed transcription of atrogins. In addition, the high levels of phosphorylated Akt induce increased protein synthesis (not shown). All these adaptations result in muscle growth.

Furthermore, pronounced muscle wasting ultimately results in increased morbidity and mortality when key muscles (i.e. respiratory muscles) become atrophied (Figure 1). For example, a large number of cachectic cancer, septic, burned, or traumatized patients die when muscle protein loss exceeds 70% (which corresponds to a loss of body weight of about 30%). Thus preventing muscle wasting is of major clinical importance and is a critical issue in terms of

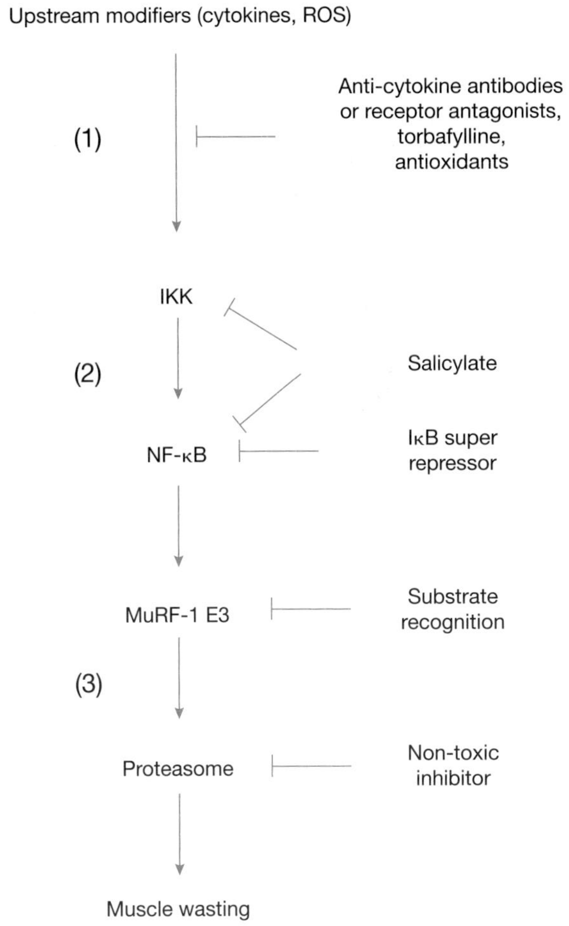

Upstream modifiers (cytokines, ROS)

(1)

Anti-cytokine antibodies
or receptor antagonists,
torbafylline,
antioxidants

IKK

(2)

Salicylate

NF-κB

IκB super
repressor

MuRF-1 E3

Substrate
recognition

(3)

Proteasome

Non-toxic
inhibitor

Muscle wasting

Figure 5. Possible strategies to block muscle wasting
The numbers in parentheses refer to three different possible approaches (see text). For more detailed information on torbafylline and salicylate or IκB (inhibitory κB) super repressor, see [3] and [9] respectively. IKK, IκB kinase complex; ROS, reactive oxygen species

health care costs (Figure 1). Recent studies have shown that there are at least three possible strategies to prevent the stimulation of the UPS in muscle wasting diseases (Figure 5). The first involves inhibitors of upstream modifiers like glucocorticoid, cytokine, and/or free radical production. A second possibility is to target the NF-κB pathway that is induced by one or several of the upstream modifiers. Finally, one may target some components of the ubiquitination (or perhaps deubiquitination) machinery or the proteasome itself. Any approach has advantages but also drawbacks and limitations (reviewed in [25]).

Conclusion

How the UPS degrades muscle proteins, and more particularly contractile proteins, remains largely unknown. Crucially, we need to identify the precise substrates of the UPS in muscle wasting and the precise signal(s) that target(s) myofibrillar proteins for breakdown. The complexity of the UPS itself and of its signalling pathways will clearly impede the identification of such mechanisms. Microarray analyses of transcription profiles [5] and (so far lacking) proteomic surveys of atrophying muscles should provide extremely valuable information and reveal new players in the muscle UPS. For example, the only two E3s that are believed to play a major role in muscle wasting have been initially characterized in three different models of inactivity (denervation atrophy, unweighting and immobilization [7]). Although the expression of these enzymes is also enhanced in other catabolic conditions [6], it is likely that other muscle-critical E3s remain to be identified in other catabolic conditions. Elucidating proteolytic mechanisms both upstream and downstream of the UPS that result in the complete degradation of muscle proteins is also of major importance. In theory the inhibition of any proteolytic enzyme involved in the sequential breakdown of the contractile proteins should prevent or at least limit muscle wasting.

Summary

- *Muscle wasting is a key metabolic adaptation that is initially beneficial to the organism in many severe pathological conditions. However, sustained muscle wasting is ultimately very deleterious and represents a major cause of increased morbidity and mortality.*
- *The UPS plays a major role in the control of muscle mass and is believed to degrade major contractile proteins. However, as yet only a single polyubiquitinated contractile protein (cardiac troponin I) has been identified.*
- *Multiple steps (ubiquitination/deubiquitination, proteasome activities) in the pathway are up-regulated in muscle wasting. However, few key components of the UPS that are strictly necessary for muscle wasting have been characterized.*
- *The complete breakdown of contractile proteins into free amino acids requires other proteolytic enzymes or systems acting both upstream and downstream of the UPS.*
- *Multiple and complex signalling pathways control the activation of the UPS in muscle wasting.*
- *Several potential approaches that are effective for blocking or reducing enhanced ubiquitin–proteasome-dependent proteolysis are now available in animal models of muscle wasting. In the future, such approaches should become effective in weight-losing and cachectic patients.*

Studies in the laboratory of the authors that led to some concepts reported herein are supported by the Institut National de la Recherche Agronomique, the Institut National de la Santé et de la Recherche Médicale, the Ministère Français de la Recherche, and Nestlé.

References

1. Attaix, D., Combaret, L., Kee, A.J. & Taillandier, D. (2003) Mechanisms of ubiquitination and proteasome-dependent proteolysis in skeletal muscle. In *Molecular Nutrition* (Zempleni, J. & Daniel, H., eds.), pp. 219–235, CAB International, Wallingford, Oxon, U.K.

2. Jagoe, R.T. & Goldberg, A.L. (2001) What do we really know about the ubiquitin–proteasome pathway in muscle atrophy? *Curr. Opin. Clin. Nutr. Metab. Care* **4**, 183–190

3. Combaret, L., Tilignac, T., Claustre, A., Voisin, L., Taillandier, D., Obled, C., Tanaka, K. & Attaix, D. (2002) Torbafylline (HWA 448) inhibits enhanced skeletal muscle ubiquitin–proteasome-dependent proteolysis in cancer and septic rats. *Biochem. J.* **361**, 185–192

4. Price, S.R. (2003) Increased transcription of ubiquitin–proteasome system components: molecular responses associated with muscle atrophy. *Int. J. Biochem. Cell Biol.* **35**, 617–628

5. Wing, S.S. (2005) Control of ubiquitination in skeletal muscle wasting. *Int. J. Biochem. Cell Biol.,* in the press

6. Lecker, S.H., Jagoe, R.T., Gilbert, A., Gomes, M., Baracos, V., Bailey, J., Price, S.R., Mitch, W.E. & Goldberg, A.L. (2004). Multiple types of skeletal muscle atrophy involve a common program of changes in gene expression. *FASEB J.* **18**, 39–51

7. Bodine, S.C., Latres, E., Baumhueter, S., Lai, V.K., Nunez, L., Clarke, B.A., Poueymirou, W.T., Panaro, F.J., Na, E., Dharmarajan, K. et al. (2001) Identification of ubiquitin ligases required for skeletal muscle atrophy. *Science* **294**, 1704–1708

8. Li, H.H., Kedar, V., Zhang, C., McDonough, H., Arya, R., Wang, D.Z. & Patterson, C. (2004) Atrogin-1/muscle atrophy F-box inhibits calcineurin-dependent cardiac hypertrophy by participating in an SCF ubiquitin ligase complex. *J. Clin. Invest.* **114**, 1058–1071

9. Glass, D.J., Witt, S.H., Granzier H., Witt, C.C. & Labeit, S. (2005) MURF-1 and MURF-2 target a specific subset of myofibrillar proteins redundantly: towards understanding MURF-dependent muscle ubiquitination. *J. Mol. Biol.* **350**, 713–722

10. Sandri, M., Sandri, C., Gilbert, A., Skurk, C., Calabria, E., Picard, A., Walsh, K., Schiaffino, S., Lecker, S.H. & Goldberg, A.L. (2004) Foxo transcription factors induce the atrophy-related ubiquitin ligase atrogin-1 and cause skeletal muscle atrophy. *Cell* **117**, 399–412

11. Cai, D., Frantz, J.D., Tawa, Jr, N.E., Melendez, P.A., Oh, B.C., Lidov, H.G., Hasselgren, P.O., Frontera, W.R., Lee, J., Glass, D.J. & Shoelson, S.E. (2004) IKKβ/NF-κB activation causes severe muscle wasting in mice. *Cell* **119**, 285–298

12. Combaret, L., Adegoke, O.A.J., Bedard, N., Baracos, V., Attaix, D. & Wing, S.S. (2005) USP19 is a ubiquitin-specific protease regulated in rat skeletal muscle during catabolic states. *Am. J. Physiol. Endocrinol.* Metab. **288**, E693–E700

13. Tiao, G., Fagan, J.M., Samuels, N., James, J.H., Hudson, K., Lieberman, M., Fischer, J.E. & Hasselgren, P.O. (1994) Sepsis stimulates nonlysosomal, energy-dependent proteolysis and increases ubiquitin mRNA levels in rat skeletal muscle. *J. Clin. Invest.* **94**, 2255–2264

14. Solomon, V., Baracos, V., Sarraf, P. & Goldberg, A.L. (1998) Rates of ubiquitin conjugation increase when muscles atrophy, largely through activation of the N-end rule pathway. *Proc. Natl. Acad. Sci. U.S.A.* **95**, 12602–12607

15. Combaret, L., Taillandier, D., Dardevet, D., Béchet, D., Rallière, C., Claustre, A., Grizard, J. & Attaix, D. (2004) Glucocorticoids regulate mRNA levels for subunits of the 19S regulatory complex of the proteasome in fast-twitch rat muscles. *Biochem. J.* **378**, 239–246

16. Bassaglia, Y., Cebrian, J., Covan, S., Garcia, M. & Foucrier, J. (2005) Proteasomes are tightly associated to myofibrils in mature skeletal muscle. *Exp. Cell Res.* **302**, 221–232

17. Farout, L., Lamare, M.C., Cardozo, C., Harrisson, M., Briand, Y. & Briand, M. (2000) Distribution of proteasomes and of the five proteolytic activities in rat tissues. *Arch. Biochem. Biophys.* **374**, 207–212

18. Tilignac, T., Temparis, S., Combaret, L., Taillandier, D., Pouch, M.N., Cervek, M., Cardenas, D.M., Le Bricon, T., Debiton, E., Samuels, S.E. et al. (2002) Chemotherapy inhibits skeletal muscle ubiquitin–proteasome-dependent proteolysis. *Cancer Res.* **62**, 2771–2777

18a. Tilignac, T., Temparis, S., Combaret, L., Taillandier, D., Pouch, M.N., Cervek, M., Cardenas, D.M., Le Bricon, T., Debiton, E., Samuels, S.E. et al. (2002) *Erratum. Cancer Res.* **62**, 7133

19. Taillandier, D., Aurousseau, E., Combaret, L., Guezennec, C.Y. & Attaix, D. (2003) Regulation of proteolysis during reloading of the unweighted soleus muscle. *Int. J. Biochem. Cell Biol.* **35**, 665–675

20. Kedar, V., McDonough, H., Arya, R., Li, H.H., Rockman, H.A. & Patterson, C. (2004) Muscle-specific RING finger 1 is a bona fide ubiquitin ligase that degrades cardiac troponin I. *Proc. Natl. Acad. Sci. U.S.A.* **101**, 18135–18140

21. Tintignac, L.A., Lagirand, J., Batonnet, S., Sirri, V., Leibovitch, M.P. & Leibovitch, S.A. (2005) Degradation of MyoD mediated by the SCF (MAFbx) ubiquitin ligase. *J. Biol. Chem.* **280**, 2847–2856

22. Du, J., Wang, X., Miereles, C., Bailey, J.L., Debigare, R., Zheng, B., Price, S.R. & Mitch, W.E. (2004) Activation of caspase-3 is an initial step triggering accelerated muscle proteolysis in catabolic conditions. *J. Clin. Invest.* **113**, 115–123

23. Deval, C., Mordier, S., Obled, C., Béchet, D., Combaret, L., Attaix, D. & Ferrara, M. (2001) Identification of cathepsin L as a differentially expressed message associated with skeletal muscle wasting. *Biochem. J.* **360**, 143–150

24. Jackman, R.W. & Kandarian, S.C. (2004) The molecular basis of skeletal muscle atrophy. *Am. J. Physiol. Cell Physiol.* **287**, C834–C843

25. Attaix, D., Ventadour, S., Taillandier, D. & Combaret, L. (2005) The ubiquitin–proteasome pathway: limitations and opportunities. *J. Support. Oncol.* **3**, 221–222

13

The ubiquitin–proteasome system and cancer

Anny Devoy, Tim Soane, Rebecca Welchman and R. John Mayer[1]

School of Biomedical Sciences, University of Nottingham Medical School, Queen's Medical Centre, Nottingham NG7 2UH, U.K.

Abstract

The ubiquitin proteasome system (UPS) has emerged from obscurity to be seen as a major player in all regulatory processes in the cell. The concentrations of key proteins in diverse regulatory pathways are controlled by post-translational ubiquitination and degradation by the 26 S proteasome. These regulatory cascades include growth-factor-controlled signal-transduction pathways and multiple points in the cell cycle. The cell cycle is orchestrated by a combination of cyclin-dependent kinases, kinase inhibitors and protein phosphorylation, together with the timely and specific degradation of cyclins and kinase inhibitors at critical points in the cell cycle by the UPS. These processes provide the irreversibility needed for movement of the cycle through gap 1 (G_1), DNA synthesis (S), gap 2 (G_2) and mitosis (M). The molecular events include cell-size control, DNA replication, DNA repair, chromosomal rearrangements and cell division. It is doubtful whether these events could be achieved without the temporally and spatially regulated combination of protein phosphorylation and ubiquitin-dependent degradation of key cell-cycle regulatory proteins. The oncogenic transformation of cells is a multistep process that can be triggered by mutation of genes for proteins involved in regulatory processes from the cell surface to the nucleus. Since the

[1]To whom correspondence should be addressed
(email john.mayer@nottingham.ac.uk).

UPS has critical functions at all these levels of control, it is to be expected that UPS activities will be central to cell transformation and cancer progression.

Intracellular proteolysis

The Nobel Prize for Chemistry was awarded in 2004 to the discoverers of the ubiquitin system of protein degradation. Intracellular proteolysis occurs by several mechanisms: the UPS (ubiquitin–proteasome system), autophagy (wrapping a double membrane around cytoplasm to form an autophagosome, with subsequent fusion with a lysosome) and the endosome–lysosome system (endocytosis of membrane components to form endosomal vesicles followed by fusion with a lysosome) It turns out that molecular events in these distinct cellular protein-degradation systems are controlled by the covalent attachment of ubiquitin or ubiquitin-like molecules to target proteins. This illustrates the diverse utilization of the 'ubiquitin superfold' in the course of evolution. The ubiquitin fold can be attached (covalently linked) to target proteins or can be genetically built into proteins for diverse downstream functions. A generic term for the complete family of covalently linked ubiquitin-like molecules and built-in ubiquitin folds is 'ubiquitons'. The conjugatable ubiquitons are used for a variety of purposes in the cell, in addition to acting as a signal for degradation by the 26 S proteasome. The diverse uses of the ubiquiton in the life process is a tribute to the parsimonious nature of evolution and the reason for the award of the Nobel Prize [1].

It is worth noting that a mere 30 years ago, the widely accepted dogma was that the degradation of proteins in cells was improbable or did not occur, since such a process would 'waste' energy. It was thought that the ATP invested in protein synthesis was too valuable to expend by subsequently destroying the proteins. However, it has been known for 52 years [2] that intracellular proteolysis proceeds by mechanisms requiring ATP! That proteins should be degraded by energy-dependent reactions seemed unlikely, since proteolytic enzymes in the gut and blood did not require ATP hydrolysis for their activities. The requirement of ATP for intracellular proteolysis was considered theoretically unnecessary and therefore probably experimentally wrong! This is not the case: ATP is required by the UPS at several stages and is necessary for the use of ubiquitin and ubiquitin-like molecules for autophagy and the endosome–lysosome systems.

The process of protein ubiquitination is driven by three classes of enzymes: E1, E2 and E3. Ubiquitin is activated by a ubiquitin-activating enzyme (E1), transferred to a ubiquitin-conjugating enzyme (E2) and then handed to a ubiquitin ligase (E3) for covalent attachment to the ε amino group of a lysine residue of a target protein (Figure 1). A ubiquitin chain, consisting of at least four ubiquitins linked via Lys^{48} of the previous ubiquitin, acts as a signal for protein degradation. The polyubiquitinated protein is recognized and binds the 26 S proteasome. The 26 S proteasome consists of a 20 S catalytic

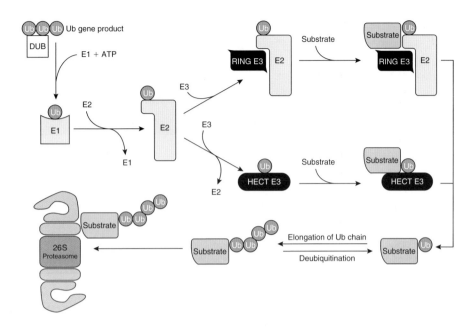

Figure 1. The UPS

Ubiquitin-fusion gene products are cleaved to release monomeric ubiquitin by a subgroup of DUBs. Ubiquitin (Ub) is activated by E1 and ATP. Activated ubiquitin is passed to an E2. There are two major classes of E3s: HECT ligases, which directly conjugate ubiquitin before ligating it to the targeted substrate, and RING ligases, which chaperone the Ub-bound E2 to, and facilitate the ubiquitination of the, targeted substrate. Polyubiquitin chains can be assembled by further rounds of ubiquitination, or disassembled by DUBs. Proteins with at least four Ubs in a chain are targeted for degradation by the proteasome.

barrel-like core with a multiprotein 19 S regulator at each end of the 20 S core. Each target protein is deubiquitinated, unwound by the hexameric ring of ATPases in the base of the 19 S regulator, and fed into the central chambers of the 20 S core for fragmentation into small peptides [3].

This UPS has a central role in the degradation of cytosolic and nuclear proteins and therefore in the control of the cell cycle and cancer.

The cell cycle

The cell cycle can be divided into stages, as indicated in Figure 2. In rapidly growing and dividing cells, the cycle describes two major phases: interphase and mitosis. In the former process (interphase), a sequential unidirectional set of events occurs that can be divided into a gap (G_1) between mitosis and where DNA synthesis and chromosomal replication take place (S phase), followed by another gap (G_2) before mitosis (M) takes place. In the latter process (mitosis), chromosomes are segregated to the two daughter cells followed by cell division (cytokinesis). The cell cycle is a critical time for every cell since any mistake may lead to DNA damage, genome instability, cell death or cancer. At

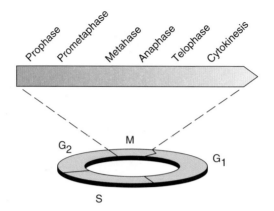

Figure 2. The eukaryotic cell cycle
The eukaryotic cell cycle can be divided into four distinct phases: G_1, S and G_2 together are called interphase. This is the period during which DNA synthesis takes place. During mitosis (M phase), chromosome segregation into two daughter cells occurs.

every step in the cycle there must be checks and balances to ensure that only normally replicated DNA is incorporated into the daughter cells.

The key questions are: first, what mechanisms ensure that one process is complete before the next process starts and, secondly, what mechanisms ensure the strict alternation of S-phase and M-phase? The answer to the first question is 'checkpoints', which are safe stopping points where progress can be halted and previous events subjected to biochemcial quality control. The answer to the second question is a carefully constructed set of regulator proteins that are controlled by phosphorylation and dephosphorylation and by ubiquitin-dependent degradation. Cells deemed to have failed the checkpoint scrutiny may be eliminated by apoptosis. If the checkpoints and apoptosis fail to operate properly, then a cell with damaged DNA may survive, eventually to become a cancer cell.

Accelerators and brakes

The orderly irreversible progression of the cell cycle is controlled by molecular machines. These molecular machines consist of many protein components, including Cdks (cyclin-dependent kinases) and kinase inhibitors (Figure 3). The concentration of every protein in the cell is determined by the balance between a rate of synthesis of the protein (Ks) that depends on transcription of the gene and translation of the mRNA, and a rate of degradation (Kd) of the protein. The concentration of each protein (P) in a steady state is given by:

$P=Ks/Kd$

The complexity of the cell cycle requires both the ordered synthesis and degradation of proteins to ensure the unidirectionality of the process. A seminal finding supporting the overall notion was made in 1983, by Tim Hunt

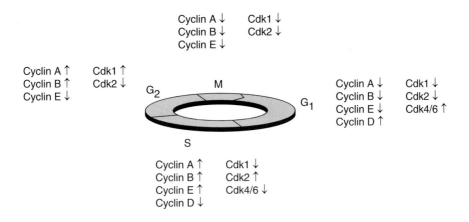

Figure 3. The regulation of the cell cycle by Cdks
The activities of the major Cdks oscillate during the cell cycle, as a result of the levels of cyclins present at each stage.

and colleagues, for which he was awarded a Nobel Prize. They found that several proteins in rapidly dividing sea-urchin embryos varied in concentration with a cyclical periodicity dependent on continuous synthesis and periodic degradation at the end of the cell cycle [4]. These proteins were named cyclins and were subsequently found to be essential for the activity of the cell cycle by controlling kinases, hence the term Cdk. However, the ubiquitin story was still in its infancy and it took many years to realize that the cyclical disappearance of the cyclins was due to ubiquitin-dependent proteolysis. It is now known that the concentrations of these key cell-cycle regulators are controlled by both phosphorylation and ubiquitination, followed by proteasomal degradation.

Ubiquitin ligases involved in cell-cycle control

The interplay between the UPS, Cdks and inhibitors is shown in Figure 4. The devil is, as usual, in the detail. Two classes of related ubiquitin-protein ligases: the SCF (Skp1–Cdc53/Cul1–F-box protein) ligase and the APC/C (anaphase-promoting complex/cyclosome) are used to ubiquitinate cell-cycle proteins at defined transition points in the cycle. There are three groups of E3s: the single subunit RING-finger type, e.g. the p53 targeting Mdm2 (muring double minute clone 2 oncoprotein) E3; the multisubunit RING-finger type, e.g the SCF and APC/C E3s; and the HECT (homologous to E6-AP C-terminus)-domain type, e.g. the cellular E6-AP (E6-associated protein) ligase that is ambushed by the papilloma virus E6 protein and used to ubiquitinate p53 for proteasomal degradation as part of the process of causing cervical carcinoma.

Most of the multi-subunit RING-finger types of E3 ligases contain a cullin protein (Figure 5), so named because these proteins appear to be

G₁ phase

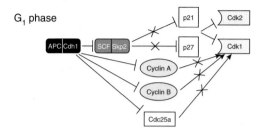

G₁–S, S and G₂ phase

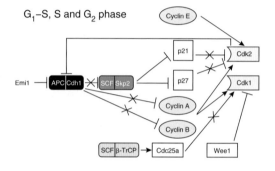

G₂–M phase

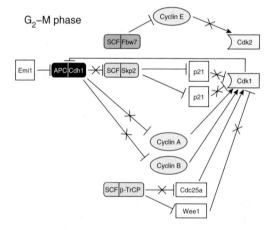

Mitotic progression and exit

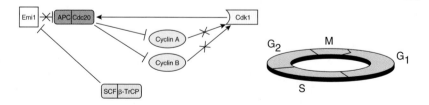

involved in a 'cull' of proteins by degradation. Each cullin (there are seven different cullins) acts as a molecular scaffold that interacts simultaneously with an adaptor protein Skp1 (S-phase associated protein-1) and a RING-finger protein (Rbx1–Roc1–Roc2) and a specific E2. In turn, Skp1 binds to one of many F-box proteins, the specificity factors that recognize phosphorylated proteins that are to be ubiquitinated by the SCF ubiquitin ligase complex. Different F-box proteins are used to identify different cell-cycle protein substrates at different stages of the cell cycle, adding to the regulatory power of the ubiquitin-ligase system to control the cell cycle.

The APC/C ubiquitin ligase is a more complex variant of the SCF ubiquitin ligase. The catalytic core of the APC/C consists of a cullin-like protein (Apc2), a RING-finger protein (APC/C11) and an E2. In addition to an F-box protein, the APC/C contains ten proteins that appear to create a hollow particle that functions as a scaffold for the cullin-like protein, and probably controls protein-substrate entry to the ligase complex. Another distinguishing feature of the APC/C is that the complex has two alternative substrate selection subunits, Cdc20 (cell-division cycle 20) and Cdh1, that are critical for substrate selection at different stages of the cell cycle. The comparative structures of the complexes are shown in Figure 5.

Kinase regulation and the cell cycle

As shown in Figure 4, each phase of the cell cycle is controlled by a complex, yet beautifully orchestrated, set of interactions between Cdks and E3s [5]. The kinases set the pace of the cyclic activities, with the ligases acting as executioners of key players to maintain irreversible progression. The kinases have an extra tier of regulation, i.e. the kinase inhibitors, p21 and p27. These inhibitors are crucial for kinase regulation and are, in turn, substrates for ubiquitination and degradation, so that kinases become active on demand as required for cell-cycle progression. The key kinases, Cdk1 and Cdk2, are present, but inactivated by these inhibitors in G_1. At the G_1–S checkpoint, DNA synthesis starts and duplication of the centrosome takes place. The centrosome is the microtubule-organizing centre adjacent to the nucleus that controls the microtubules of the mitotic spindle. These events are accompanied by a large increase in the activity of Cdk2 and subsequent phosphorylation of Cdk2 substrates, peaking during DNA synthesis and centrosome duplication in G_2, after which Cdk2 is inactivated. The activities, of Cdk2 can be

Figure 4. The UPS and cell-cycle regulation
The arrowhead indicates activation, the T-bar indicates inhibition and the crosses indicate abrogation of the activity. The levels of each cyclin are tightly controlled by the presence of ubiquitin ligases APC and SCF. The activity of these multi-subunit complexes are in turn controlled by the presence of particular substrate-determining subunits, e.g. the Cdh1 and Cdc20 subunits of the APC E3. The picture is further complicated by the roles of Cdk inhibitors p21, p27, Wee1 and Cdc25a. Modified from Figure 3 in Cardozo, M. and Pagano, M. (2004) *Nat. Rev. Mol. Cell Biol.* **5**, 739–751 (reproduced with permission from Nature; http://www.nature.com).

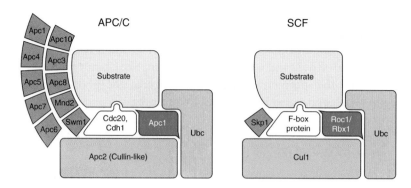

Figure 5. The APC/C and SCF ligases
The multi-subunit ubiquitin ligases SCF and APC/C contain many analogous components. The substrate specificity is determined by either Cdc20 or Cdh1 in APC/C, and by the specific F-box proteins in SCF.

complimented by low Cdk1 and possible further kinase activities i.e. cell-cycle progression can continue in the absence of Cdk2. Redundancy of kinase activities is a feature of cell-cycle control, as in other critical regulatory kinase cascades in the cell.

Coincident with the decline in Cdk2 activity in G_2, there is a large increase in Cdk1 activity to create the phosphorylated proteins necessary for mitosis. Anaphase (where each duplicated chromosome separates and moves apart) is defined by a sudden decline in Cdk1 activity. The activities of Cdk1 and Cdk2 are maintained at low levels until the next G_1–S transition. The known roles of the APC/C and SCF ubiquitin ligases in these transitions are shown in Figure 3. A key feature is that the ligases ubiquitinate not only key protein substrates, but also each other, to attenuate respective ligase activities in the cycle. The interplay of the APC/C and SCF ligases is at the heart of the regulation of the cell cycle. The cell-cycle proteins are synthesized in anticipation of their eventual need for cycle progression. However, the cycle can idle because of the ubiquitin-dependent elimination of cell-cycle-protein targets to keep cycle proteins at low levels. In this way, cell-cycle progression is kept in check, at least in normal cells. In cancer cells it is a different story.

In G_1, the levels of the p21 and p27 inhibitors are high and levels of cyclin A (that controls both Cdk1 and Cdk2) and cyclin B (that controls Cdk1) are low. The reason is that the APC/C^{Cdh1} ligase (the F-box substrate receptor of a ligase, e.g. Cdh1, is always represented by a superscript) is active, and destroys the SCF ubiquitin ligase, preventing degradation of p21 and p27 Additionally, APC/C^{Cdh1} degrades cyclin A and cyclin B to keep Cdk1 activity low. When the cycle is triggered by growth factors to move into G_1–S, S and G_2, the p21 and p27 inhibitors are degraded and cyclins A and B accumulate to drive up the activity of Cdk2. The concentration of Cdk1 is kept low. A key event is the transcription and translation of the Emi1 (early mitotic inhibitor-1) protein. This is driven by the adenovirus E2 promoter-binding transcription fac-

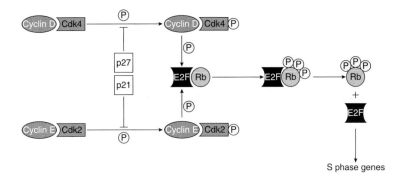

Figure 6. The pRb and the G₁/S phase of the cell cycle
Cdk hyperphosphorylation and inactivation of pRb in the E2F–pRb complex releases E2F, a transcription factor for S-phase genes. P, phosphate.

tor E2F (see Figure 6), which also up-regulates the synthesis of cyclins A, B and E. The Emi1 protein inhibits APC/C^{Cdh1} activity. This decrease in APC/C activity increases the concentration of SCF^{Skp2} and cyclins A and B, which results in the degradation of p21 and p27 and the activation of Cdk2. This raises the question of why Cdk1 does not accumulate. The reason is that another ubiquitin ligase, SCF$^{β-TrCP}$ (SCF β-transducin repeat-containing protein), enters the scene. This ligase ubiquitinates the Cdc25a phosphatase, which is degraded. Therefore, Cdc25a cannot dephosphorylate Cdk1, which is maintained inactive by the kinase Wee1. The end result is accumulation and high activity of Cdk2–cyclin E and Cdk2–cyclin A to drive DNA synthesis and chromosome replication. The G₂–M transition is accompanied by a decrease in the concentration of cyclin E after ubiquitination of cyclin E by another ubiquitin ligase, SCF^{Fbw7}. The APC/C^{Cdh1} is still inhibited, as well as APC/C^{Cdc20}, by Emi1, but the concentration of Cdk1 now increases because of an increase in the activity of Cdc25a, which is only degraded in S and G₂ by SCF$^{β-TrCP}$ and by the demise of Wee1 kinase, again through the ubiquitination activity of SCF$^{β-TrCP}$. In late mitosis, both Cdk1 and Cdk2 are attenuated. The block on both APC/Cs is now lifted by the ubiquitination of Emi1 by SCF$^{β-TrCP}$ and its degradation. This results in activation of APC/C^{Cdc20}, which ubiquitinates securin, an inhibitor of the separase protease, that cleaves the cohesins and facilitates sister-chromatid separation. The Cdc20 protein needed for securin ubiquitination is predominately expressed late in the cell cycle, which is consistent with Cdc20 functioning in the metaphase–anaphase transition, during which chromosomes become arranged at the cell midline (metaphase) and then separate (anaphase). Significantly, Cdc20 becomes ubiquitinated and degraded once its functions are over, limiting the essential functions of Cdc20 to this part of the cell cycle [5].

A crucial point to emphasize is that the APC/C and SCF ligases are activated in different ways to integrate with the kinase activities of the cell cycle. The APC/C ubiqutin ligase is activated by phosphorylation, whereas the SCF-ubiquitin-ligase substrates are activated by phosphorylation [6]. No doubt, other protein cofactors are involved in the activities of the ligases, and these cofactors will contribute to the exquisite control of the cell cycle, which is so necessary to avoid genomic instability and cancer.

The APC/C promotes cyclin degradation in order to exit mitosis. The re-accumulation of cyclin A causes the inactivation of the APC/C and entry into S-phase. However, it was not clear until recently, how cyclin A could accumulate in the presence of active APC/C. This problem has been solved by the demonstration that, during G_1, APC/C^{Cdh1} autonomously becomes inactivated to allow cyclin A accumulation [7]. This is achieved by auto-ubiquitination and degradation of the E2 UbcH10 (ubiquitin-conjugating enzyme H10), that serves APC/C^{Cdh1}. It appears that other (possibly numerous) protein substrates of APC/C^{Cdh1} can prevent the ubiquitination of UbcH10, as long as these protein targets remain in G_1. After these substrates are degraded, UbcH10 becomes ubiquitinated and degraded, and cyclin A accumulates and causes entry into S phase. These data are interpreted to mean that alternating and self-perpetuating destruction of the E2 is central to the down-regulation of APC/C, allowing cyclin A accumulation and perpetuation of the cell cycle [7].

Note, however, that new data on the kinases regulating the cell cycle emerge continuously. For example, in the last few years, protein kinase B/Akt has come to centre stage as a cell-cycle regulator [8]. No doubt, interactions between protein kinase B/Akt and the UPS will emerge in the future.

The tumour suppressor gene product pRb (retinoblastoma protein)

Cell-cycle progression from G_1 through S and M clearly is controlled by protein phosphorylation and ubiquitination. There are several extracellular and intracellular cues that orchestrate these cyclical events. The replication of DNA and division of cells needs to be tightly regulated to prevent anomalous cell division and cancer. One method of regulation is through tumour suppressors. The first tumour suppressor to be discovered was pRb. Germ-line mutation in one allele of the pRb gene, together with somatic mutation in the other allele, causes retinoblastoma.

pRb is a key regulator upstream of the phases of the cell cycle, as it controls the E2F transcription factors (Figure 6) that control the expression of DNA-synthesis genes and collaborating gene products, e.g. the cyclins. The E2F transcription factors are complexed with active pRb. pRb can be hyperphosphorylated by Cdk4 and Cdk6. Normally, the activities of these kinases are blocked by p21 and 27, plus the inhibitors of kinases (INKs). Hyperphosphorylation of pRb causes inactivation of pRb, releasing E2F, with subsequent transcription of genes for proteins involved in DNA synthesis and cell-cycle progression [9]. Several viral proteins can interfere with the tumour-suppressor function of Rb and trigger DNA synthesis, and therefore facilitate viral replication and cancer, e.g. simian virus 40. Once the p21, p27 and INK blocks on Cdk4/6 are relieved and E2F activation of the expression of cyclin E–Cdk2 is commenced, cells are sometimes said to have crossed the 'restriction point'. The cells will proceed with DNA synthesis and chromosome replication with little upstream control, as is apparent in cells with mutant pRb that have lost the ability to restrain E2F. This results in cancer in the eye.

DNA repair and p53

The synthesis of DNA is not without error, particularly when subjected to environmental interference, e.g. radiation and carcinogens. Cells have elaborate DNA-repair mechanisms to repair different sorts of DNA damage, e.g. single-strand breaks or deletions. Protein ubiquitination and sumolylation (SUMO is a cousin of ubiquitin) are involved in the molecular machines that repair DNA damage. Additionally, protein ubiquitination is involved in the regulation of transcription, e.g. in chromatin remodelling through histone ubiquitination. The ubiquitination of proteins involved in DNA repair and gene expression again places ubiquitin at the hub of activities involved in genome stability, which becomes deranged in tumour cells [10].

The cell cycle pauses during DNA repair. If the DNA cannot be repaired then DNA synthesis and cell-cycle progression are aborted and apoptosis (programmed cell death) takes place. The DNA-repair process is regulated by a transcription factor called p53 [9]. The expression of p53 is dramatically increased in cells subjected to physical or chemical insults, affecting DNA quality. The p53 transcription factor activates the transcription of genes for proteins involved in DNA repair and apoptosis, e.g. caspases. If the DNA cannot be properly repaired then the apoptotic cascades are activated and cells with irrevocably damaged DNA are eliminated. Approximately 50% of human tumours have mutated p53 which is unable to cause apoptosis. Even with normal (wild-type) p53, any compromise of the transcription of DNA repair and apoptotic genes will be deleterious for the cell. The concentration of p53 is regulated by transcription and translation in response to DNA damage and other toxic cell stresses, and also by degradation. The ubiquitination of p53 is tightly controlled by several ubiquitin ligases, but the major ligase is called Mdm2 [11]. This solitary RING ligase is mutated in many tumours. Clearly, if p53 cannot function properly, then apoptosis will be impaired and cells will lose the option of p53-dependent apoptosis. Tumour cells, through genomic instability and alterations in response to intracellular and extracellular regulatory cues, progressively become autonomously dividing cells independent of any method of preventing cell division. In the absence of functioning p53 they are deprived of one mechanism of apoptosis. If the cells cannot deliberately die, they may acquire more genomic damage and become rampantly dividing cells. Such cancer cells may move throughout the body causing metastases. Metastatic cell growth is a characteristic of cancer progression. Many current treatments, e.g. chemotherapy and radiation, seem to activate p53-dependent apoptotic mechanisms in tumour cells, retaining active p53.

Growth factors and tumorigenesis

Cell division is controlled by extracellular growth factors in multicellular organisms. There are several signal-transduction pathways activated by the growth factors. The MAPK (mitogen-activated protein kinase) system is a major regulator of cell division [12]. The MAPK system consists of several parallel biochemical pathways (modules) that can be activated by growth-factor receptors. The general principle is that a MAPKKK (MAPK kinase kinase) phosphorylates a MAPKK (MAPK kinase), which phosphorylates a MAPK to drive cell-cycle events in the nucleus. For example, Raf kinase (MAPKKK) phosphorylates MEK1/2 [MAPK/ERK (extracellular-signal-regulated kinase) kinase] (MAPKK) that phosphorylates ERK1/2 (MAPK) to drive cell division.

The receptors that drive the MAPK pathways include the epidermal growth factor receptor and the platelet-derived growth factor receptor, and several other RTKs (receptor tyrosine kinases). The activity of these receptors must be switched off (down-regulated) to control cell division. One mechanism involves the ubiquitination of the cytosolic tails of the receptors as well as several of the downstream adaptor proteins that relay the activation signal to the nucleus to cause cell division. Receptor ubiquitination is part of the signalling system that causes receptor-mediated endocytosis to bring the receptors and associated proteins into the cell for degradation in endosome–lysosomes [13]. The ubiquitination of the cytosolic tails of the receptors is a crucial event in down-regulating the potent activity of these growth factor receptors. The ligands for these receptors often induce receptor oligomerization, which then activates the kinase pathways. Oligomerization of mutant forms of the receptors in the absence of ligand can trigger activation of the kinases and cause uncontrolled cell division, as occurs in several tumours, including breast cancer. Mutant ubiquitin ligases, with decreased catalytic activity directed at receptor tails, can prevent receptor internalization into endosomes and cause continuous kinase signalling and cancer. This occurs with mutated Cbl, a RING-finger ubiquitin ligase involved in RTK down-regulation [14]. Receptor ubiquitination is additionally controlled by deubiquitination. Mutations in the DUB (deubiquitinating enzyme) and tumour suppressor CYLD, which deubiquitinates proteins in the IKK [IκB (inhibitory κB) kinase complex] and negatively regulates NF-κB (nuclear factor κB) signalling, inhibits apoptosis and causes cylindromatosis, an autosomal-dominant skin-tumour condition [15]. A twist, emphasizing the importance of protein ubiquitination in signal transduction pathways, is that Raf-regulated MEKK1 (MEK kinase 21) is not only a kinase but also a ubiquitin ligase [16].

The attachment of a chain of ubiquitins to a target protein via Lys^{63} of each ubiquitin is not a degradation signal, but a signal for kinase activation, e.g. in the NF-κB regulatory pathway involved in activating the immune and inflammatory responses. The kinase pathway adaptor enzyme A20, a potent inhibitor of the NF-κB pathway, contains an N-terminal Lys^{63}-linked ubiquitin-chain deubiquitinating activity to deubiquitinate the RIP (receptor-interacting protein), and a C-terminal ubiquitinating activity to synthesize Lys^{48}-linked ubiquitin chains on RIP [17]. This catalytic strategy ensures the removal of Lys^{63}-linked ubiquitin chains and the construction of the degradation-specifying Lys^{48}-linked ubiquitin chains (perhaps simultaneously) to ensure efficient control of the NF-κB pathway. Tight regulation of the NF-κB pathway is again needed, since, for example, activation of the NF-κB pathway prevents apoptosis and could therefore contribute to cancer progression.

UPS defects in tumour cells

The UPS has multiple roles in the regulation of growth-signalling pathways, from cell-surface receptors and MAPK pathways, to the control of DNA replication and repair, chromosomal separation and cytokinesis. Therefore, mutations in genes of the UPS are increasingly seen to contribute to tumour progression and metasteses [18]. For example, mutation in the F-box-related receptor, the VHL (von Hippel–Lindau) tumour-suppressor protein that is a component of a CDL (cullin-dependent ligase), is causative of renal cell carcinoma [19]. The motif in a target protein recognized by F-box-like protein receptors for ubiquitin-ligase activity is not always a phosphorylated residue: the VHL protein recognizes a hydroxylated proline residue in a target protein. The most well-characterized protein substrate of the VHL receptor is called HIFα (hypoxia-inducible factor α). Mutations in the VHL protein prevent recognition of the motif in the target protein by the CDL^{VHL}, preventing regulated degradation of the HIF transcription factor. This results in continuous activation of the expression of HIF target genes, including that encoding VEGF (vascular endothelial growth factor), causing dysregulated endothelial cell proliferation. The pathological hallmark of renal cell carcinomas and their metasteses is high vascularization, because HIF cannot be degraded properly. Mutations in the F-box protein Skp2, and in other components of the ubiquitin ligases controlling the concentration of cyclins, e.g. cyclin E, are also oncogenic [20].

The subtleties of the UPS regulation of the cell cycle are illustrated by the roles of the first liver oncoprotein, gankyrin. This protein is a newly discovered 26 S proteasome subunit, but is also present in other protein complexes, including a complex containing Cdk4 that regulates the phosphorylation status of pRb and controls its degradation. Gankyrin was discovered in a yeast two-hybrid screen, as a specific interactor with one of the six ATPases (S6b) in the base of the 19 S regulator of the 26 S proteasome [21], and by subtractive hybridization, to detect genes overexpressed in hepatocellular carcinoma [22]. Gankyrin is a promiscuous ankyrin-repeat protein and, besides being present in complexes with pRb, is also in a complex with the ubiquitin ligase Mdm2. Consequently, gankyrin, via Mdm2, regulates the ubiquitination of p53. Overexpression of gankyrin causes ubiquitination and degradation of p53. The reduced concentration of p53 prevents apoptosis of liver cells that are experiencing growth stimulation and genomic instability. This eventually results in hepatocellular carcinoma [23]. Gankyrin, by binding to the 26 S proteasome via the S6b ATPase, may bring complexes containing Mdm2/ubiquitinated p53 (and pRb and other cell-cycle regulators) to the proteasome to facilitate the rapid unfolding of these proteins and their degradation. There are a number of other 'go-betweens' that can ferry ubiquitinated proteins to the 26 S proteasome for degradation [24], as illustrated in Figure 7.

Conclusion: the UPS and novel therapeutic intervention

As they say, 'the proof of the pudding is in the eating': could potent drugs that inhibit specific components of the UPS have a role in the treatment of cancer?

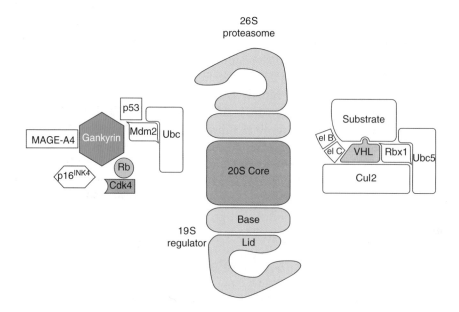

Figure 7. The delivery of ubiquitinated proteins to the 26 S proteasome
The 26 S proteasome consists of a 20 S core and a 19 S regulator subdivided into a 'base' containing six ATPases and a multisubunit 'lid'. Polyubiquitinated substrates can be chaperoned to the proteasome by E3 complexes: gankyrin can bind to an ATPase subunit to bring ubiquitinated p53 (in complex with its E3, Mdm2) to the proteasome for degradation. The VHL F-box protein can also bind an ATPase subunit. INK4, inhibitor of CDK4; MAGE-A4, melanoma antigen A4.

In a rather counterintuitive manner, an inhibitor (peptide boronic ester) of the catalytic activity of the proteasome named bortezomib (Velcade) is very efficacious in the treatment of intractable multiple myeloma [25]. This drug probably works by preventing the degradation of ubiquitinated IKK in myeloma cells and, therefore, preventing the anti-apoptotic activities of NF-κB in myeloma cells.

Intuitively, inhibitors of specific SCF ubiquitin ligases, e.g. enzymes targeting the p21 and p27 inhibitors of the Cdks, may have much more generalized effects on tumour-cell growth. The principle behind drug discovery (so far) is to find small compounds (less than approx. 1 kDa) that will bind to small structural pockets in proteins, such as the ligand binding site of a receptor, and prevent some biological activity, e.g. enzyme catalytic activity. The next challenge for the UPS is to determine whether small molecules can be found to block the activities of SCFs where the transfer of ubiquitin from the E2 to the target protein substrate requires a relatively large surface of the Rbx–Cul1–Skp1 F-box complex. Recently, compounds have been discovered that can block protein–protein interactions, e.g. Mdm2–p53. However, these compounds (Nutlins) rely on a structurally defined rigid area on Mdm2 [26]. The F-box binding sites for post-translationally modified residues in substrates might be suitable targets for interaction with small compounds, e.g. sites that bind phosphorylated residues, hydroxylated prolines and N-glycosylated residues in target proteins.

There is certainly the need for a chemical gear-change in drug discovery to find such drugs, since much of the intracellular chemistry of life involves protein–protein interactions generated by relatively weak non-covalent bonding over long distances on the protein surface.

The involvement of the UPS in probably all regulatory processes in the cell, including cell division and therefore cancer, has opened up a totally new view of cell physiology. It has been known for decades that exquisitely controlled extracellular proteases regulate vascular homoeostasis — blood clotting and complement activation. It is interesting that highly regulated intracellular proteases — the UPS and caspases — control cell life (division) and cell death!

Summary

- *The regulated cell cycle is at the heart of normal cell division.*
- *Dysfunctional regulation of the cell cycle is at the heart of cancer.*
- *The regulation of cell division from growth factor receptors to DNA replication, repair and chromosomal separation is controlled by phosphorylation/dephosphorylation and by ubiquitination/deubiquitination.*
- *Mutations in kinases/phosphatases and ubiquitin ligases/DUBs cause cancer.*
- *Drugs that target kinases and the UPS are effective in treating cancers.*

The Biotechnology and Biological Sciences Research Council, European Union, Wellcome Trust and Alzheimer's Research Trust are thanked for support of some of the work described.

References

1.   Mayer, R.J. (2005) The Nobel Prize for Chemistry 2004. *Eur. Biopharm. Rev.*, **Summer**, 34–39
2.   Simpson, M.V. (1953) The release of labeled amino acids from proteins in liver slices. *J. Biol. Chem.* **201**, 143–154
3.   Glickman, M.H. & Ciechanover, A. (2002) The ubiquitin–proteasome proteolytic pathway: destruction for the sake of construction. *Physiol. Rev.* **82**, 373–428
4.   Evans, T., Rosenthal, E.T., Youngblom, J., Distel, D. & Hunt, T. (1983) Cyclin: a protein specified by maternal mRNA in sea urchin eggs that is destroyed at each cleavage division. *Cell* **33**, 389–396
5.   Cardozo, T. & Pagano, M. (2004) The SCF ubiquitin ligase: insights into a molecular machine. *Nat. Rev. Mol. Cell Biol.* **5**, 739–751
6.   Reed, S.I. (2003) Ratchets and clocks: the cell cycle, ubiquitylation and protein turnover. *Nat. Rev. Mol. Cell Biol.* **4**, 855–864
7.   Rape, M. & Kirschner, M.W. (2004) Autonomous regulation of the anaphase-promoting complex couples mitosis to S-phase entry. *Nature (London)* **432**, 588–595
8.   Brazil, P., Yang, Z.-Z. & Hemmings, B.A. (2004) Advances in protein kinase B signalling: AKTion on multiple fronts. *Trends Biochem. Sci.* **29**, 233–242
9.   Sherr, C.J. & McCormack, F. (2002) The RB and p53 pathways in cancer. *Cancer Cell* **2**, 103–112
10. Gill, G. (2004) SUMO and ubiquitin in the nucleus: different functions, similar mechanisms? *Genes Dev.* **18**, 2046–2059
11. Kubbutat, M.H., Jones, S.N. & Vousden, K.H. (1997) Regulation of p53 stability by Mdm2. *Nature (London)* **387**, 299–303
12. Pearson, G., Robinson, F., Beers Gibson, T., Xu, B.-E., Karandikar, M., Berman, K. & Cobb, M.H. (2001) Mitogen activated protein (MAP) kinase pathways: regulation and physiological functions. *Endocr. Rev.* **22**, 153–183
13. Hicke, L. (2001) Protein regulation by monoubiquitin. *Nat. Rev. Mol. Cell Biol.* **2**, 195–201
14. Joazeiro, C.A., Wing, S.S., Huang, H., Leverson, J.D., Hunter, T. & Liu, Y.C. (1999) The tyrosine kinase negative regulator c-Cbl as a RING-type, E2-dependent ubiquitin-protein ligase. *Science* **286**, 309–312
15. Brummelkamp, T.R., Nijman, S.M., Dirac, A.M. & Bernards, R. (2003) Loss of the cylindromatosis tumour suppressor inhibits apoptosis by activating NF-κB. *Nature (London)* **424**, 797–801
16. Lu, Z., Xu, S., Joazeiro, C., Cobb, M.H. & Hunter, T. (2002) The PHD domain of MEKK1 acts as an E3 ubiquitin ligase and mediates ubiquitination and degradation of ERK1/2. *Mol. Cell* **9**, 945–956
17. Wertz, I.E., O'Rourke, K.M., Zhou, H., Eby, M., Aravind, L., Seshagiri, S.D.L., Wu, P., Wiesmann, C., Baker, R., Boone, D.L. et al. (2004) De-ubiquitination and ubiquitin ligase domains of A20 downregulate NF-κB signalling. *Nature (London)* **430**, 694–699
18. Pagano, M. & Benmaamar, R. (2003) When protein destruction runs amok, malignancy is on the loose. *Cancer Cell* **4**, 251–256
19. Corn, P.G., McDonald, III, E.R., Herman, J.G. & El-Deiry, W.S. (2003) Tat-binding protein-1, a component of the 26 S proteasome, contributes to the E3 ubiquitin ligase function of the von Hippel–Lindau protein. *Nat. Genet.* **35**, 229–237
20. Gstaiger, M., Jordan, R., Lim, M., Catzavelos, C., Mestan, J., Slingerland, J. & Krek, W. (2001) Skp2 is oncogenic and overexpressed in human cancers. *Proc. Natl. Acad. Sci. U.S.A.* **98**, 5043–5048
21. Dawson, S., Mee, M., Apcher, S., Higashitsuji, H., Baker, R., Uhle, S., Dubiel, W., Fujita, J. & Mayer, R.J. (2002) Gankyrin: an ankyrin-repeat oncoprotein interacts with Cdk4 kinase and the S6 ATPase of the 26 S proteasome. *J. Biol. Chem.* **277**, 10893–10902

22. Higashitsuji, H., Itoh, K., Nagao, T., Dawson, S., Nonoguchi, K., Kido, T., Mayer, R.J., Arii, S. & Fujita, J. (2000) Reduced stability of retinoblastoma protein by gankyrin, an oncogenic ankyrin-repeat protein overexpressed in hepatomas. *Nat. Med.* **6**, 96–99

23. Higashitsuji, H., Higashitsuji, H., Nagao, T., Itoh, K., Dawson, S., Mayer, R.J. & Fujita, J. (2003) Gankyrin, an oncoprotein commonly overexpressed in hepatocellular carcinomas, is anti-apoptotic and accelerates degradation of the tumor suppressor p53. *Cancer Cell* **8**, 75–87

24. Hartmann-Petersen, R., Seeger, M. & Gordon, C. (2003) Transferring substrates to the 26 S proteasome. *Trends Biochem. Sci.* **28**, 26–31

25. Goy, A. & Gilles, F. (2004) Update on the proteasome inhibitor bortezomib in hematologic malignancies. *Clin. Lymphoma* **4**, 230–237

26. Vassilev, L.T., Vu, B.T., Graves, B., Carvajal, D., Podlaski, F., Filipovic, Z., Kong, N., Kammlott, U., Lukacs, C., Klein, C. et al. (2004) In vivo activation of the p53 pathway by small-molecule antagonists of Mdm2. *Science* **303**, 844–848

14

Proteasome inhibitors as therapeutics

Constantine S. Mitsiades*†, Nicholas Mitsiades*†, Teru Hideshima*†, Paul G. Richardson*† and Kenneth C. Anderson*†

*Jerome Lipper Multiple Myeloma Center, Department of Medical Oncology, Dana-Farber Cancer Institute, Boston, MA, U.S.A., and †Department of Medicine, Harvard Medical School, Boston, MA, U.S.A.

Abstract

The ubiquitin–proteasome pathway is a principle intracellular mechanism for controlled protein degradation and has recently emerged as an attractive target for anticancer therapies, because of the pleiotropic cell-cycle regulators and modulators of apoptosis that are controlled by proteasome function. In this chapter, we review the current state of the field of proteasome inhibitors and their prototypic member, bortezomib, which was recently approved by the U.S. Food and Drug Administration for the treatment of advanced multiple myeloma. Particular emphasis is placed on the pre-clinical research data that became the basis for eventual clinical applications of proteasome inhibitors, an overview of the clinical development of this exciting drug class in multiple myeloma, and a appraisal of possible uses in other haematological malignancies, such non-Hodgkin's lymphomas.

[1]To whom correspondence should be addressed (email Constantine_Mitsiades@dfci.harvard.edu).

Introduction

The elucidation of the role of ubiquitin–proteasome pathway, as a principle intracellular route for controlled protein degradation, represented a major conceptual advancement in our understanding of cell biology [1], reflected by the recent Nobel prize awarded to Drs Ciechanover, Hershko and Rose. Importantly, it also paved the way for therapeutic targeting of protein degradation in human diseases, such as cancer. In this chapter, we review the current state of the field of proteasome inhibitors, with particular emphasis on the bench-to-bedside research studies that led to the development of bortezomib (Velcade™, formerly known as PS-341), as the prototypical proteasome inhibitor for the treatment of human neoplasias, such as multiple myeloma (MM).

Over the years, an extensive list of proteins (previously reviewed in [2–4]) involved in tumour cell proliferation, survival and drug resistance were shown to be regulated by proteasome-mediated degradation. This list includes cell-cycle regulators, e.g. various cyclins; cyclin-dependent kinase inhibitors (i.e. p21$^{WAF1/CIP1}$ and p27^{KIP1}); regulators of oncogenic transformation, e.g. c-Fos, c-Jun or c-Myc; tumour suppressors, such as p53; pro-apoptotic and anti-apoptotic regulators, including Bax and Bcl-2 (B-cell lymphocytic-leukaemia proto-oncogene 2); and the inhibitor of NF-κB (nuclear factor κB), IκBα (inhibitory κB α) [5]. The critical roles of these proteins in tumour cell biology raised the hypothesis that interfering with proteasome function might perturb their intracellular levels in a manner conducive to antitumour effects, e.g. cell-cycle arrest owing to accumulation of cyclin-dependent kinase inhibitors p21$^{WAF1/CIP1}$ and/or p27^{KIP1}, facilitation of tumour cell apoptosis owing to accumulation of p53 or Bax, as well as accumulation of IκB and inhibition of nuclear translocation of NF-κB, which is known to activate multiple anti-apoptotic genes [6]. However, because proteasomal degradation regulates diverse processes pertinent to both healthy and abnormal cells, there were initially concerns that this pathway cannot be therapeutically manipulated without major perturbations in proteins critical for normal cellular physiology, thereby causing extensive toxicities that would be incompatible with use in a clinical setting.

Despite these concerns, small molecule proteasome inhibitors were developed with the goal at least to use them as chemical probes to interrogate the biological roles of proteasome function. Five main groups of such inhibitors have been synthesized so far: peptide aldehydes, peptide vinyl sulphones, peptide boronates, peptide epoxyketones (the less extensively studied group), and β-lactones (lactacystin and its derivatives) [2,7]. Peptide aldehydes, peptide vinyl sulphones and β-lactones were not considered amenable to clinical development, for several reasons, including instability *in vivo* [8], suboptimal enzyme specificity, and irreversible binding to the proteasome [9]. Nonetheless, these inhibitors were used in informative pre-clinical studies, which provided proof-of-concept of

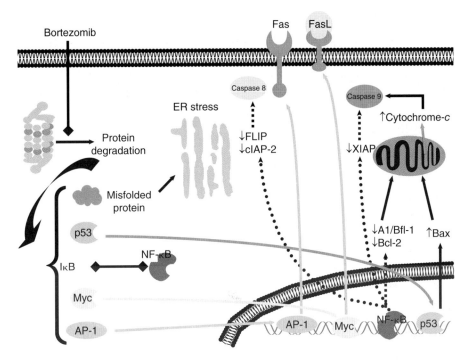

Figure 1. Schematic representation of pleiotropic molecular sequelae triggered by bortezomib-induced proteasome inhibition in myeloma cells

The inhibition of 20 S chymotryptic proteasome activity by bortezomib leads to a multitude of specific molecular events related to accumulation of undegraded proteins, such as or IκB, p53, Myc, or AP-1. The accumulation of IkB prevents the nuclear translocation of NF-κB and blocks the transcription of anti-apoptotic genes regulated (at least in part) by NF-κB, including cIAP-2, XIAP, or A1/Bfl-1. The accumulation of Myc and AP-1 triggers increased production of FasL and Fas, which interact to trigger apoptosis of myeloma cells via a caspase-8-dependent pathway. In addition, the accumulation of p53 and Bax, as well as the suppression of mitochondrial anti-apoptotic molecules (e.g. A1/Bfl-1 or Bcl-2) or of caspase 9 inhibitors (e.g. XIAP), leads to activation of a caspase-9-dependent pro-apoptotic pathway. Furthermore, the accumulation of undegraded proteins leads to ER stress and subsequent activation of a caspase-12-dependent pathway for induction of apoptosis. In contrast to other antimyeloma agents, which may activate only one of these pathways (e.g. caspase 9 activation by dexamethasone), proteasome inhibition by bortezomib triggers simultaneous activation of these pro-apoptotic pathways, which can explain not only the ability of bortezomib to kill myeloma cells resistant to multiple other agents, but also its properties to sensitize myeloma tumour cells to a broad spectrum of conventional and novel therapeutics.

in vitro and *in vivo* antitumour effects of proteasome inhibitors, including studies showing their selective cytotoxicity against transformed cells, rather than their normal counterparts [10,11]; and their ability to sensitize tumour cells to other anticancer therapies, including radiotherapy or cytotoxic chemotherapy [12]. These data provided a rationale for more research on peptide boronic acids, which were synthesized as derivatives of peptidyl aldehydes with substitution of the leucine carbon for a boron atom [8]. This was a critical step in proteasome-inhibitor research because peptidyl aldehydes are not only potent inhibitors of proteasome-mediated proteolysis, but are also potent inhibitors of thiol proteases such as cathepsin B and calpains [8]. However, the three-dimensional structure of the boronated derivatives of peptide aldehydes could not only allow them to form stable tetrahedral intermediates with the N-terminal threonine residues of the catalytically active proteasome β-subunits, but also prevent similar interactions with common serine proteases (e.g. leucocyte elastase, chymotrypsin or thrombin) or with cysteine proteases (e.g. cathepsin G) [8]. Furthermore, the potent (with even sub-nanomolar K_i values) and selective binding of boronic dipeptides to the β-proteasome subunits is accompanied by other favourable features for possible clinical applications, including reversible activity [9], *in vivo* stability, and potent anti-proliferative effects against diverse types of tumour cells (e.g. non-small-cell lung, colon, central nervous system, melanoma, ovarian, renal, prostate, and breast cancers) in the NCI-60 panel of tumour cell lines [13]. Of the peptide boronic acids, bortezomib (originally designated as PS-341) exhibited a unique cytotoxicity profile, in comparison with historical data of the NCI on 60000 compounds tested in the NCI-60 panel [13], and was selected for further pre-clinical studies and clinical development.

Spectrum of pre-clinical antitumour activity and mechanism(s) of actions of bortezomib

Bortezomib (PS-341, Velcade™) is the prototypical small-molecule proteasome inhibitors that has been used clinically, mainly in MM, an incurable neoplasia of malignant plasma cells. Preceding or concomitant pre-clinical studies evaluated the activity of bortezomib against other haematological neoplasias and solid tumours, including MM itself [14–17], mantle cell lymphoma [18] and various histological subtypes of lung [19], ovarian [20], pancreatic [21], prostate [13] and breast [19] cancers.

Bortezomib probably kills tumour cells via multi-factorial mechanisms (Figure 1), which conceivably involve tumour type-specific features. For example, p53 expression is essential for proteasome inhibitor-induced apoptosis in breast epithelial cells [22], but it is dispensable for induction of G_2/M cell-cycle arrest and apoptosis of the p53 null PC-3 prostate cancer cells [13]. Bortezomib triggers cell-cycle arrest attributable to stabilization of p21 and p27 [13], but eventually induces apoptosis even in tumour cells with low proliferative rates [11,14,23]. In MM cells, the prototypic tumour model for antitumour activity of proteasome inhibitors, bortezomib triggers concomitant activation of a dual caspase 8 and caspase 9 pro-apoptotic pathway, which is accompanied by inhibition of anti-apoptotic pathways, such NF-κB transcriptional activity [15]. Indeed, bortezomib leads to intracellular accumulation of c-Jun [which leads to increased transcriptional activity of AP-1 (activator protein 1)] and c-Myc [15], which in turn increase the expression, in MM cells, of Fas and Fas ligand (FasL) respectively [15], resulting in activation of caspase-8. Furthermore, Bax-triggered release of cytochrome *c* from the mitochondria activates caspase-9-mediated apoptosis, and recent data in MM and other tumour models suggest the activation of caspase 12 by ER (endoplasmic reticulum) stress related to the accumulation of undegraded proteins ([24] and C.S. Mitsiades, unpublished work).

Bortezomib not only directly triggers pro-apoptotic cascades but also facilitates their activation, by suppressing the function of a series of anti-apoptotic pathways, such as NF-κB transcriptional activity. NF-κB stimulates expression of caspase 8 inhibitors, such as FLIP (FADD-like interleukin-1β-converting enzyme inhibitory protein) and cIAP-2 (cellular inhibitor of apoptosis protein 2) [25,26], caspase 9 inhibitors, such as XIAP (X-linked inhibitor of apoptosis protein) [6,26], or anti-apoptotic Bcl-2 family members [6,25,26], such as A1/Bfl-1 and Bcl-2 itself. Consequently, by causing accumulation of IκB and preventing nuclear translocation of NF-κB, proteasome inhibition facilitates both extrinsic (caspase-8-dependent routes after, for example, Fas/FasL interaction) and intrinsic mitochondrial-dependent (caspase-9-dependent) apoptotic cascades [15].

The antitumour effects of bortezomib cannot be attributed exclusively to just one of the aforementioned pathways. It is more likely that bortezomib's antitumour activity is due to simultaneous effects on multiple such pathways. These pleiotropic effects can also help to explain the activity of bortezomib, even against tumour cells resistant to conventional or other investigational agents [14]. For instance, bortezomib simultaneously activates three distinct pathways of caspase-mediated apoptosis (caspase 8, 9 and 12), which suggests that it can be active even against cells in which, for example, one of these cascades is not operational. The pleiotropic effects of bortezomib also allow it to sensitize tumour cells to a broad range of antitumour agents. Bortezomib-induced suppression of caspase 8 inhibitors, such as FLIP and cIAP-2, sensitizes MM cells to caspase-8-depenent pro-apoptotic stimuli, including ligands or agonistic antibodies against Fas or TRAIL (tumour necrosis factor-related apoptosis-inducing ligand) receptors [6,15], as well as thalidomide and its immunomodulatory derivatives [16]. Bortezomib-induced suppression of the caspase 9 inhibitor XIAP explains the (at least) additive effect of bortezomib with dexamethasone against MM cells [14,15]. In addition, bortezomib sensitizes MM cells to diverse DNA-damaging chemotherapeutic agents [17,19], which is attributed to inhibition of NF-κB, suppression of caspase inhibitors (which generally increase the resistance of tumour cells to various anticancer agents [26,27]) and, more specifically, suppression of various DNA repair enzymes [17].

Proteasome inhibitors also influence the non-malignant cells of the tumour micro-environment. It is well established that MM cells, which generally reside in the bone marrow of patients, adhere to bone marrow stromal cells (BMSCs), triggering an NF-κB-dependent secretion of IL-6 (interleukin-6) by, mainly, BMSCs [28]. IL-6 is a key proliferation factor for MM cells [29] and its NF-κB-dependent (and proteasome-dependent) up-regulation due to MM–BMSC interaction is also targeted by bortezomib. This allows proteasome inhibition to target not only the MM cell itself, but also the BMSCs and their ability to support the tumour cell population with paracrine proliferative stimulation [14].

It is still unclear why bortezomib has a therapeutic window *in vitro* and *in vivo*. Quiescent HL60 leukaemia cells or contact-inhibited quiescent endothelial cells are less susceptible to proteasome inhibitors than rapidly proliferating HL60 cells or primary endothelial cells respectively [30,31]. However, other types of tumour cells are more sensitive to proteasome inhibitors than their normal counterparts, even when their proliferation rates are not substantially different, e.g. in chronic lymphocytic leukaemia (CLL) [32], acute myelogenous leukaemia (AML) stem cells [23], or primary myeloma tumour cells [14]. In view of these data, an alternative, but less discretely formed, hypothesis is that tumour cells are more susceptible to proteasome inhibition, not necessarily just because of higher proliferation rates, but because of concomitant dysregulation of cell-cycle regulators, such as cyclin-dependent kinases, and the defective cell-cycle check points in tumour cells [2,9,33].

Clinical development of proteasome inhibitors

Bortezomib was first administered as a single agent in four different phase I clinical trials (two in hematologic malignancies [34,35] and two in solid tumours [36,37]) as bolus intravenous injections in various schedules, including 6-week cycles (4 weeks of therapy followed by a 2-week rest) at doses of 0.40, 1.04, 1.20, or 1.38 mg/m^2 for patients with advanced B-cell malignancies [34], or at doses of 0.75, 1.25, or 1.5 mg/m^2 for patients with acute leukaemias refractory to or relapsing after prior therapy [35]. In the phase I trials for solid tumours, bortezomib was administered (again by bolus intravenous injections) weekly, at doses ranging from 0.13–2.0 mg/m^2 per dose for 4 weeks of 5-week cycles, for mostly patients with advanced prostate cancer) [37], or twice weekly (at doses ranging from 0.13–1.56 mg/m^2 per dose) for 2 weeks, followed by a 1-week recovery period, in patients with advanced solid tumour malignancies [36].

In the phase I trial in advanced prostate-cancer patients, PK (pharmacokinetic) data were obtained from analyses of peripheral blood samples by LC/MS/MS (liquid chromatography with tandem mass spectrometry) detection assay. This PK assessment was performed for patients receiving doses between 1.45 and 2.0 mg/m^2 per dose. The majority of these plasma profiles are described by a two-compartment PK model with a rapid initial distribution half-life ($t_{1/2\alpha}$: 0.22–0.46 h), followed by a more sustained terminal elimination half-life ($t_{1/2\beta}$>10 h) and a large (>500 litres) volume of distribution [37]. These data, taken together with tissue distribution results from pre-clinical animal models, indicated that after its intravenous administration, bortezomib is rapidly distributed into extravascular tissues, cleared slowly from them, and returns to the systemic circulation to be eliminated by the hepatic and renal routes [37]. In that same phase I trial, the relationship between bortezomib plasma concentration and proteasome inhibition was assessed over a 24-h period from borte-zomib injection. The 1-h plasma concentrations of bortezomib had a hetero-geneous 8-fold range, in contrast to the rather homogenous response in reduction of 20 S activity of approx. 70% (and a homogeneous pattern of recovery in 20 S proteasome activity in 24-h measurements) [37], which suggest a disconnection between plasma bortezomib levels and suppression of 20 S activity. These results suggested that either the early part of bortezomib administration (e.g. 0 to 1-h interval) is very important for determining the clinical outcome of the drug, or perhaps that the intracellular biovailability of bortezomib is more informative than its plasma PK. Furthermore, the observed clinically relevant efficacy and toxicity occurred at saturation (plateau) levels of inhibition of 20 S proteasome activity (65–80%), whereas no relationship appears to exists between plasma bortezomib concentration and 20 S activity [37]. Overall, in several trials, bortezomib treatment was associated with a dose-related inhibition of 20 S proteasome activity in peripheral blood samples, suggesting that these measurements can be viewed as a surrogate pharmacodynamic marker. Generally, doses of bortezomib that achieve up to approx. 80% inhibition of chymotryptic 20 S proteasome activity in the peripheral blood can be well tolerated [38]. The fact that no direct correlation has yet been established between the precise percentage inhibition of 20 S proteasome activity in the peripheral blood and the clinical response of patients to bortezomib could perhaps reflect the fact that the sensitivity of tumour cells to proteasome inhibitors depends not only on the degree of inhibition of the target, but also on downstream pathways that regulate how dependent tumour cells are on proteasome function for their proliferation and viability.

In view of the different schedules, dose escalation schemes and patient populations in the various trials of the phase I programme for the clinical development, the recommended phase II doses differed, e.g. 1.56 mg/m^2 per dose for twice weekly administration (2 weeks on, 1 week off treatment) [36], 1.6 mg/m^2 per dose for weekly administration (for 4 weeks of a 5-week cycle) [37], 1.04 mg/m^2 per dose for twice weekly administration (for 4 weeks of a 6-week cycle) [34] and 1.25 mg/m^2 per dose for twice weekly administration (for 4 weeks of a 6-week cycle) [35].

Two major conclusions emerged from these phase I clinical trials. The first was that bortezomib can be safely administered with acceptable and manageable toxicity (e.g. for thrombocytopaenia, diarrhoea, electrolyte imbalances, and peripheral neuropathy [34–37]), in contrast to initial concerns that proteasome inhibition would lead to clinically unacceptable and catastrophic toxicities. The second was that bortezomib achieved very encouraging clinical responses in patients with plasma cell neoplasias, such as MM. Among nine fully assessable patients with heavily pretreated plasma-cell malignancies, one patient had complete response and eight others had reductions in tumour burden (assessed by serum paraprotein levels and/or marrow plasmacytosis). In addition, one patient with mantle cell lymphoma and another with follicular lymphoma had shrinkage of lymph node involvement of their disease [34]. One major response was observed in a non-small-cell-lung-carcinoma patient [36], yet the activity of bortezomib in MM patients was so favourable that it warranted extensive phase II tesing in this disease.

Two phase II clinical trials of single agent bortezomib in advanced MM have been conducted [39,40] In the SUMMIT (Study of Uncontrolled MM managed with Proteasome Inhibition Therapy) trial, 202 heavily pretreated patients with relapsed and refractory myeloma received bortezomib at 1.3 mg/m^2 intravenously on days 1, 4, 8, and 11 of a 3-week cycle for up to eight cycles [39]. In 193 patients that could be evaluated, bortezomib achieved a 35% overall response rate, including 4% complete responses [complete clinical remission and undetectable myeloma-related monoclonal protein (M-protein) by electrophoresis and immunofixation], 6% near-complete responses (M-protein detectable only by immunofixation), 18% partial responses (>50% decrease of M-protein levels compared with the baseline), and 7% minimal responses (25–50% reduction of M-protein levels). Response to bortezomib was independent of most prognostic factors, including type of MM or type or number of previous therapies, as well as chromosomal abnormalities of tumour cells (e.g. chromosome 13 deletion) [39]. These clinical responses were not only durable (median time to disease progression of 7 months), but were observed in cases resistant to multiple other therapies [39], which was quite encouraging.

In the CREST (Clinical Response and Efficacy Study of Bortezomib in the Treatment of Relapsing MM) trial, 67 patients with relapsed or refractory MM following front-line therapy were randomized to receive bortezomib at either 1.0 or 1.3 mg/m^2 [40] on the same schedule used in the SUMMIT trial. Clinical responses were observed at either dose level, indicating that dose reduction to 1.0 mg/m^2 could still be therapeutic in cases of patients experiencing side effects at 1.3 mg/m^2. In both the SUMMIT and CREST trials, patients with progressive disease after two cycles or stable disease after the first four cycles could receive 20 mg of oral dexamethasone on the day of, and the day after, bortezomib administration. Additional responses were observed in both trials when dexamethasone was combined with bortezomib, consistent with the prior preclinical data, suggesting that the molecular effects of proteasome inhibition can sensitize MM cells to various treatments [14,15], including dexamethasone.

The profile of side effects of bortezomib-treated patients is generally manageable with routine therapeutic measures. The most frequently reported treatment-emergent side effects are nausea, fatigue, and diarrhoea [40,41]. Thrombocytopaenia, fatigue, peripheral neuropathy, neutropaenia, lymphopaenia, and hyponatraemia correspond to the most frequently reported drug-related grade 3/4 adverse events [40,41]. Bortezomib-emergent thrombocytopaenia is cyclical, and is characterized by a drop in platelet count during the first 2 weeks of each cycle of treatment and gradual recovery to baseline counts during the third week (i.e. the rest phase of each cycle, according to the schedule of bortezomib administration in the phase II and III clinical trials of this agent). The nadir platelet count within each cycle usually corresponds to approx. 40% of the baseline value, suggesting that the risk of treatment-emergent clinically significant thrombocytopaenia primarily pertains to patients with already low baseline platelet counts [41]. Bortezomib-emergent peripheral neuropathy was the cause for discontinuation of therapy in 9% and 4% of patients in the CREST and SUMMIT trials respectively, which corresponded to the highest proportion of treatment discontinuations among adverse events in these trials [40,41]. It is important to emphasize that symptoms of peripheral neuropathy were present at baseline (prior to initiation of bortezomib therapy) in many patients enrolled in these trials and were largely attributed to previous treatment with neurotoxic agents, incorporated in the therapeutic management of myeloma (e.g. thalidomide, vincristine). Importantly, peripheral neuropathy improved or resolved in the majority of patients after completion or discontinuation of therapy [41].

Based on the results of the pivotal SUMMIT phase II trial, the U.S. Food and Drug Administration approved, in May 2003, bortezomib for the treatment of patients with MM who have received at least two prior therapies and who have demonstrated disease progression on their last therapy. In addition, bortezomib was approved in April 2004 for use in the European Union.

The phase III trial APEX (Assessment of Proteasome Inhibition for Extending Remissions) was a large international study, in which 669 relapsed myeloma patients (who were known not to be refractory to dexamethasone) were randomized to receive either bortezomib (administered for the first eight cycles using the phase II schedule, and thereafter at 1.3 mg/m^2 on day one of the first 4 weeks of a 5-week cycle for an additional three cycles) or high-dose dexamethasone [41]. A pre-specified interim analysis demonstrated superiority of the bortezomib arm over dexamethasone with regard to the primary end point, median time to disease progression, and median overall survival [41].

At least two phase I trials of bortezomib, one in combination with melphalan and the other in combination with doxorubicin, are ongoing in patients with relapsed or refractory haematological malignancies, based on the pre-clinical observations on the bortezomib-induced chemosensitization of MM cells [17]. Activity reported to date in these trials has been promising, and importantly, approx. 50% of patients with prior resistance to melphalan or doxorubicin responded to the original agent combined with bortezomib.

Studies of bortezomib in NHL (non-Hodgkin's lymphoma) and other malignancies

Although the main emphasis of the clinical development of bortezomib was on MM, clinical responses in the phase I trials were also observed in patients with other types of haematological malignancies, e.g. one patient with Waldenstrom's macroglobulinaemia (WM; lymphoplasmacytic lymphoma), one patient with mantle cell lymphoma (MCL) and another with follicular lymphoma [34]. These considerations, along with pre-clinical data indicating that bortezomib can be active against tumour cells from WM patients [42] or against MCL cell lines [18], provided sufficient support for the notion that bortezomib warranted further clinical testing in haematological malignancies other than MM. Results of two such phase II trials were recently published [43,44] and showed that bortezomib, which was well tolerated, has significant single-agent activity in patients with certain subtypes of NHL, such as MCL [43,44].

Several phase II clinical trials of bortezomib in patients with advanced solid tumours are ongoing or have been reported recently [45–52]. Many of these trials explore the chemosensitizing properties of bortezomib, using it in combination with other anti-neoplastic agents. So far, no histological type or subtype of solid tumour has been shown to respond clinically to bortezomib to the same degree of clinical response observed in MM. However, there is still potential for bortezomib use in solid tumours, mainly in combination with cytotoxic chemotherapy, although more pre-clinical studies will be needed to define which solid tumours may be more amenable to such combination regimens.

Conclusion

Proteasome inhibitors constitute a novel class of drugs for the treatment of human cancer. Bortezomib, the prototypical member of this class, has been approved in the U.S. and Europe for the treatment of advanced myeloma. Clinical trials of bortezomib as first-line treatment of myeloma are underway, and further investigation should be carried out to evaluate the role of bortezomib in other haematological malignancies, including MCL, in view of the encouraging data from phase II studies, which show substantial clinical activity in this subtype of NHL.

Summary

- *Despite the role of the proteasome in both normal and transformed cells, inhibition of the chymotryptic activity of the 20 S proteasome has more significant functional consequences for malignant cells.*
- *Bortezomib is the first-in-class proteasome inhibitor used for treatment of human neoplasias.*
- *Bortezomib kills tumour cells via pleiotropic mechanisms, including both simultaneous activation of multiple caspase-mediated apoptotic cascades and inhibition of anti-apoptotic pathways.*
- *Bortezomib is active in vitro and in vivo against even cells resistant to multiple conventional antitumour therapies.*
- *Bortezomib can be combined with diverse other anticancer therapeutics to achieved enhanced antitumour effect in vitro or in vivo.*

- *Ongoing clinical studies are evaluating the role of proteasome inhibitors in diseases other than myeloma (e.g. various subtypes of lymphomas).*

This work has been supported in part by grants (to C.S.M. and N.M.) from the Multiple Myeloma Research Foundation, the Career Development Award of the NCI (National Cancer Institute) SPORE (Specialized Programs of Research Excellence) Grant for Multiple Myeloma, the Lauri Strauss Leukemia Foundation, and the International Waldenstrom's Macroglobulinemia Foundation. C.S.M is a Special Fellow of the Leukemia and Lymphoma Society. The authors apologize in advance for the inability, due to space limitations, to reference all studies relevant to the scope of this article.

References

1   Ciechanover, A. (1994) The ubiquitin–proteasome proteolytic pathway. *Cell* **79**, 13–21

2   Adams, J. (2004) The development of proteasome inhibitors as anticancer drugs. *Cancer Cell* **5**, 417–421

3   DeMartino, G.N. & Slaughter, C.A. (1999) The proteasome, a novel protease regulated by multiple mechanisms. *J. Biol. Chem.* **274**, 22123–22126

4   Goldberg, A.L., Akopian, T.N., Kisselev, A.F., Lee, D.H. & Rohrwild, M. (1997) New insights into the mechanisms and importance of the proteasome in intracellular protein degradation. *Biol. Chem.* **378**, 131–140

5   Palombella, V.J., Rando, O.J., Goldberg, A.L. & Maniatis, T. (1994) The ubiquitin–proteasome pathway is required for processing the NF-κB1 precursor protein and the activation of NF-κB. *Cell* **78**, 773–785

6   Mitsiades, N., Mitsiades, C.S., Poulaki, V., Chauhan, D., Richardson, P.G., Hideshima, T., Munshi, N., Treon, S.P. & Anderson, K.C. (2002) Biologic sequelae of nuclear factor-κB blockade in multiple myeloma: therapeutic applications. *Blood* **99**, 4079–4086

7   Kisselev, A.F. & Goldberg, A.L. (2001) Proteasome inhibitors: from research tools to drug candidates. *Chem. Biol.* **8**, 739–758

8   Adams, J., Behnke, M., Chen, S., Cruickshank, A.A., Dick, L.R., Grenier, L., Klunder, J.M., Ma, Y.T., Plamondon, L. & Stein, R.L. (1998) Potent and selective inhibitors of the proteasome: dipeptidyl boronic acids. *Bioorg. Med. Chem. Lett.* **8**, 333–338

9   Almond, J.B. & Cohen, G.M. (2002) The proteasome: a novel target for cancer chemotherapy. *Leukemia* **16**, 433–443

10 Orlowski, R.Z., Eswara, J.R., Lafond-Walker, A., Grever, M.R., Orlowski, M. & Dang, C.V. (1998) Tumor growth inhibition induced in a murine model of human Burkitt's lymphoma by a proteasome inhibitor. *Cancer Res.* **58**, 4342–4348

11 Masdehors, P., Merle-Beral, H., Magdelenat, H. & Delic, J. (2000) Ubiquitin–proteasome system and increased sensitivity of B-CLL lymphocytes to apoptotic death activation. *Leuk. Lymphoma* **38**, 499–504

12 Cusack, Jr, J.C., Liu, R., Houston, M., Abendroth, K., Elliott, P.J., Adams, J. & Baldwin, Jr, A.S. (2001) Enhanced chemosensitivity to CPT-11 with proteasome inhibitor PS-341: implications for systemic nuclear factor-κB inhibition. *Cancer Res.* **61**, 3535–3540

13 Adams, J., Palombella, V.J., Sausville, E.A., Johnson, J., Destree, A., Lazarus, D.D., Maas, J., Pien, C.S., Prakash, S. & Elliott, P.J. (1999) Proteasome inhibitors: a novel class of potent and effective antitumor agents. *Cancer Res.* **59**, 2615–2622

14 Hideshima, T., Richardson, P., Chauhan, D., Palombella, V.J., Elliott, P.J., Adams, J. & Anderson, K.C. (2001) The proteasome inhibitor PS-341 inhibits growth, induces apoptosis, and overcomes drug resistance in human multiple myeloma cells. *Cancer Res.* **61**, 3071–3076

15   Mitsiades, N., Mitsiades, C.S., Poulaki, V., Chauhan, D., Fanourakis, G., Gu, X., Bailey, C., Joseph,
      M., Libermann, T.A., Treon, S.P. et al. (2002) Molecular sequelae of proteasome inhibition in
      human multiple myeloma cells. *Proc. Natl. Acad. Sci. U.S.A.* **99**, 14374–14379

16   Mitsiades, N., Mitsiades, C.S., Poulaki, V., Chauhan, D., Richardson, P.G., Hideshima, T., Munshi,
      N.C., Treon, S.P. & Anderson, K.C. (2002) Apoptotic signaling induced by immunomodulatory
      thalidomide analogs in human multiple myeloma cells: therapeutic implications. *Blood* **99**, 4525–4530

17   Mitsiades, N., Mitsiades, C.S., Richardson, P.G., Poulaki, V., Tai, Y.T., Chauhan, D., Fanourakis, G.,
      Gu, X., Bailey, C., Joseph, M. et al. (2003) The proteasome inhibitor PS-341 potentiates sensitivity
      of multiple myeloma cells to conventional chemotherapeutic agents: therapeutic applications.
      Blood **101**, 2377–2380

18   Pham, L.V., Tamayo, A.T., Yoshimura, L.C., Lo, P. & Ford, R.J. (2003) Inhibition of constitutive NF-
      kB activation in mantle cell lymphoma B cells leads to induction of cell cycle arrest and apoptosis.
      J. Immunol. **171**, 88–95

19   Teicher, B.A., Ara, G., Herbst, R., Palombella, V.J. & Adams, J. (1999) The proteasome inhibitor
      PS-341 in cancer therapy. *Clin. Cancer Res.* **5**, 2638–2645

20   Frankel, A., Man, S., Elliott, P., Adams, J. & Kerbel, R.S. (2000) Lack of multicellular drug resistance
      observed in human ovarian and prostate carcinoma treated with the proteasome inhibitor PS-
      341. *Clin. Cancer Res.* **6**, 3719–3728

21   Shah, S.A., Potter, M.W., McDade, T.P., Ricciardi, R., Perugini, R.A., Elliott, P.J., Adams, J. &
      Callery, M.P. (2001) 26 S proteasome inhibition induces apoptosis and limits growth of human
      pancreatic cancer. *J. Cell. Biochem.* **82**, 110–122

22   MacLaren, A.P., Chapman, R.S., Wyllie, A.H. & Watson, C.J. (2001) p53-dependent apoptosis
      induced by proteasome inhibition in mammary epithelial cells. *Cell Death Differ.* **8**, 210–218

23   Guzman, M.L., Swiderski, C.F., Howard, D.S., Grimes, B.A., Rossi, R.M., Szilvassy, S.J. & Jordan,
      C.T. (2002) Preferential induction of apoptosis for primary human leukemic stem cells. *Proc. Natl.
      Acad. Sci. U.S.A.* **99**, 16220–16225

24   Lee, A.H., Iwakoshi, N.N., Anderson, K.C. & Glimcher, L.H. (2003) Proteasome inhibitors disrupt
      the unfolded protein response in myeloma cells. *Proc. Natl. Acad. Sci. U.S.A.* **100**, 9946–9951

25   Mitsiades, C.S., Mitsiades, N., Poulaki, V., Schlossman, R., Akiyama, M., Chauhan, D., Hideshima,
      T., Treon, S.P., Munshi, N.C., Richardson, P.G. & Anderson, K.C. (2002) Activation of NF-kB and
      upregulation of intracellular anti-apoptotic proteins via the IGF-1/Akt signaling in human multiple
      myeloma cells: therapeutic implications. *Oncogene* **21**, 5673–5683

26   Mitsiades, N., Mitsiades, C.S., Poulaki, V., Anderson, K.C. & Treon, S.P. (2002) Intracellular
      regulation of tumor necrosis factor-related apoptosis-inducing ligand-induced apoptosis in human
      multiple myeloma cells. *Blood* **99**, 2162–2171

27   Mitsiades, N., Mitsiades, C.S., Poulaki, V., Anderson, K.C. & Treon, S.P. (2001) Concepts in the
      use of TRAIL/Apo2L: an emerging biotherapy for myeloma and other neoplasias. *Expert Opin.
      Invest. Drugs* **10**, 1521–1530

28   Chauhan, D., Uchiyama, H., Akbarali, Y., Urashima, M., Yamamoto, K., Libermann, T.A. &
      Anderson, K.C. (1996) Multiple myeloma cell adhesion-induced interleukin-6 expression in bone
      marrow stromal cells involves activation of NF-κB. *Blood* **87**, 1104–1112

29   Barut, B.A., Zon, L.I., Cochran, M.K., Paul, S.R., Chauhan, D., Mohrbacher, A., Fingeroth, J. &
      Anderson, K.C. (1992) Role of interleukin 6 in the growth of myeloma-derived cell lines. *Leuk.
      Res.* **16**, 951–959

30   Drexler, H.C. (1997) Activation of the cell death program by inhibition of proteasome function.
      Proc. Natl. Acad. Sci. U.S.A. **94**, 855–860

31   Drexler, H.C., Risau, W. & Konerding, M.A. (2000) Inhibition of proteasome function induces
      programmed cell death in proliferating endothelial cells. *FASEB J.* **14**, 65–77

32   Masdehors, P., Omura, S., Merle-Beral, H., Mentz, F., Cosset, J.M., Dumont, J., Magdelenat, H. &
      Delic, J. (1999) Increased sensitivity of CLL-derived lymphocytes to apoptotic death activation by
      the proteasome-specific inhibitor lactacystin. *Br. J. Haematol.* **105**, 752–757

33   Adams, J. (2004) The proteasome: a suitable antineoplastic target. *Nat. Rev. Cancer* **4**, 349–360

34 Orlowski, R.Z., Stinchcombe, T.E., Mitchell, B.S., Shea, T.C., Baldwin, A.S., Stahl, S., Adams, J., Esseltine, D.L., Elliott, P.J., Pien, C.S. et al. (2002) Phase I trial of the proteasome inhibitor PS-341 in patients with refractory hematologic malignancies. *J. Clin. Oncol.* **20**, 4420–4427

35 Cortes, J., Thomas, D., Koller, C., Giles, F., Estey, E., Faderl, S., Garcia-Manero, G., McConkey, D., Patel, G., Guerciolini, R. et al. (2004) Phase I study of bortezomib in refractory or relapsed acute leukemias. *Clin. Cancer Res.* **10**, 3371–3376

36 Aghajanian, C., Soignet, S., Dizon, D.S., Pien, C.S., Adams, J., Elliott, P.J., Sabbatini, P., Miller, V., Hensley, M.L., Pezzulli, S. et al. (2002) A phase I trial of the novel proteasome inhibitor PS341 in advanced solid tumor malignancies. *Clin. Cancer Res.* **8**, 2505–2511

37 Papandreou, C.N., Daliani, D.D., Nix, D., Yang, H., Madden, T., Wang, X., Pien, C.S., Millikan, R.E., Tu, S.M., Pagliaro, L. et al. (2004) Phase I trial of the proteasome inhibitor bortezomib in patients with advanced solid tumors with observations in androgen-independent prostate cancer. *J. Clin. Oncol.* **22**, 2108–2121

38 Adams, J. (2002) Development of the proteasome inhibitor PS-341. *Oncologist* **7**, 9–16

39 Richardson, P.G., Barlogie, B., Berenson, J., Singhal, S., Jagannath, S., Irwin, D., Rajkumar, S.V., Srkalovic, G., Alsina, M., Alexanian, R. et al. (2003) A phase 2 study of bortezomib in relapsed, refractory myeloma. *N. Engl. J. Med.* **348**, 2609–2617

40 Jagannath, S., Barlogie, B., Berenson, J., Siegel, D., Irwin, D., Richardson, P.G., Niesvizky, R., Alexanian, R., Limentani, S.A., Alsina, M. et al. (2004) A phase 2 study of two doses of bortezomib in relapsed or refractory myeloma. *Br. J. Haematol.* **127**, 165–172

41 Richardson, P.G., Sonneveld, P., Schuster, M.W., Irwin, D., Stadtmauer, E.A., Facon, T., Dalton, W.S., Harousseau, J.L., San Miguel, J.F. & Anderson, K.C. (2005) Bortezomib vs. dexamethasone in relapsed multiple myeloma: a phase 3 randomized study. *N. Engl. J. Med.* in the press

42 Mitsiades, C.S., Mitsiades, N., McMullan, C.J., Poulaki, V., Shringarpure, R., Hideshima, T., Chauhan, D., Treon, S.P., Richardson, P.G., Munshi et al. (2003) The proteasome inhibitor bortezomib (PS-341) is active against Waldenstrom's macroglobulinemia (WM). *Blood* **102** (suppl), Abstract no. 631

43 Goy, A., Younes, A., McLaughlin, P., Pro, B., Romaguera, J.E., Hagemeister, F., Fayad, L., Dang, N.H., Samaniego, F., Wang, M. et al. (2005) Phase II study of proteasome inhibitor bortezomib in relapsed or refractory B-cell non-Hodgkin's lymphoma. *J. Clin. Oncol.* **23**, 667–675

44 O'Connor, O.A., Wright, J., Moskowitz, C., Muzzy, J., MacGregor-Cortelli, B., Stubblefield, M., Straus, D., Portlock, C., Hamlin, P., Choi, E. et al. (2005) Phase II clinical experience with the novel proteasome inhibitor bortezomib in patients with indolent non-Hodgkin's lymphoma and mantle cell lymphoma. *J. Clin. Oncol.* **23**, 676–684

45 Kondagunta, G.V., Drucker, B., Schwartz, L., Bacik, J., Marion, S., Russo, P., Mazumdar, M. & Motzer, R.J. (2004) Phase II trial of bortezomib for patients with advanced renal cell carcinoma. *J. Clin. Oncol.* **22**, 3720–3725

46 Davis, N.B., Taber, D.A., Ansari, R.H., Ryan, C.W., George, C., Vokes, E.E., Vogelzang, N.J. & Stadler, W.M. (2004) Phase II trial of PS-341 in patients with renal cell cancer: a University of Chicago phase II consortium study. *J. Clin. Oncol.* **22**, 115–119

47 Dragovich, T., Lenz, H.J., Rocha Lima, C.M.S., Kozuch, P., Hochster, H., O'Neil, B., Atiq, O., Pipas, J.M., Kashala, O. & Schenkein, D.P. (2004) Bortezomib ± irinotecan in relapsed/refractory colorectal cancer (CRC): interim analysis results from a phase 2b study. *J. Clin. Oncol.* **22** (Suppl.), 267s (Abstract)

48 Fanucchi, M.P., Belt, R.J., Fossella, F.V., Natale, B., Robert, F., Fidias, P., Kelly, K., Kashala, O., Schenkein, D.P. & Schiller, J.H. (2004) Phase (ph) 2 study of bortezomib ± docetaxel inpreviously treated patients (pts) with advanced non-small cell lung cancer (NSCLC). Preliminary results. *J. Clin. Oncol.* **22** (Suppl.), 643s (Abstract)

49 Dreicer, R., Roth, B., Petrylak, D., Agus, D., Meyers, M., Esseltine, D., Rodriquez, D., Oppedisano, P., Wang, K. & Boral, A.(2004) Phase I/II trial of VELCADE® plus docetaxel in patients with advanced androgen-independent prostate cancer. *J. Clin. Oncol.* **22** (Suppl.), 420s (Abstract)

50   Shah, M.H., Young, D., Kindler, H.L., Webb, I., Kleiber, B., Wright, J. & Grever, M. (2004) Phase II
      study of the proteasome inhibitor bortezomib (PS-341) in patients with metastatic
      neuroendocrine tumors. *Clin. Cancer Res.* **10**, 6111–6118
51   Stevenson, J., Nho, C.W., Johnson, S.W. et al. (2004) Phase II/pharmacodynamic trial of PS-341
      (bortezomib, VELCADE®) in advanced non-small cell lung cancer. *J. Clin. Oncol.* **22** (Suppl.), 652s
      (Abstract)
52   Hegewisch-Becker, S., Sterneck, M., Schubert, U., Rogiers, X., Guerciolini, R., Pierce, J.E. &
      Hossfeld, D.K. (2004) Phase I/II trial of bortezomib (VELCADE®) in patients with unresectable
      hepatocellular carcinoma. *J. Clin. Oncol.* **22** (Suppl.), 335s (Abstract)

Subject index

A

AAA motif, 34, 89
ACC domain, 24
adenovirus, 144, 145
adenovirus proteinase, 149
aggresome, 162
AIP1, 91
AIP4, 94
Alix, 91
Alzheimer's disease, 17, 114, 124, 159–167
anaphase-promoting complex (see APC/C)
Angelman syndrome, 17, 21, 72
APC/C, 20, 26, 27, 57, 191, 193–196
apoptosis, 206, 208, 209
Arabidopsis thaliana, 131
archaeal proteasome, 37, 41
ataxin-3, 2, 8–10, 133
ATP-dependent nucleasome remodeling
    enzyme, 76
atrogin-1/MAFbx, 176, 177
autophagic pathway, 166

B

Blm3/PA200, 44
bortezomib, 206–214
Bro1, 91

C

Caenorhabditis elegans, 5, 6, 10, 132
calpain, 180, 181
caspase, 180, 181, 208, 209
β-catenin, 26, 71
cathepsin, 180, 181
Cbl, 21, 86, 93

Cdc20, 193
Cdc48, 58, 59, 104–107
Cdh1, 193
Cdk, 190–197
cell cycle, 189, 190
chaperone (see molecular chaperone)
charged multivesicular protein 91
CHIP, 5–7, 25, 27, 166
chromatin modification, 76
clathrin, 89
c-myc, 71
COP9 signalosome, 45
CUE domain, 51, 52
cullin–RING E3, 19, 20, 25–27
cyclin, 191, 192, 195
cyclin-dependent kinase (see Cdk)
cyclosome (see APC/C)
cytomegalovirus (see human cytomegalovirus)

D

Deg1 signal, 121
dementia with Lewy bodies, 161
derlin-1, 106, 107
deubiquitinating enzyme, 7, 19, 36, 50, 57, 59,
    83, 84, 118, 131, 134, 147, 148, 177
deubiquitination (see *also* deubiquitinating
    enzyme), 36, 176
Drosophila melanogaster, 132
drug resistance, 206, 209, 213

E

E1, 2, 3, 50
E2, 2, 3, 16, 50, 100, 102, 175, 176
E3, 2, 3, 16, 50, 100, 102, 175, 176
    and disease, 17